The Little Black Book

of London

timeout.com

Published by Time Out Guides Ltd, a wholly owned subsidiary of Time Out Group Ltd.
Time Out and the Time Out logo are trademarks of Time Out Group Ltd.

Printer GGP Media GmbH, Karl-Marx-Str 24, 07318 Pößneck, Germany.
Time Out Group uses paper products that are environmentally friendly, from well managed forests and mills
that use certified (PEFC) Chain of Custody pulp in their production.

ISBN 978-1-905042-53-1
ISSN 204258400

Distribution by Comag Specialist (01895 433 800).
For further distribution details, see www.timeout.com.

Published by
Time Out Guides Limited
Universal House
251 Tottenham Court Road
London W1T 7AB
Tel +44 (0)20 7813 3000
Fax +44 (0)20 7813 6001
email guides@timeout.com
www.timeout.com

Editorial

Editor Emma Howarth
Copy Editor Janice Fuscoe
Listings Editors William Crow,
Gemma Pritchard, Jamie Warburton
Proofreader Patrick Mulkern
Indexer William Crow

Managing Director Peter Fiennes
Editorial Director Sarah Guy
Series Editor Cath Phillips
Business Manager Daniel Allen
Editorial Manager Holly Pick
Assistant Management Accountant
Ija Krasnikova

Design

Art Director Scott Moore
Art Editor Pinelope Kourmouzoglou
Senior Designer Kei Ishimaru
Guides Commercial Designer Jodi Sher

Picture Desk

Picture Editor Jael Marschner
Picture Desk Assistant/Researcher Ben Rowe

Advertising

New Business & Commercial Director Mark Phillips
Magazine & UK Guides Commercial Director
St John Betteridge
Advertising Sales Ten Alps
Production Controller Chris Pastfield
Copy Controller Alison Bourke

Marketing

Group Commercial Art Director Anthony Huggins
Circulation & Distribution Manager Dan Collins
Marketing Co-ordinator Alana Benton

Production

Group Production Manager Brendan McKeown
Production Controller Katie Mulhern

Time Out Group

Director & Founder Tony Elliott
Chief Executive Officer David King
Group Financial Director Paul Rakkar
Group General Manager/Director Nichola Coulthard
Time Out Communications Ltd MD David Pepper
Time Out International Ltd MD Cathy Runciman
Time Out Magazine Ltd Publisher/MD Mark Elliott
Group Commercial Director Graeme Tottle
Group IT Director Simon Chappell

Contributors Tim Arthur, Simone Baird, Nuala Calvi, Katie Dailey, Neela Debnath, Emma Howarth, Dan Jones, John Lewis, Charmaine Mok, Jenni Muir, Meryl O'Rourke, Candice Pires, Gemma Pritchard, Kate Riordan, Cyrus Shahrad, Daniel Smith, Caroline Stacey, Peter Watts, Elizabeth Winding, Yolanda Zappaterra.

The Editors would like to thank Sarah Guy, Janice Fuscoe, Kate Hutchinson, Holly Pick and Elizabeth Winding, plus all the Time Out contributors whose work provided a basis for this book, and everyone who came up with suggestions and recommendations.

Illustrations Anna Spencer (www.raspberrykisses.co.uk).

Introduction

Even if you've lived in London for a lifetime, there's always something new to discover. And no matter how well you know the capital, some mysteries always remain, such as where to find a pet-sitter at short notice or how to get your hands on one-for-the-road after last orders.

This is a city where it pays to be well connected, so we've ransacked our contact books – and those of our Address Book Secrets interviewees – to make this the ultimate insiders' guide to London living. So, whether you're looking for a haircut on the cheap, the perfect pair of jeans, a great garden centre or just someone to come and fix your broken boiler in a hurry, you'll find it here.

This is not an A-Z of London's shops, bars, restaurants, museums and galleries, nor is it a sightseeing guide. Instead of focusing on the well known and familiar, we're tried to track down unexpected, unusual or overlooked shops, services, venues and contacts.

We've scoured the streets and forced those-in-the-know to give up their closest-guarded secrets to unearth the best party entertainers and supper clubs, salvage yards and car-share schemes, manicurists and masseurs, locksmiths and computer repair geniuses – all the practical essentials and quirky pleasures that make London life worth living.

Contents

Before you book your **London hotel** check the **London hotel map** on LondonTown.com

London's hotels all on one map

Visually compare best hotel rates and availability

View entertainment, including ticket prices and availability

Hotel Price Guarantee: "Find it cheaper, get £100"

See real customer feedback on all hotels

full screen, fully interactive

The new ∧ hotel map on LondonTown.com

www.londontown.com/hotelmap

Your Best Friend in London

About the guide

LISTINGS

We've tried to make this book as useful – and user-friendly – as possible. Addresses, telephone numbers, websites, transport information, opening times and admission prices are included in the listings, along with price categories for cafés and restaurants. We've indicated how much an average main course costs by using one to four £ signs (£-££££), representing budget, moderate, expensive and luxury.

While every effort has been made to ensure the accuracy of information within this guide, the publishers cannot accept responsibility for any errors it may contain. Businesses can change their arrangements at any time, so before you go out of your way, we strongly advise that you phone ahead to check opening times, prices and other particulars.

Certain shops, restaurants, pubs and services are marked with a star symbol ★ – which indicates that we consider them to be particularly worthy of note.

CREDIT CARDS

If credit cards are not accepted, we've said so; otherwise, establishments should accept major credit cards (MasterCard, Visa and usually AmEx).

TELEPHONE NUMBERS

All telephone numbers listed in this guide assume that you are calling from within London. If you're ringing from outside the city, you will need to use the area code (020) before the phone number. If you're calling from abroad, dial your international access code, then 44 for the UK; follow that with 20 for London, then the eight-digit number.

ADVERTISERS

No payment or PR invitation of any kind has secured inclusion in this guide, or influenced its content. No establishment appears because it has advertised in any of our publications. The editors select the venues and activities listed, and reviews were compiled before any advertising space was sold. The opinions given in this book are those of Time Out writers, and are entirely independent.

WHAT DO YOU THINK?

Did we miss anything? We welcome suggestions for services and places you think we should include in future editions, and take note of your criticism of our choices. You can email us at guides@timeout.com.

Cinema

Look in the right places and you'll find a thriving alternative cinema scene in the capital.

Independent cinemas

We've focused on smaller indie cinema gems, but you can't go wrong with the grandes dames of London's cinema scene – the **BFI Southbank** (Belvedere Road, SE1 8XT, 7928 3232, www.bfi.org.uk) and the **Barbican** (Silk Street, EC2Y 8DS, 7638 8891, www.barbican.org.uk).

CENTRAL

Curzon Soho
99 Shaftesbury Avenue, W1D 5DY (7292 1686, booking line 0871 7033 988, www.curzoncinemas.com). Leicester Square tube. Tickets £7-£12.50; £6 reductions.
Arguably the city's leading indie cinema, the Curzon Soho also boasts a bar and a street-level café, run by the fab Konditor & Cook.

ICA
The Mall, SW1Y 5AH (7930 0493, box office 7930 3647, www.ica.org.uk). Charing Cross tube/rail. Tickets £7-£9; £8 reductions.
Two cinemas show an eclectic variety of feature-length films and shorts, as well as hosting talks by film industry luminaries.

Prince Charles
7 Leicester Place, WC2H 7BP (7494 3654, www.princecharlescinema.com). Leicester Square tube. Tickets £5.50-£10; £1.50-£6 reductions.
This place has been known to sell seats for as little as £1, but it's always cheap.

Renoir Cinema
The Brunswick, WC1N 1AW (7837 8402, box office 0871 7033 991, www.curzoncinemas.com/renoir). Russell Square tube. Tickets £6-£10.50; £6 reductions.
The two-screen Renoir Cinema shows an international array of arthouse releases, and has changing art exhibitions in its bar.

NORTH

Everyman
203 Haverstock Hill, NW3 4QG (0871 906 9060, www.everymancinema.com). Belsize Park tube. Tickets £12.
Popular local cinema with a great sound system, roomy seats and a varied schedule.

Phoenix
52 High Road, N2 9PJ (8444 6789, www.phoenixcinema.co.uk). East Finchley tube. Tickets £6-£9; £6 reductions.
Reopened after a refurb in late 2010, screenings at this East Finchley art deco treasure include the latest indie flicks, and films accompanied by live music.

EAST

Rich Mix
35-47 Bethnal Green Road, E1 6LA (7613 7498, www.richmix.org.uk). Liverpool Street tube/rail. Tickets £8.50; £6 reductions.
Shoreditch's cultural foundation screens big-budget releases alongside unconventional festival fare, and there's a large bar.

Rio Cinema
107 Kingsland High Street, E8 2PB (7241 9410, www.riocinema.org.uk). Dalston Kingsland rail. Tickets £8.50; £6.50 reductions.
The Rio screens everything from major releases to Turkish, Kurdish and gay cinema.

SOUTH

Dulwich Paradiso Film Society

Magnolia, 211 Lordship Lane, SE22 8HA (8299 1136, www.paradisofilm.co.uk). East Dulwich rail. Tickets £5; £3 reductions. No credit cards

This community-run society holds left-of-mainstream screenings on Tuesdays during the spring and autumn.

Ritzy Picturehouse

Brixton Oval, Coldharbour Lane, SW2 1JG (0871 704 2065, www.picturehouses. co.uk). Brixton tube/rail. Tickets £6.50-£9; £5-£8 reductions.

Kids' Club, cheap offers for over-60s and autism-friendly screenings all feature here.

WEST

Cine Lumière

17 Queensferry Place, SW7 2DT (7073 1350, www.institut-francais.org.uk). South Kensington tube. Tickets £7-£9; £5-£7 reductions.

Founded in 1910 to introduce Londoners to artists and writers from across La Manche, London's French cultural institute shows European and world cinema classics.

Coronet Cinema

103 Notting Hill Gate, W11 3LB (7727 6705, www.coronet.org). Notting Hill Gate tube. Tickets £7; £4.50 reductions.

In its days as a theatre, Ellen Terry and Sara Bernhardt trod the boards here, but

GOING OUT

BEAUTY

FASHION

PARTIES

FOOD

HEALTH

ECO

OUTDOORS

HOME

CHILDREN

PETS

TRANSPORT

RESOURCES

LUXURY CINEMA

Take your next trip to the flicks up a level with sofas, footstools and G&Ts on tap.

Charlotte Street Hotel

15-17 Charlotte Street, W1T 1RJ (7806 2000, www.firmdale.com). Goodge Street or Tottenham Court Road tube. Tickets £35 incl afternoon tea or a 3-course dinner.

For the ultimate Sunday indulgence watch a film in this swanky hotel's screening room with either a three-course dinner or a champagne afternoon tea. Firmdale's Covent Garden and Soho (*see p14*) hotels put on similar weekend film events.

Electric Cinema

191 Portobello Road, W11 2ED (7908 9696, www.electriccinema. co.uk). Ladbroke Grove or Notting Hill tube. Tickets £12.50-£14.50; £7.50-£10 Mon.

Think luscious luxury with leather seats and sofas (book early for these), footstools and a bar inside

the auditorium. There's also has a fashionable brasserie next door.

Everyman

5 Hollybush Vale, NW3 6TX (0871 906 9060, www.everymancinema. com). Hampstead tube. Tickets £12.

The Everyman has a glamorous bar and two-seaters (£32) in its 'screening lounges', complete with footstools and wine coolers.

Exhibit

12 Balham Station Road, SW12 9SG (8772 6556, www.theexhibit.co.uk). Balham tube. Tickets £5.

This boutique cinema has no fewer than 24 leather sofas for two, plus a great drinks menu.

Thefilmworks

Odeon Greenwich, Bugsby Way, SE10 0QJ (0871 2244 007, www.odeon.co.uk). North Greenwich tube. Sofas £18-£20 for 2 people.

Upgrade to the gallery and it's a different world. Stretch out and enjoy the ample legroom, drink in hand.

City Secret

Sign up for **Secret Cinema** (www.secretcinema.org) and you could be in for a surprise. Monthly mystery screenings take place in the most unlikely of locations, from derelict theatres to children's playgrounds. Subscribers are only given details on the morning of the event – but rest assured, you won't be watching an anodyne Hollywood rom com.

contemporary Londoners know it as the last cinema where you could enjoy the film through a haze of cigarette smoke.

Riverside Studios

Crisp Road, W6 9RL (8237 1111, www.riversidestudios.co.uk). Hammersmith tube. Tickets £7.50; £6.50 reductions.

The Riverside is famed for its inspired double bills – a bargain at £7.50. The airy café and terrace are lovely in summer too.

Tricycle

269 Kilburn High Road, NW6 7JR (7328 1000, www.tricycle.co.uk). Kilburn tube or Brondesbury rail. Tickets £6-£9.50; £5-£8.50 reductions.

This well-loved cultural centre offers a lively mix of theatre, visual arts and cinema.

Private hire

Whether you're after a lavish screening of your favourite Hepburn film with your 200 closest friends or a cosy viewing of an old family holiday, venues across the city provide facilities to suit all budgets.

Big cinemas – including the **Prince Charles**, **Rio** and **Electric** (*see p12-p13*) plus chains such as **Everyman** (0871 906 9060, www.everymancinema.com) – also hire out auditoriums. Note that not all prices include screening rights, which start at £100.

The Garrison

99-101 Bermondsey Street, SE1 3XB (7367 6351, www.thegarrison.co.uk). London Bridge tube/rail. Capacity 30. Cost £50-£150.

This buzzy gastropub offers intimate screenings on a decent-sized screen (5ft x 4ft) in its cosy, living room-like basement.

One Aldwych

1 Aldwych, WC2B 4RH (7300 0700, www.onealdwych.com). Covent Garden tube. Capacity 30. Cost £100-£150/hr.

The slick screening room features 35mm hotel projection with Dolby SR widescreen and cinemascope; popcorn's on the house.

Phoenix Cinema

For listings, see p12. Capacity 255. Cost call for details.

Available for hire outside normal screening hours, the Phoenix Cinema is a big hit for children's parties.

Roxy

128-132 Borough High Street, SE1 1LB (7407 4057, www.roxybarandscreen.com). Borough tube. Capacity 220. Cost £200/hr.

Book ahead at this spacious bar, whose four-metre screen has full projection capabilities. Great cocktails and lovely staff make it a very popular choice.

16mm Café

19 D'Arblay Street, W1F 8ED (7287 8892, www.16mm-soho.co.uk). Oxford Circus tube. Capacity 16. Cost £100/hr.

The downstairs room at this warmly welcoming little café can be used to show films on its four-metre screen, while the owners are happy to arrange refreshments.

Soho Hotel

4 Richmond Mews, WC2H 9HB (7559 3000, www.firmdalehotels.com). Tottenham Court Road tube. Capacity 45 & 100. Cost £250/hr-£350/hr.

Two luxurious screening rooms are available at the Soho Hotel – and also at its sister operations, the Covent Garden Hotel and Charlotte Street Hotel.

GOING OUT

BEAUTY

FASHION

PARTIES

FOOD

HEALTH

ECO

OUTDOORS

HOME

CHILDREN

PETS

TRANSPORT

RESOURCES

Clubbing

London's ever-changing club scene remains innovative, creative and hedonistic.

Alternative nights out

London's alternative club nights are constantly evolving. Some favourite nights are listed below; for the latest overview, check out *Time Out London* (www.timeout.com).

As most of the nights listed below are held at various venues, we've given the websites where you'll be able to find details of upcoming events.

Book Slam ★
www.bookslam.com. Admission £10.
Invariably a sell-out, this monthly literary soirée (usually, but not always, on the last Thursday of the month) is leagues ahead of your average book club. Major authors read from recently published works, while spoken word and slam poets step up alongside soon-to-be big musical names. Venues vary, but line-ups are constantly impressive: think Dave Eggers, Hanif Kureishi, Nick Hornby, Adele, Kate Nash and the like.

Cabaret Room at Bistrotheque
For venue listings, see p95.
Admission £5-£20.
The small cabaret room at Bistrotheque is much loved by edgier performance artists. Regular performers include drag superstar Jonny Woo, Bourgeois & Maurice and the Lipsinkers.

Gaz's Rockin Blues
St Moritz, 161 Wardour Street, W1F 8WJ (www.gazrockin.com). Tottenham Court Road tube. Admission £8.
Long-running and popular ska, R&R, rocksteady and jive night, with bands featured each week.

Hula Boogie
8672 5972, www.hulaboogie.co.uk.
Admission £7.
When the grey-on-grey weather gets you down, there's a tiny bit of the sunny South Pacific to be found in... Kennington. One Sunday a month sees Hula Boogie – a colourful, floor-stomping rock'n'roll party that's hosted by Miss Aloha and Reverend Boogie – take over the South London Pacific Tiki Bar (340 Kennington Road, SE11 4LD, 7820 9189). If the hula and jive classes can't get you moving, nothing will.

I Knit London
www.iknit.org.uk. Admission free.
Knitting circles might sound like something your gran once went to, but young Londoners are flocking to I Knit London's gatherings in their droves. Events alternate between the I Knit shop (106 Lower Marsh, SE1 7AB, 7261 1338) and various central London pubs, and are particularly popular with gay knitters.

Killing Kittens
www.killingkittens.com. Admission varies; check online for details.
Girls who like boys but sometimes like girls too will love Killing Kittens, the monthly party for London swingers, held in a secret location. Participants are strictly vetted (young, attractive couples and single girls only), and the girls say what goes. You can keep your kit on, but the brave plunge straight in to the bacchanalia.

London Rollergirls
www.londonrollergirls.com. Admission £5-£6.
Enormously popular in Depression-era America, and now the subject of a worldwide revival, roller derby is a sometimes violent

GOING OUT

BEAUTY

FASHION

PARTIES

FOOD

HEALTH

ECO

OUTDOORS

HOME

CHILDREN

PETS

TRANSPORT

RESOURCES

EARLY OPENING

Been out at night and still wide awake? Carry on the excess with a cheeky breakfast pint at one of the city's early-opening pubs.

Smithfields' **Fox & Anchor** (115 Charterhouse Street, EC1M 6AA, 7250 1300, www.foxandanchor. com, opens 7am) remains popular and in sparkling form, while on the other side of the market, the **Hope** (94 Cowcross Street, EC1M 6BH, 0871 984 1334, opens 6am) has also been serving the traders for years.

Borough Market has a decent drinking spot in the **Market Porter** (9 Stoney Street, SE1 9AA, 7407 2495, www.markettaverns.co.uk, opens 6-8.30am Mon-Fri), where film buffs can enjoy the fact that scenes from *Mission Impossible* were shot here.

Non-market-related drinking can be had at the oddly-named **Only Running Footman** (5 Charles Street, W1J 5DF, 7499 2988, www.therunningfootman. biz, opens 7.30am Mon-Fri) in Mayfair, while at King's Cross, **06 St Chad's Place** (6 St Chad's Place, WC1X 9HH, 7278 3355, www.6stchadsplace.com, opens 8am Mon-Fri) occupies a modish, stripped-down warehouse. Further afield, the **George** (159 High Street, E11 2RL 8989 2921, opens 7am) in Wanstead is run by Wetherspoons, and remains an exceedingly handsome hostelry.

---

girls-only sport on skates. In a nutshell: two teams race around a track, each trying to block the other team's key player, called a jammer. What makes it a riot, though, are the girls' amazing punk-meets-burlesque costumes, the themes chosen by the teams, and the fund-raising rockabilly parties held most months.

Musical Bingo

www.musicalbingo.co.uk. Admission varies.
Like ordinary bingo but instead of numbers you cross songs off your card before hitting the dancefloor. Venues vary but include Concrete (www.concretespace.co.uk) at the Tea Building in Shoreditch among others.

Oh My God I Miss You! ★

www.ohmygodimissyou.com. Admission £5-£8.
With seemingly endless imagination, the Oh My God I Miss You! team transforms the Bethnal Green Working Men's Club (44-46 Pollard Row, E2 6NB, 7739 7170, www. workersplaytime.net) each month for its tremendous themed parties. Go Go Grind rewinds to a 1960s television set, filled with dancers on podiums and girls in teeny miniskirts, while the Birthday Club is like no party you went to as a small child. Always dress to the theme – a good time is guaranteed.

Stitch & Bitch

www.stitchldn.com. Admission free.
Craft is still where it's at as far as Stitch London is concerned. Their Stitch & Bitch sessions, held at various venues across town, have London's trendy types learning to knit, purl and cast-off amid lots of chat, drinks and a significant amount of cake. The collective has been involved with various charity events over the years and recently created a herd of sheep and picnic baskets made from plastic bags (or 'plarn') as part of Prince Charles's Garden Party To Make a Difference at Clarence House.

Torture Garden

www.torturegarden.com. Admission £22-£28.
All roads in London's fetish scene lead to Torture Garden, arguably the world's biggest S&M club. The monthly balls aren't half as intimidating as fetish virgins assume: people dress in sleazy vintage as well as small bits of rubber, and there's a zero-tolerance policy on leches.

GOING OUT

BEAUTY

FASHION

PARTIES

FOOD

HEALTH

ECO

OUTDOORS

HOME

CHILDREN

PETS

TRANSPORT

RESOURCES

Clubs

Where we've listed specific nights held at particular clubs (such as Jaded at Cable), the opening times given are for that particular club night, rather than the club's general opening hours.

In addition to the venues listed below, Nathan Gregory Wilkins' (*see p25*) tiny venue **The Drop** (Three Crowns, 175 Stoke Newington High Street, N16 0LH) is well worth checking out for its eclectic programming, edgy crowd and intimate feel.

Best for...
A tearing sound system

Fabric ★
77A Charterhouse Street, EC1M 3HN (7336 8898, www.fabriclondon.com). Farringdon tube/rail. Open 10pm-6am Fri; 10pm-7am Sat. Admission £13-£16; £10-£12 reductions
When Fabric opened to much excitement in 1999, the Bodysonic speaker system under its floorboards left punters completely lost for words – not that they'd have heard them anyway – and its spine-melting, trouser-flapping bass still wipes the dancefloor with every other club in London. Still retaining clubbing icon status after more than a decade in the business.

See also *East Village, 89 Great Eastern Street, EC2A 3HX (7739 5173, www.eastvillageclub.com).*

Best for...
Freaky electro fun

Bugged Out @ XOYO
32-37 Cowper Street, EC2A 4AP (www.xoyo.co.uk). Old Street tube/rail. Open check website for detail. Admission check website for details.
Bugged Out's new London residency at XOYO (a joint venture from Cymon Eckel, the Vinyl Factory, Bugged Out's own Johnno Burgess, Tom Baker and Marcus Weedon) is set to be as popular as its legendary one at the End. Think bubbly, brilliant, bleeding-edge electro euphoria, with appearances by everyone from Daft Punk to Dave Clarke, Squarepusher to Simian Mobile Disco.

See also *Fabric ON, for listings, see left.*

Best for...
Messy after-parties

Jaded @ Cable
Cable, 33a Bermondsey Street Tunnel, SE1 2EI (7403 7730, www.cable-london.com). London Bridge tube/rail. Open 5am-1pm. Admission £5-£12.
Anyone still on the dancefloor at 5am clearly wants to stay there until lunchtime – and they can thanks to Jaded, which combines spine-tingling electro mayhem with all manner of sleep-deprived skylarking. One of London's most hardcore parties, it's no wonder plenty of attendees opt to stay in the night before then head here after breakfast.

See also *Breakfast @ EGG (www.myspace.com/breakfastategg).*

Best for...
An eclectic booking policy

Plastic People
147-149 Curtain Road, EC2A 3QE (7739 6471, www.plasticpeople.co.uk). Old Street tube/rail or Shoreditch High Street rail. Open 10pm-2am Thur; 10pm-3.30am Fri, Sat. Admission £5-£12.
Complaints about clubs regurgitating the same floor-filling formats should be checked in at the door. An innovative programme sees nights from the likes of FWD (*see p19*), Dance Obscura, Warm and Ben Watts' Buzzin Fly Records.

See also *Basing House, 25-27 Kingsland Road, E2 8AA (7033 1900, www.basinghouse.co.uk).*

GOING OUT

BEAUTY

FASHION

PARTIES

FOOD

HEALTH

ECO

OUTDOORS

HOME

CHILDREN

PETS

TRANSPORT

RESOURCES

Best for...
Clubbing with a garden

Cargo
83 Rivington Street, EC2A 3AY (7749 7840, www.cargo-london.com). Old Street tube/rail or Shoreditch High Street rail. Open noon-1am Mon-Thur; noon-3am Fri, Sat; noon-midnight Sun. Admission free-£10.
Having the option of grabbing five minutes of fresh air is an important clubbing asset, and not just for smokers. Cargo's garden is one of London's finest outdoor clubbing spaces, with seating aplenty and heat lamps for chilly winter evenings.

See also *EGG, 200 York Way, N7 9AP (7609 8364, www.egglondon.net).*

Best for...
Jungle fever

Hospitality
Various venues (www.hospital records.com/hospitality).
Following four successful years at Heaven, Hospitality's legendary drum 'n' bass nights now take place at various venues across the capital (and nationwide).

See also *Ram Records @ various venues (www.ramrecords.co.uk).*

Best for...
Underground sounds

FWD @ Plastic People
Plastic People, 147-149 Curtain Road, EC2A 3QE (7739 6471, www.ilovefwd. com). Old Street tube/rail or Shoreditch High Street rail. Open 10am-2pm 1st & 3rd Thur of mth. Admission £7.
The jury remains out on how well dubstep translates from the studio to the dancefloor, but there's no denying that FWD is the most exciting night at which to catch it in experimental action.

See also *DMZ @ Mass (www.myspace.com/dmzuk).*

Best for...
Old-skool rave

Vintage House Foundation @ East Village
East Village, 89 Great Eastern Street, EC2A 3HX (7739 5173, www.eastvillage club.com). Old Street tube/rail or Shoreditch High Street rail. . Open 9pm-3.30am. Admission £5-£8.
This fantastic vintage house night digs through the crates from '88 to '08 unearthing the forgotten gems that have made and continue to make the capital groove. Events in summer 2010 proved a resounding success all round.

See also *Bang Face @ various venues (www.bangface.com)*

Best for...
Eclectic hip hop nights

On the Real @ Plan B
Plan B, 418 Brixton Road, SW9 7AY (7737 7372, www.plan-brixton.co.uk). Brixton tube. Open 9pm-4am. Admission £5.
Head to this monthly night for underground hip hop, classic soul and West Coast to Dirty South with DJs including Jimmy Screech and Scandal and Hobbit. Truly the kings of the capital's hip hop scene.

See also *Breakin' Bread @ various venues (www.breakinbread.org).*

Best for...
Gay clubbing

Popstarz@ The Den
The Den, 18 West Central Street, WC1A 1JJ (7240 1083, www.popstarz.org). Tottenham Court Road tube. Open 10pm-4am Fri. Admission £8 or free before 11pm.
The easy-going, affable Popstarz has found a winning formula: indie music (bands followed by DJs), credible pop and crunching electronic carnage across three rooms.

See also *Caligula @ Basing House (www.facebook.com/caligulauk).*

Comedy

Discover new acts and catch old favourites warming up for big gigs.

CENTRAL

Comedy Camp
Barcode, 3-4 Archers Street, W1D 7AP (tickets 0844 477 1000, www.comedy camp.co.uk). Leicester Square or Piccadilly Circus tube. Shows 8.30pm Tue. Admission £8 plus £2 membership.
This intimate, straight-friendly gay club is one of the best nights out in town. Resident host and promoter Simon Happily only books truly fabulous acts: Jo Caulfield, Harry Hill and Graham Norton are among those who have performed here.

Comedy Store
1A Oxendon Street, SW1Y 4EE (0844 847 1728, www.thecomedystore.co.uk). Leicester Square or Piccadilly Circus tube. Shows 8pm-10.30pm Tue-Thur, Sun; 8pm & midnight Fri, Sat. Admission £14-£20.
Apart from the corking bills every Thursday to Saturday, check out the brilliant Comedy Store Players (Wed, Sun) or the fantastic Cutting Edge Team (Tue). The Gong Show on the last Monday of the month is also not to be missed.

The Funny Side...
Upstairs at The George, 213 The Strand, WC2R 1AP (0844 478 0404, www.the funnyside.info). Charing Cross tube/rail or Covent Garden or Leicester Square tube. Shows 8pm Fri, Sat. Admission £12.50.
Two nights a week this award-winning club puts on a terrific line-up of well-established comedians in its medium-sized space in central London.

Soho Theatre
21 Dean Street, W1D 3NE (7478 0100, www.sohotheatre.com). Tottenham Court Road tube. Shows vary. Admission £10-£20.
Soho Theatre has become one of the best places in the capital to catch major comedy talents breaking out of their normal club sets to perform more substantial – and often more creative – solo shows.

NORTH

Downstairs at the King's Head
2 Crouch End Hill, N8 8AA (8340 1028, www.downstairsatthekingshead.com). Finsbury Park tube/rail then W7 bus. Shows 8pm Thur-Sun. Admission £4-£9. No credit cards.
Founded back in 1981, this Crouch End venue is still run with huge enthusiasm by the immensely knowledgeable promoter Pete Grahame. It's a pleasingly friendly sort of place too.

Hampstead Comedy Club
The Pembroke Castle, 150 Gloucester Road, NW1 8JA (7633 9539, www. hampsteadcomedy.co.uk). Chalk Farm or Swiss Cottage tube. Shows 8pm Sat. Admission £9.50; £8.50 reductions. No credit cards.
Ivor Dembina, host of this Saturday night club, hates the sound of people scoffing food during a show, and detests the idea of a disco afterwards. Instead, he invests everything in booking exciting, interesting acts.

Hen & Chickens ★
109 St Paul's Road, Highbury Corner, N1 2NA (7704 2001, www.henandchickens. com). Highbury & Islington tube/rail. Shows 7.30pm, 9.30pm. Admission £7-£10. No credit cards.
This dinky black box theatre (seating just 54) above the cosy Hen & Chickens is *the* place

to see great solo shows and catch major acts trying out their material before they head out on tour. Recent performers have included the likes of Jimmy Carr and Frankie Boyle.

EAST

Comedy Café
66-68 Rivington Street, EC2A 3AY (7739 5706, www.comedycafe.co.uk). Liverpool or Old Street tube/rail. Shows 9pm Wed, Thur, Sat; 8pm Fri. Admission £8-£15. Free Wed.
At this purpose-built Shoreditch club you're given a table for the evening and have to dine; the menu offers hearty burgers, pies and meze, among other things. Comedian and host Noel Faulkner mainly keeps to the back room now, but his influence can be felt in the emphasis on inviting, interesting bills and satisfied punters.

Theatre Royal Stratford East
Gerry Raffles Square, E15 1BN (8279 1160, www.stratfordeast.com). Stratford tube/rail. Shows 8pm Mon. Admission free.
Set in the opulent surroundings of the Theatre Royal, this little gem of a night is held every Monday and is completely free. The gig takes place in the long bar upstairs and has some great line-ups – especially considering you're not paying a penny to see them. A great choice for a comical night out on the town.

SOUTH

Banana Cabaret ★
The Bedford, 77 Bedford Hill, SW12 9HD (8682 8940, www.bananacabaret.co.uk). Balham tube/rail. Shows 9pm Fri, Sat. Admission £14-£16. No credit cards.
Satisfaction's guaranteed every Friday and Saturday in the roundhouse setting of Balham's Bedford Arms. Comics tend to enjoy playing here, and the bills are always strong.

99 Club Brixton
Babalou, The Crypt, St Matthew's Church, Brixton Hill, SW2 1JF (07760 488119,
www.99clubcomedy.com). Brixton tube/rail. Shows 8pm Sat. Admission £10.*
99 Club's critically acclaimed comedy nights (also hosted at the club's sister venues in Leicester Square and Islington) guarantee maximum laughs, good quality acts (Noel Fielding, Spencer Brown, Josh Widdicombe, Patrick Monahan, Ria Lina, Will Smith have gigged at 99 Club venues in recent months) and good, honest fun all round.

WEST

Bearcat Comedy
The Turk's Head, 28 Winchester Road, TW1 1LF (8891 1852, www.bearcatcomedy.co.uk). St Margaret's rail. Shows 8pm Sat. Admission £15, £12 members. No credit cards.
Way out west in suburban Twickenham, this is one of London's oldest comedy clubs, with an impressive list of past guests and current performers worth shouting about.

Headliners
George IV, 185 Chiswick High Road, W4 2DR (8566 4067, www.headlinerscomedy.com). Turnham Green tube. Shows 9pm Fri, Sat. Admission £12. No credit cards.
Surprisingly perhaps, Headliners is the only purpose-built comedy club in West London – but it's a very good one.
At the helm is the very experienced Simon Randall, who also runs the popular Ha Bloody Ha night at nearby Ealing Studios – also worth a look.

GOING OUT

BEAUTY

FASHION

PARTIES

FOOD

HEALTH

ECO

OUTDOORS

HOME

CHILDREN

PETS

TRANSPORT

RESOURCES

BEAUTY

FASHION

PARTIES

FOOD

HEALTH

ECO

OUTDOORS

HOME

CHILDREN

PETS

TRANSPORT

RESOURCES

GOING OUT

Music

Check out some of the city's lesser-known musical gems, from jazz nights to karaoke clubs.

Acoustic nights

Bedford
77 Bedford Hill, SW12 9HD (8682 8940, www.thebedford.co.uk). Balham tube/rail. Shows 7.30pm Mon-Thur. Admission free.
Above-average musos take to the stage in the Bedford's Elizabethan-style balconied theatre – Paolo Nutini cut his teeth here, while Pete Townshend and Willy Mason have both chosen it for secret shows.

Cavendish Arms
128 Hartington Road, SW8 2HJ (7498 7464, www.thecavendisharmsstockwell. co.uk). Stockwell tube. Shows 7pm daily. Admission free Mon-Fri, Sun; £5 Saturday.
The Cavendish Arms is one of south London's most passionate purveyors of live acoustic music. The first-class PA ensures the charming rear room venue sounds as good as it looks.

Cross Kings
126 York Way, N1 0AX (7278 8318, www.thecrosskings.co.uk). King's Cross tube/rail. Shows 8pm daily. Admission free-£10.
In an area forging towards the future, the Cross Kings parties like it's 1969. Communal living room aesthetics meet hallucinatory art-house inclinations, and regular music nights mingle with day-long festivals.

Green Note
106 Parkway, NW1 7AN (7485 9899, www. greennote.co.uk). Camden Town tube. Shows 9pm daily. Admission £4-£15.
This vegetarian restaurant and bar hosts a programme of suitably thoughtful live music – from folk and blues to jazz and country. The small space makes for an intimate atmosphere, but means queues around the block when big acts are treading the boards.

Regal Room
Distillers Arms, 64 Fulham Palace Road, W6 9PH (8748 2834, www.theregalroom. com). Hammersmith tube. Shows 7.30pm Wed-Fri. Admission free.
A rather glamorous venue above a less-than-glamorous boozer, the Regal Room offers a well-edited roster of artful acoustic acts.

Slaughtered Lamb
34-35 Great Sutton Street, EC1V 0DX (7253 1516, www.electroacousticclub.com). Barbican tube. Shows 8pm Mon-Thur. Admission £5-£8.
The Lamb's Electroacoustic Club nights pull in emotionally charged balladeers from around the UK to the Lamb's diminutive, candlelit downstairs room.

Troubadour
263-267 Old Brompton Road, SW5 9JA (7370 1434, www.troubadour.co.uk). Earls Court tube. Shows 8pm, days vary (at least 5 days a week); check website for details. Admission £5-£10.
Its sound system may be far from satisfying, but the cellar at this characterful pub is a live music mecca that has hosted the legendary likes of Hendrix and Dylan.

12 Bar Club ★
22-23 Denmark Street, WC2H 8NL (7240 2120, www.12barclub.com). Tottenham Court Road or Leicester Square tube. Gigs 8pm daily. Admission £3-£15. No credit cards.
The 12 Bar boasts one of London's most intimate stages, with ground-floor seating

and a snug gallery. Blues, folk and rock acts perform nightly to an appreciative crowd.

Jazz

In addition to the venues listed, the **100 Club** (100 Oxford Street, W1D 1LL, 7636 0933, www.the100club.co.uk) hosts occasional trad jazz sessions, the **Pigalle** (215 Piccadilly, W1J 9HN, 0800 988 5470, www.vpmg.net/pigalle) specialises in the jazzier end of pop and cabaret, and the **Jazz Café** (5 Parkway, NW1 7PG, 7485 6834, www.jazzcafe.co.uk) lives up to its name about half a dozen times a month. Both the **Barbican** and the **South Bank Centre** (for both, *see p12*) also host dozens of big jazz names every year, including the bulk of the **London Jazz Festival** (www.londonjazz festival.org.uk).

See www.timeout.com or www.jazzin london.net for the latest details on current and upcoming jazz events.

Bull's Head
373 Lonsdale Road, SW13 9PY (8876 5241, www.thebullshead.com). Barnes Bridge rail. Gigs 8.30pm Mon-Sat; 1-3.30pm, 8.30-11pm Sun. Admission £5-£12.
The rows of seating at this riverside boozer may resemble a school assembly hall, but acoustics are good and the music is of a high standard; regulars include pianist Stan Tracey and sax maestro Peter King.

Pizza Express Jazz Club
10 Dean Street, W1D 3RW (0845 602 7017, 7439 8722, www.pizzaexpress live.com). Tottenham Court Road tube. Gigs 8.30pm Mon-Thur; 9pm Fri, Sat; 8pm Sun. Admission £15-£25.
This 120-capacity basement club hosts excellent swing, mainstream, contemporary and fusion residencies from the likes of Lea DeLaria and Mose Allison. Tip: if it's sold out, try and you may just be able to cadge a seat at the bar.

Le QuecumBar
42-44 Battersea High Street, SW11 3HX (7787 2227, www.quecumbar.co.uk). Clapham Junction rail. Gigs 8pm Mon-Sat; call for details Sun. Admission £5-£15. Free before 8pm.
This lovely art deco bar and brasserie attracts a surprisingly young crowd with top drawer Gypsy jazz, alongside old-school swing, crooners, swing and nostalgia.

Ronnie Scott's
47 Frith Street, W1D 4HT (7439 0747, www.ronniescotts.co.uk). Leicester Square tube. Gigs 7.30pm daily. Admission (non-members) £15-£46 Mon-Sat.
After a change in ownership several years back, tickets, food and booze became super-pricey at this Soho legend. Things have been back on track of late though, with jazz heavyweights once more dominating in place of the mainstream pop acts who held sway for a while. The acoustics and the sightlines are pleasingly perfect.

606 Club ★
90 Lots Road, SW10 0QD (7352 5953, www.606club.co.uk). Earl's Court or Fulham Broadway tube/11, 211 bus. Gigs times vary; call for details. Admission (music charge) £8-£12.
There's no entry fee at this charmingly ramshackle 150-capacity venue: instead, the bands are funded from a 'music charge' that's added to your bill at the end of the night. Note alcohol can only be served with food.

Spice of Life
6 Moor Street, Cambridge Circus, W1D 5NA (7739 3025, www.spiceoflifesoho.com). Leicester Square tube. Gigs times vary; phone for details. Admission free-£10.
The basement of this old-school boozer hosts excellent mainstream jazz singers and instrumentalists, and there are weekly open mic nights too.

Vortex Jazz Club ★
11 Gillet Square, N16 8AZ (7254 4097, www.vortexjazz.co.uk). Dalston Kingsland rail. Gigs 8.30pm daily. Admission £8-£15.

GOING OUT

BEAUTY

FASHION

PARTIES

FOOD

HEALTH

ECO

OUTDOORS

HOME

CHILDREN

PETS

TRANSPORT

RESOURCES

GOING OUT

BEAUTY

FASHION

PARTIES

FOOD

HEALTH

ECO

OUTDOORS

HOME

CHILDREN

PETS

TRANSPORT

RESOURCES

The Vortex continues to draw a vibrant boho crowd. Line-ups remain as varied as ever, with left-field musicians mixing with cabaret divas and folkies.

Karaoke

Bloomsbury Lanes
Basement of Tavistock Hotel, Bedford Way, WC1H 9EU (7183 1979, www.bloomsbury bowling.com). Russell Square tube. Open 1pm-midnight Mon-Thur; 1pm-3am Fri, Sat; 1-11pm Sun. Room hire £30-£60/hr.
Two no-frills, retro-style rooms overlook the popular bowling lanes. There's an abundance of tunes to choose from and plenty of time to belt 'em out, with minimum time slots set at two-hours.

The Dolphin
165 Mare Street, E8 3RH (8985 3727). London Fields rail. Open 4pm-2.30am Mon-Thur; 4pm-4.30am Fri; noon-4.30am Sat; noon-2.30am Sun. Admission £3 after 11pm. No credit cards
With a beguilingly mixed crowd of arty, alternative types and old geezers, this Hackney boozer packs them in for a weekend sing-song – generally on Fridays.

Karaoke Box
18 Frith Street, W1D 4RQ (7494 3878, www.karaokebox.co.uk). Leicester Square or Tottenham Court Road tube. Open noon-1am Mon-Thur; noon-2am Fri, Sat; noon-11pm Sun. Admission free Mon-Wed, £3 after 6pm Thur-Sat. Room hire from £20/hr.
Regulars avow Karaoke Box is the best of the bunch, thanks to its value for money, friendliness and – vitally – reliable mics. There's also a branch in Smithfield (12 Smithfield Street, EC1A 9LA, 7329 9991).

K-Box
Cranbourn Mansions, 7-9 Cranbourn Street, WC2H 7AG (7287 8868, www.k-box.co.uk). Leicester Square tube. Open 6pm-midnight Mon-Wed; 6pm-3am Thur-Sat. Room hire from £40/2hrs.

Japanese cocktails help loosen the vocal cords at this four-floor temple to karaoke, along with gloriously tacky '80s videos.

Lucky Voice
52 Poland Street, W1F 7NH (7439 3660, www.luckyvoice.co.uk). Oxford Circus tube. Open 5.30pm-1am Mon-Thur; 3pm-1am Fri, Sat; 5.30-10.30pm Sun. Room hire £20-£110/hr.
Kitsch pink lighting and sleek, dimly lit private rooms make Lucky Voice the swishest karaoke joint in town (there's another branch in Islington, 173-174 Upper Street, N1 1RG, 7354 6280). Some of the rooms have stashes of props (think hats, wigs and toy tambourines) to inspire you.

Ribon
6 Holborn Viaduct, EC1A 2AE (7329 3254, www.ribonrestaurant.co.uk). St Paul's tube. Open 6-10.30pm Mon-Sat. Room hire £25-£50/hr.
The karaoke at this pleasingly authentic (if not particularly pretty) Japanese restaurant kicks off from about 6pm for parties who have booked.

Shanghai
41 Kingsland Road, E8 2JS (7254 2878, www.shanghaidalston.co.uk). Dalston Junction or Dalston Kingsland rail. Open 6-11pm daily. Room hire call for details.
What could be finer than tucking into a Chinese banquet before belting out Celine Dion tracks at the top of your voice? Nothing, that's what. There are two karaoke rooms for hire here, both can fit 40-50 people – perfect for birthdays, hen parties, engagement dos and the like.

Tiroler Hut
27 Westbourne Grove, W2 4UA (7727 3981, www.tirolerhut.co.uk). Bayswater or Royal Oak tube. Open 6.30pm-1am Tue-Sat; 6.30-11pm Sun.
This kitsch-tastic eaterie serves solid Alpine fare and has musicians playing and yodelling every night. It's not karaoke as such, but group sing-a-longs are encouraged.

Address Book Secrets
Nathan Gregory Wilkins

DJ, co-founder of History Clock label and owner of the Drop

I am a pub person and I love pubs in Soho like the **Coach & Horses** (29 Greek Street, W1F 7HG, 7437 5920, www.coachandhorsessoho.co.uk). I sometimes go there on a Sunday. They have lots of classic British dishes like fish and chips and sausages and mash. It's an old-fashioned pub and it's exactly what I think a British pub should be, especially as many are closing down.

Dalston Superstore (177 Kingsland High Street, E8 2PB, 7254 2273) is somewhere I've been going for however long it's been open. It's a really nice mix of the gay and straight crowd – which I like. It's not like other places in Shoreditch. They always have really interesting nights and there's lots of things going on.

I have been a member of **Close Up** (139 Brick Lane, E1 6SB, 7739 3634, www.closeupfilmcentre.com), a DVD rental shop, for three years now. They have an amazing selection of old films. I have discovered so many there. If you're not sure what to watch they can recommend great films.

Yalla Yalla (1 Green's Court Soho, W1F 0HA, 7287 7663, www.yalla-yalla.co.uk) does exceptional food. They describe it as Beirut street food. But it's not really like something on Edgware Road because it's quite modern and a lot more cosmopolitan. They do pastries – both sweet and savoury – and the staff are really friendly. There's nothing else like it in the West End.

I sometimes go to **Daunt Books** (83 Marylebone High Street, W1U 4QW, 7224 2295, www.dauntbooks.co.uk). It sells predominantly travel books (or books relating to travel) but it's great mainly because it's such a beautiful building. I love the architecture and like the fact that it's just as interesting historically as it is as a lovely bookshop.

Tayyabs (83-89, Fieldgate Street, E1 1JU, 7247 6400, www.tayyabs.co.uk), a Pakistani restaurant, is fantastic. Everything is done to perfection. People from the local community go there, which is a good sign because you don't always get that. I really like their lamb chops and all their grilled stuff is amazing.

For an evening out, **Bistrotheque** (23-27 Wadeson Street, E2 9DR, 8983 7900, www.bistrotheque.com) is great. It's run by two friends of mine who are true visionaries. They have the Midas touch when it comes to restaurants and the chef is incredibly talented. There is also a cabaret room with a bar downstairs – so you can spend a whole night flitting from one room to another.

Lounge Bohemia (1E Great Eastern Street, EC2A 3EJ, 07720 707000, www.loungebohemia.com) does great cocktails. It's a lovely little space that not a lot of people know about and it's one of the few places in Shoreditch where you can really relax, and the music is quiet enough so you can talk. It has a really interesting atmosphere.

GOING OUT

BEAUTY

FASHION

PARTIES

FOOD

HEALTH

ECO

OUTDOORS

HOME

CHILDREN

PETS

TRANSPORT

RESOURCES

GOING OUT

BEAUTY

FASHION

PARTIES

FOOD

HEALTH

ECO

OUTDOORS

HOME

CHILDREN

PETS

TRANSPORT

RESOURCES

Pubs & bars

Summer pints and late-night cocktails are all covered here.

Beer gardens

CENTRAL

Chapel
*48 Chapel Street, NW1 5DP (7402 9220,
www.thechapellondon.com). Edgware Road
tube. Open noon-11pm Mon-Sat; noon-
10.30pm Sun.*
Hedges screen busy Old Marylebone Road
from the Chapel's beer garden, where you can
wash down (unponcey) gastropub fare with
a pint of Adnams or glass of Addlestones'
cloudy cider.

Coach & Horses
*26-28 Ray Street, EC1R 3DJ (7278 8990,
www.thecoachandhorses.com). Farringdon
tube/rail. Open noon-11pm Mon-Fri.*
This Farringdon gastropub offers top-notch
English and French country food, and a
sterling list of beers. There's also a small but
appealing garden with a handful of tables.

Crutched Friar
*39-41 Crutched Friars, EC3N 2AE
(7488 3243). Tower Hill tube. Open 10am-
11pm daily.*
The neatly tucked-away garden is perfect for
leisurely summer lunches in the City. Staff
are friendly, and the wine list affordable.

NORTH

Albert
*11 Princess Road, NW1 8JR (7722 1886).
Chalk Farm tube. Open 11am-11pm Mon-
Sat; noon-10.30pm Sun.*
Everyone's welcome in this 11-table garden
– kids and dogs included. There's loads of
standing room, and a suitably bucolic apple
tree growing in the middle of it.

Albion
*10 Thornhill Road, N1 1HW (7607 7450,
www.the-albion.co.uk). Highbury & Islington
tube/rail. Open 11am-11pm Mon-Fri; 10am-
11pm Sat; 10am-10.30pm Sun.*
The Albion's serene, sizeable garden is a
thing of beauty, with its shady veranda,
flower beds and wooden tables and chairs.

Compton Arms
*4 Compton Avenue, N1 2XD (7359 6883).
Highbury & Islington tube/rail. Open noon-
11pm Mon-Sat; noon-
10.30pm Sun.*

Diminutive it may be, but the Compton has a lovely little paved courtyard, full of greenery and with space for about 25 drinkers.

Engineer
65 Gloucester Avenue, NW1 8JH (7722 0950, www.the-engineer.com). Chalk Farm tube. Open 9am-11pm Mon-Sat; 9am-10.30pm Sun.
The garden at this perennially trendy Primrose Hill pub is small but inviting, with lots of blooms. Kids are welcome.

Flask ✖
77 Highgate West Hill, N6 6BU (8348 7346). Archway or Highgate tube. Open noon-11pm Mon-Sat; noon-10.30pm Sun.
Tables in the front garden fill up alarmingly fast on clement days, so get there early to bag a spot, then camp out for the day. If you're in luck, the barbecue may make an appearance.

Red Lion & Sun
25 North Road, N6 4BE (8340 1780, www.theredlionandsun.com). Highgate tube. Open noon-11pm Mon-Wed, Sun; noon-midnight Thur-Sat.
Highgate's Red Lion & Sun offers two beer gardens, with a courtyard at the back and larger patio area at the front.

EAST

Approach Tavern
47 Approach Road, E2 9LY (8980 2321). Bethnal Green tube/rail. Open noon-11pm Mon-Thur, Sun; noon-midnight Fri, Sat.
This classic East End boozer with a contemporary twist has a large, pleasant patio, good beer and unpretentious food.

Eagle
2 Shepherdess Walk, N1 7LB (7250 0507, www.theeaglehoxton.co.uk). Old Street tube/rail. Open noon-midnight Mon-Thur; noon-1am Fri, Sat; noon-11pm Sun.
This big, old boozer (apparently immortalised in the song 'Pop Goes the Weasel') is rammed on Friday nights but usually pleasantly quiet for much of the rest of the weekend. All the better for taking over

its sizeable (and very pleasant) suntrap beer garden with a gang of mates and settling in for the afternoon.

Prospect of Whitby
57 Wapping Wall, E1W 3SH (7481 1095). Shadwell tube. Open noon-11pm Mon-Sat; noon-10.30pm Sun.
With views of the river and Canary Wharf, both the flagstone riverside garden and rooftop terrace are generally packed on summer weekends, when the pub also opens early (from 11am on Saturdays and Sundays between May-September).

Royal Inn on the Park
111 Lauriston Road, E9 7HJ (8985 3321). Mile End tube then 227 bus. Open noon-11pm Mon-Sat; noon-10.30pm Sun.
With a beer garden backing on to Victoria Park, an alfresco pint at this Victorian pub is a delight. There are barbecues in high season, and heaters for nippy evenings.

SOUTH

Avalon
16 Balham Hill, SW12 9EB (8675 8613, www.theavalonlondon.com). Clapham South tube. Open noon-11pm Mon-Wed; noon-midnight Thur; noon-1am Fri, Sat; noon-10.30pm Sun.
The Avalon has a deep, awning-covered terrace facing a busy road, a pretty side garden, a big and beautifully landscaped rear garden (complete with barbecue station), and a spacious bar area that wouldn't look out of place in *Country Living*.

Crooked Billet
14-15 Crooked Billet, SW19 4RQ (8946 4942). Wimbledon tube/rail. Open 11am-11pm Mon-Thur; 11am-midnight Fri, Sat; noon-10.30pm Sun.
On summer afternoons, Pimm's-quaffing customers bask in the Billet's lush garden, or order food to eat on Wimbledon Common.

Crown & Greyhound
73 Dulwich Village, SE21 7BJ (8299 4976, www.thecrownandgreyhound.co.uk).

GOING OUT

BEAUTY

FASHION

PARTIES

FOOD

HEALTH

ECO

OUTDOORS

HOME

CHILDREN

PETS

TRANSPORT

RESOURCES

GOING OUT

BEAUTY

FASHION

PARTIES

FOOD

HEALTH

ECO

OUTDOORS

HOME

CHILDREN

PETS

TRANSPORT

RESOURCES

North Dulwich rail. Open 11am-11pm Mon-Wed; 11am-midnight Thur-Sat; 11am-10.30pm Sun.
The two-tier garden and terrace come into their own on warmer days, when you can enjoy the barbecue or scoff a substantial Sunday lunch.

Dolphin
121 Sydenham Road, SE26 5HB (8778 8101, www.thedolphinsydenham.com). Sydenham rail. Open noon-midnight Mon-Thur; noon-1am Fri, Sat; noon-11pm Sun.
It's worth coming here for the garden alone, a formal criss-cross of box, privet and gravel around a central water sculpture, edged by attractive apple trees.

Duke of Edinburgh
204 Ferndale Road, SW9 8AG (7326 0301). Brixton tube/rail. Open noon-midnight Mon-Thur, Sun; noon-2am Fri, Sat.
Happy kids, leafy trees and plenty of picnic tables characterise this superior pub garden.

Dulwich Wood House
39 Sydenham Hill, SE26 6RS (8693 5666, www.dulwichwoodhouse.com). Sydenham Hill rail. Open noon-11.30pm Mon-Wed; noon-midnight Thur-Sat; noon-11pm Sun.
This elegant Young's pub has a charming, part-decked garden running around its side, which also hosts the odd jazz session.

WEST

Grand Junction Arms
Canal Bridge, Acton Lane, NW10 7AD (8965 5670). Harlesden tube. Open noon-11pm Mon-Wed; noon-midnight Thur-Sat; noon-10.30pm Sun.
The attractive three-part garden here has a decked balcony overlooking the canal.

Old Ship
25 Upper Mall, W6 9TD (8748 2593, www.oldshipw6.co.uk). Hammersmith tube. Open 9am-11pm daily.
One of the most coveted spots in the capital during the Boat Race, the Old Ship's terrace is a lovely place to drink at any time.

Swan
1 Evershed Walk, W4 5HH (8994 8262, www.theswanchiswick.co.uk). Chiswick Park tube. Open 5-11pm Mon-Fri; noon-11pm Sat; noon-10.30pm Sun.
Sweltering in central London? Then jump on the 94 bus heading west and don't alight until the engine is turned off. Within seconds, you can be sitting in the dappled light of the Swan's lush and leafy 30-table garden.

White Horse
1-3 Parson's Green, SW6 4UL (7736 2115, www.whitehorsesw6.com). Parsons Green tube. Open 9.30am-11.30pm Mon-Wed, Sun; 9.30-midnight Thur-Sat.
The White Horse is rated as one of the top beer pubs in the country and really saddles up in the summer with an enormous outdoor patio, a brilliant barbecue and a well-heeled local crowd.

Cocktail bars

As well as those listed below, Shoreditch's **Lounge Bohemia** (*see p25*) is beloved of locals for its excellent quality cocktails.

CENTRAL

For innovative cocktails in deliciously opulent surrounds, the bar at **Hakkasan** (*see p95*) is well worth investigating. So too is the low-lit basement bar at **Crazy Bear** (*see p95*), also in Fitzrovia – just don't quaff too many cocktails before attempting to negotiate the famously disorientating mirrored loos.

LAB
12 Old Compton Street, W1D 4TQ (7437 7820, www.lab-townhouse.com). Leicester Square or Tottenham Court Road tube. Open 4pm-midnight Mon-Sat; 4-10.30pm Sun.
Newer spots have overtaken the '70s-meets-'90s decor, but few can match the sheer enthusiasm and knowledge of the staff at the London Academy of Bartending. Cocktails

are king here, and many original combinations are mixed using LAB's own infusions and syrups (chorizo tequila, anyone?). Pull up a chair and let one of the ultra-helpful mixologists guide you through the menu. The party vibe means this place fills up early.

Milk & Honey
61 Poland Street, W1F 7NU (7065 6841, www.mlkhny.com). Oxford Circus tube. Open Non-members 6-11pm Mon-Sat (2hrs max, last admission 9pm).
Members bar Milk & Honey is open to all comers at certain times, if you call ahead. Sours, swizzles, punches and fizzes (from £8.50) are first-rate.

Polo Bar
Westbury Hotel, New Bond Street, W1S 2YF (7629 7755, www.westburymayfair.com). Bond Street or Oxford Circus tube. Open 11am-midnight Mon-Sat; noon-midnight Sun.
Polo eschews the bland international style of many hotel bars in favour of a gorgeous art deco look that's just the right side of opulent.

Purl ★
50 Blandford Street, W1U 7HX (7935 0835, www.purl-london.com). Baker Street or Marble Arch tube. Open 5pm-midnight Mon-Sat.

City Secret

For those times when your quest for a late-night drinking den fails – or you find yourself enthusiastically yelling 'all back to mine' at chucking out time – **Booze Up**'s (0800 3101707, www.booze-up.com) late-night alcohol delivery service is your fourth emergency service. They aim to deliver in 20-40 minutes and cover south London, most of southwest and south-east London, central London and the most central parts of east and west London.

Head for this ultra-stylish and discreet basement bar for some of the finest cocktails in the capital. Skilled staff mix up expert margaritas – perfect for kicking off that weekend feeling. Or bag yourself a loungey sofa and try a Clover Club (Tanqueray gin, fresh lemon, egg white and grenadine; £7).

NORTH

Gilgamesh
Stables Market, Chalk Farm Road, NW1 8AH (7482 5757, www.gilgameshbar.com). Chalk Farm tube. Open 6-11.30pm Mon-Thur; noon-11.30pm Fri-Sun.
Once you've gawped at the Babylonian-style decor, turn your attention to the lapis lazuli bar and fruity house cocktails (from £9.50).

25 Canonbury Lane
25 Canonbury Lane, N1 2AS (7226 0955, www.25canonburylane.com). Highbury & Islington tube/rail. Open 5pm-midnight Mon-Thur; 4pm-1am Fri; noon-1am Sat; 10am-12.30am Sun.
The premises may be small, but the baroque, chandelier-lit interior has plenty of character. Cocktails are a mere £6.50 each.

69 Colebrooke Row ★
69 Colebrooke Row, N1 8AA (07540 528593, www.69colebrookerow.com). Angel tube. Open 5pm-midnight Mon-Wed, Sun; 5pm-1am Thur; 5pm-2am Fri, Sat.
This tucked away bar has an impressive pedigree and won *Time Out*'s Best New Bar award in 2009. Opened by Tony Conigliaro, familar to keen-eyed cocktail hounds for his work at Isola, Roka and Shochu Lounge and Camille Hobby-Limon who runs the Charles Lamb pub a couple of streets away. Booking is advisable as this place is tiny. What is lacks in size it makes up for in tremendous cocktails and amazing attention to detail.

EAST

Green & Red
51 Bethnal Green Road, E1 6LA (7749 9670, www.greenred.co.uk). Liverpool Street tube/rail or Shoreditch High Street rail.

GOING OUT

BEAUTY

FASHION

PARTIES

FOOD

HEALTH

ECO

OUTDOORS

HOME

CHILDREN

PETS

TRANSPORT

RESOURCES

Open 5.30pm-midnight Mon-Thur; 5.30pm-2am Fri, Sat; 5.30-10.30pm Sun.
Named after the green and red of the Mexican flag, G&R attracts people going to the nearby Rich Mix cineplex and couples happy to pick at plates of meatballs or octopus ceviche while sampling the fabulous specialist tequilas and tequila cocktails.

Loungelover
1 Whitby Street, E1 6JU (7012 1234, www.loungelover.co.uk). Liverpool Street tube/rail. Open 6pm-midnight Mon-Thur, Sun; 5.30pm-1am Fri; 6pm-1am Sat.
This famously louche lounge offers a unique, upmarket ambience. Cocktails, listed by genre in a leopardskin menu, are around £9.

SOUTH

Hide Bar
39-45 Bermondsey Street, SE1 3XF (7403 6655, www.thehidebar.com). London Bridge tube/rail. Open 10am-midnight Mon, Tue; 10am-1am Wed, Thur; 10am-2am Fri; 5pm-2am Sat.
Expect meticulously mixed cocktails in laid-back surrounds. If you're tired of mojitos and margaritas, choose from one of the bar's books of 1920s cocktails.

Lost Society
697 Wandsworth Road, SW8 3JF (7652 6526, www.lostsociety.co.uk). Clapham Common tube/Wandsworth Road rail. Open 5pm-11pm Tue, Wed; 5pm-1am Thur; 5pm-2am Fri; 2pm-2am Sat; noon-11pm Sun. Admission £5 after 9pm Fri, Sat.
Lost has something of a roaring '20s feel, with art deco touches at every turn and glamorous cocktails of yesteryear (juleps, pina coladas).

WEST

Lonsdale
44-48 Lonsdale Road, W11 2DE (7727 4080, www.thelonsdale.co.uk). Ladbroke Grove or Notting Hill Gate tube. Open 6pm-midnight Mon-Thur; 6pm-1am Fri, Sat; 6-11.30pm Sun.

The spirit of Dick Bradsell, undisputed king of the London mixologists, lives on at his former stamping ground, with a splendid, sweeping cocktail menu.

Montgomery Place
31 Kensington Park Road, W11 2EU (7792 3921, www.montgomeryplace.co.uk). Ladbroke Grove tube. Open 5pm-midnight Mon-Fri, Sun; 2pm-1am Sat.
Any bar that takes its inspiration from the Rat Pack is aiming pretty high, but the cocktails at this slinky bar pass with flying colours.

Portobello Star
171 Portobello Road, W11 2DY (7229 8016). Ladbroke Grove tube. Open 11am-11pm Mon-Thur; 11am-12.30am Fri; 10am-12.30pm Sat; 11am-11.30pm Sun.
This 'cocktail tavern' deftly blends discerning bar and traditional boozer. The bountifully stocked bar is manned by friendly staff educated in the art of adult refreshment; 'Drink less but better' is the mantra of leading mixologist Jake Burger. His impeccable, approachable directory of discerning drinks is the last word on sophisticated intoxication. There are DJs on Friday and Saturday nights.

Fixed corkage wine bars

The following wine retailers allow you to buy your vintage of choice at retail price, then add a set corkage fee so you can consume it on the premises.

Bedales
5 Bedale Street, SE1 9AL (7403 8853, www.bedalestreet.com). London Bridge tube/rail. Open noon-8.45pm Tue; noon-10.15pm Wed; 11.30am-10.15pm Thur; 10am-10.15pm Fri; 8.30am-6pm Sat. Corkage £8.
Browse a terrific array of wines in the shop (friendly staff are happy to advise), then pop the cork and get stuck in.

Green & Blue

36-38 Lordship Lane SE22 8HJ (8693 9250, www.greenandbluewines.com). East Dulwich rail. Open 9am-11pm Mon-Wed; 9am-midnight Thur-Sat; 11am-10.30pm Sun. Corkage varies.

This shabby-chic wine shop and bar stocks around 150 wines. There's a small but enticing bar food menu, or for a £3 'chippage' charge you can bring your own grub.

Negozio Classica

283 Westbourne Grove, W11 2QA (7034 0005, www.negozioclassica.co.uk). Ladbroke Grove or Notting Hill Gate tube. Open 3pm-midnight Mon-Thur; 11am-midnight Fri, Sun; 9am-midnight Sat. Corkage £7.50.

A small selection of wines is available by the glass at this Italian eaterie and wine shop, but you can also scour the shelves and choose your own bottle to take home or drink in.

Planet of the Grapes ★

9-10 Bulls Head Passage, Leadenhall Market, EC3V 1LU (7929 7224, www.planetofthegrapes.co.uk). Bank tube. Open noon-11pm Mon-Fri. Corkage £10.

Over 450 wines are available at this unfussy wine merchant's, where you can pre-book older bottles for decanting before you arrive.

1707 Wine Bar

Lower Ground Floor, Fortnum & Mason, 181 Piccadilly, W1J 9FA (7734 8040, www.fortnumandmason.co.uk). Piccadilly Circus tube. Open noon-10pm Mon-Sat. Corkage £10.

Buying and supping wines from Fortnum's cellar is a very civilised affair. The bar itself is deliciously chic, while snacks are based on fresh, seasonal produce from the famous dfood hall.

Wine Library

43 Trinity Square, EC3N 4DJ (7481 0415, www.winelibrary.co.uk). Tower Hill tube. Open 11am-6pm Mon; 11am-8pm Tue-Fri. Corkage £6.75.

In its atmospheric vaulted cellars, the Wine Library offers a great range of retail wines, plus an impressive buffet lunch.

Late-night drinking

Finding another drink past 11pm can be surprising difficult. Here's our pick of places to try once last orders have been called; for late-night eateries, *see p90*.

CENTRAL

Ain't Nothin But... The Blues Bar

20 Kingly Street, W1B 5PZ (7287 0514, www.aintnothinbut.co.uk). Oxford Circus tube. Open 6pm-1am Mon-Wed; 6pm-2am Thur; 5pm-2.30am Fri; 3pm-2.30am Sat; 3pm-midnight Sun. Admission £5-£7 after 8.30pm Fri, Sat.

Resolutely scuffed-up and little changed in years, Ain't Nothin But... is a classic, with live blues and much toe-tapping every night.

Green Carnation

5 Greek Street, W1D 4DB (8123 4267, www.greencarnationsoho.co.uk). Tottenham Court Road tube. Open 4pm-2am Mon-Sat; 4pm-12.30am Sun. Admission £5 Mon-Thur; after 11pm Fri, Sat.

Head up to the opulent first floor of this Soho gay bar, where green and gold lacquered walls provide a sumptuous backdrop to witty banter, arty soirées and shameless flirting.

Long Bar

Sanderson, 50 Berners Street, W1T 3NG (7300 1400, www.sandersonlondon.com). Oxford Circus or Tottenham Court Road tube. Open 11am-2am Mon-Wed; 11am-3am Thur-Sat; noon-10.30pm Sun.

Cocktails in the candlelit courtyard are a sophisticated end to an evening – though at £12 a martini, you might want to stick at one.

Nueva Costa Dorada

47-55 Hanway Street, W1T 1UX (7631 5117, www.costadoradarestaurant.co.uk). Tottenham Court Road tube. Open noon-3am Mon-Fri; 5pm-3am Sat; 5pm-1am Sun.

This once down-at-heel basement bar has now been spruced up – though the kitsch live flamenco shows remain. Quaff rioja in the booth-lined bar or refuel with some tapas.

GOING OUT

BEAUTY

FASHION

PARTIES

FOOD

HEALTH

ECO

OUTDOORS

HOME

CHILDREN

PETS

TRANSPORT

RESOURCES

GOING OUT

BEAUTY

FASHION

PARTIES

FOOD

HEALTH

ECO

OUTDOORS

HOME

CHILDREN

PETS

TRANSPORT

RESOURCES

City Secret

Summer in the capital sees various pop-up bars setting up shop in unusual locations. Take the **Gin Bar**, a matt-grey 1940s Citroën H van that dished up gin cocktails on the terrace of the **Serpentine Bar & Kitchen** (www.serpentinebar andkitchen.com) in summer 2010, for example. Or **Frank's Café** (www.frankscafe.org.uk), which set up for the second year in a row atop a multi-storey car park in Peckham to serve beer, cocktails and classy bar snacks to a cheerful crowd of punters. Makes a change from the usual round of pub beer gardens, that's for sure. Check out www. timeout.com for the latest openings.

NORTH

Barrio North

For listings, see p76.
This friendly, laid-back bar on Islington's Essex Road is a prime spot for late night escapades (until 2am on Friday and Saturday nights, midnight the rest of the week). Think easy Latin vibes, great DJs and an enthusiastic crowd that's not adverse to a bit of dancing in the narrow mezzanine at the back later on.

Big Chill House

257-259 Pentonville Road, N1 9NL (7427 2540, www.bigchill.net). King's Cross tube/rail. Open noon-midnight Mon-Wed, Sun; noon-1am Thur; noon-3am Fri-Sat. Admission free-£5.
Spread across three quirky floors, this is the perfect spot for a late-night chill out. In winter, get cosy in the basement bar and in summer watch the bright lights twinkle while relaxing with a cocktail on the roof terrace. Depending on what time you rock up there's a rich mix of club nights, live music and performance-style events taking place here.

EAST

Charlie Wright's International Bar

45 Pitfield Street, N1 6DA (7490 8345, www.charliewrights.com). Old Street tube/rail. Open noon-1am Mon-Wed; noon-4am Thur, Fri; 5pm-4am Sat; 5pm-2am Sun. Admission £4 after 10pm Fri, Sat; £3 Sun.
This no-nonsense bar is an Old Street legend. It's all about pre-dawn debauchery and spirit-swigging – so don't expect polished surrounds (or glasses) and fancy cocktails.

Dalston Jazz Bar ★

4 Bradbury Street, N16 8JN (7254 9728). Dalston Kingsland rail. Open 5pm-3am Mon-Thur; 5pm-5am Fri, Sat; 5pm-2am Sun. No credit cards.
A comfortable jumble of old sofas and books, bargain cocktails and eclectic tunes make this place a classic late-night haunt.

Indo

133 Whitechapel Road, E1 1DT (7247 4926). Aldgate East or Whitechapel tube. Open noon-1am Mon-Thur, Sun; noon-3am Fri, Sat.
Indo's narrow, dimly lit premises contain a joyous mishmash of art, clutter and in-the-know locals: try to bag one of the front sofas.

SOUTH

We're also partial to London Bridge's **Hide Bar** (*see p30*), with its seemingly endless list of wines, spirits and cocktails.

Dogstar

389 Coldharbour Lane, SW9 8LQ (7733 7515, www.antic-ltd.com/dogstar). Brixton tube/rail. Open 4pm-2am Mon-Thur; 4pm-4am Fri; noon-4am Sat; noon-2am Sun. Admission £5 after 10pm Fri, Sat.
The long-running Dogstar is still going strong, with a music-savvy crowd swigging lager and dancing to hip hop and funk.

Hive

11-13 Brixton Station Road, SW9 8PA (7274 8383, www.hivebar.net). Brixton

tube/rail. Open 5pm-midnight Mon-Wed;
5pm-2am Thur; 5pm-3am Fri; 11am-3am
Sat; 10.30am-midnight Sun.
Hive's cocktail list (£6.50-£9) pays tribute to
mixologists past and present, ranging from
forgotten favourites to modern classics.

WEST

Harlem
78 Westbourne Grove, W2 5RT (7065
6814, www.harlemsoulfood.com). Bayswater
or Notting Hill Gate tube. Open 5pm-
2.30am Mon-Fri; 10am-2.30am Sat;
10am-midnight Sun.
DJs spin electro, funk and soul in the compact
basement bar; if you're peckish, all-American
soul food is served until late in the diner.

Lodge Tavern
53 The Mall, W5 3TA (8567 0173, www.
thelodgetavern.co.uk). Ealing Broadway
tube/rail. Open 11am-midnight Mon-Thur,
Sun; 11am-1am Fri; 11am-2am Sat.
There are decent DJs at weekends and a
quirky vibe, though the selection of beers
here is uninspired – best opt for a well-
mixed cocktail.

Ruby & Sequoia
6-8 All Saints Road, W11 1HH (7243
6363, www.ruby.uk.com/sequoia). Ladbroke
Grove or Westbourne Park tube. Open 6pm-
12.30am Mon-Thur; 6pm-2am Fri; 11am-
2am Sat; 11am-12.30am Sun.
It's not the latest-opening joint in town, but
this modish bar is a gem for a post-pub
cosmopolitan or two. Lay claim to one of the
olive leather booths, and admire the edgy art.

Pubs with games

Balham Bowls Club
7-9 Ramsden Road, SW12 8QX (8673
4700, www.antic-ltd.com). Balham tube/rail.
Open 4-11.30pm Mon-Thur; 4pm-midnight
Fri; noon-midnight Sat; noon-11.30pm Sun.
Sadly the bowls club has long since
disbanded and quirky memorabilia is all that
remains; sporting types can, however, play

snooker on two full-size tables. There's also
a chess set for the more cerebrally-inclined.

Balls Brothers Hay's Galleria
Tooley Street, SE1 2HD (7407 4301,
www.ballsbrothers.co.uk). London Bridge
tube/rail. Open noon-11pm Mon-Fri.
This wine bar takes its pétanque very
seriously indeed, hosting the City Pétanque
Challenge. The competition aside, its outdoor
pitch can be booked throughout the summer.

Bar Kick ★
127 Shoreditch High Street, E1 6JE (7739
8700, www.cafekick.co.uk). Old Street
tube/rail or Shoreditch High Street rail.
Open noon-11pm Mon-Wed, Sun; noon-
midnight Thur-Sat; noon-10.30pm Sun.
A boisterous crowd gathers in this flag-
bedecked bar for fast and furious table
football. If you're a dab hand, tournaments
are held on the last Thursday of the month.

Bricklayer's Arms
32 Waterman Street, SW15 1DD (8789
0222, www.bricklayers-arms.co.uk). Putney
Bridge tube/Putney rail. Open noon-11pm
Mon-Sat; noon-10.30pm Sun.
The oldest boozer in Putney offers suitably
traditional diversions: bar skittles, shove
ha'penny and the occasional pub quiz.

Freemasons Arms
32 Downshire Hill, NW3 1NT (7433 6811,
www.freemasonsarms.co.uk). Hampstead
tube or Hampstead Heath rail. Open 11am-
11pm daily.
This prize-winning gastropub features a
London skittle alley in its cellar – played with
a wooden 'cheese' and 21 skittles. The alley
can be hired, see www.londonskittles.co.uk.

Mango Landin'
40 St Matthew's Road, SW2 1NL (7737
3044, www.mangolandin.net). Brixton
tube/rail then 2, 3, 133, 159 bus. Open
5pm-midnight Mon-Thur; noon-3am Fri,
Sat; noon-11.30pm Sun.
This tropical-inspired, late-licence cocktail
bar is dotted with mates acting out grudge
matches with dominos.

GOING OUT

BEAUTY

FASHION

PARTIES

FOOD

HEALTH

ECO

OUTDOORS

HOME

CHILDREN

PETS

TRANSPORT

RESOURCES

GOING OUT

BEAUTY

FASHION

PARTIES

FOOD

HEALTH

ECO

OUTDOORS

HOME

CHILDREN

PETS

TRANSPORT

RESOURCES

Oakdale Arms

*283 Hermitage Road, N4 1NP (8800 2013,
www.individualpubs.co.uk/oakdale). Manor
House tube/Seven Sisters tube/rail. Open
noon-2pm, 5-11pm Mon-Fri; noon-11pm
Sat, Sun.*
Those of a competitive bent will be in heaven,
with air hockey, board games, chess, darts,
pool, table football and a Wii console; a
splendid array of small brewery ales provides
consolation in defeat.

Pembury Tavern

*90 Amhurst Road, E8 1JH (8986 8597,
www.individualpubs.co.uk/pembury).
Hackney Central or Hackney Downs rail.
Open noon-11pm Mon-Thur, Sun; noon-
1am Fri, Sat.*
The decor may be on the spartan side at the
local boozer, but there's a fine array of
games to play (bar billiards, pool, chess,
Scrabble and backgammon among them), plus
quality real ales from Cambridge's
Milton Brewery.

Warwick Arms

*160 Warwick Road, W14 8PS (7603
3560, www.warwickarmskensington.co.uk).
Earls Court or High Street Kensington
tube. Open noon-midnight Mon-Sat;
noon-11.30pm Sun.*
A grim location hides a little gem of a pub,
where Wednesday evenings bring 'Beat The
Dice' nights: throw two sixes after your order
and that round is free.

Quiz nights

Bull

*100 Upper Street, N1 0NP (7354 9174,
www.thebullislington.co.uk). Angel tube
or Highbury & Islington tube/rail. Open
noon-11pm Mon, Tue; noon-midnight
Wed, Thur; noon-1am Fri, Sat; noon-
10.30pm Sun. Quiz 7.30pm Mon. Entry
£1 per person.*
Always busy and buzzy, the Bull serves good
quality comfort food and an impressive
selection of continental beers. The Monday
night quiz here is always a winner.

Five Bells

*165-167 East End Road, N2 0LZ
(8883 1714). East Finchley tube. Open
11am-11pm Mon-Thur, Sun; 11am-
midnight Fri, Sat. Quiz 9pm Thur.
Entry £1 per person.*
They take their quizzes pretty seriously up in
East Finchley. A regular attendee advises
answering 'The Undertones' to any tricky
music question, as the quizmaster is a big fan;
same goes for 1980s cult classic *Back to the
Future* when the subject is film trivia.

Pineapple

*51 Leverton Street, NW5 2NX (7284 4631).
Kentish Town tube/rail. Open noon-11pm
Mon-Sat; noon-10.30pm Sun. Quiz 8.30pm
Mon. Entry £1 per person.*
Hidden away in a picturesque tangle of
backstreets, this refurbished Kentish Town
gastropub attracts a diehard band of regulars
– so it's no surprise that Monday's quiz night
often gets rammed. Arrive early to bag a
prime table in the front bar, and sample a few
real ales while you wait.

Prince George

*40 Parkholme Road, E8 3AG (7254 6060)
Dalston Junction/Kingsland rail. Open
5-midnight Mon-Thur; 5pm-1am Fri;
2pm-1am Sat; 2-10.30pm Sun. Quiz
8.30pm Mon. Entry £1 per person.*
There may not be food – this traditional
boozer prides itself on that – but there is a
superior jukebox, a decent selection of ales
on tap (London Pride, Flowers Original,
Litovel) and a friendly, locals-dominated
Monday evening quiz.

Retro Bar

*2 George Court, WC2N 6HH (7839 8760).
Charing Cross tube/rail. Open noon-11pm
Mon-Fri; 5-11pm Sat; 5-10.30pm Sun.
Quiz 9pm Tue. Entry £1 per person.*
With its decor and jukebox seemingly frozen
in the '80s (a black-and-white photograph of
Boy George hangs in pride of place), Retro
Bar is one of London's most eccentric gay
bars. The poptastic Tuesday night quiz is
tremendous fun, sometimes inspiring
impromptu singalongs to the Carpenters.

GOING OUT
BEAUTY
FASHION
PARTIES
FOOD
HEALTH
ECO
OUTDOORS
HOME
CHILDREN
PETS
TRANSPORT
RESOURCES

Beauty

Whether you're looking for a pristine blow-dry or a custom-blended foundation, here's who to call.

Bespoke beauty

Cosmetics à la Carte
19B Motcomb Street, SW1X 8LB (7235 0596, www.cosmeticsalacarte.com). Knightsbridge tube. Open 10am-6pm Mon, Tue, Fri, Sat; 9.30am-7pm Wed, Thur; 11am-6pm Sun.
'Made-to-measure' foundations are £45, while half-hour Lipstick Lovers' Lessons (£50) allow you to create your perfect colour. Staff can also precisely recreate favourite lippies, if you send a stub – though the first order costs £200.

Boutiques

Aesop Shoreditch
5A Redchurch Street, E2 7DJ (7613 3793, www.aesop.net.au). Shoreditch High Street rail or Liverpool Street tube/rail then 8, 26 or 242 bus. Open 11am-6pm Mon, Wed; 11am-7pm Tue, Thur-Sat; 11am-5pm.

> ### City Secret
>
> Lash extensions are the beauty fix of the moment, with fluttery results lasting up to seven weeks if you obey the after-care rules. Express lash extensions at Topshop's **Powder Lounge** (216 Oxford Street, W1D 1LA, 0845 224 4179, www.topshop.com) come in at £60. Short-term 'weekend' or 'holiday' extensions (lasting three days and two-four weeks respectively) are from £17.

The east London outpost of the successful Australian brand, which opened its first stand-alone store in 2008 in Mayfair, adds a fragrant touch to Redchurch Street. Aesop eschews the dubious claims made by other skincare ranges, preferring instead to focus on quality and scrupulously researched natural ingredients and gorgeous scents such as geranium, primrose and mandarin. Highlights include the Geranium Leaf body cleanser and Parsley Seed skincare range. **Other locations** *91 Mount Street, W1K 2SU (7409 2358). 227A Westbourne Grove, W11 2SE (7221 2008).*

BECCA
91A Pelham Street, SW7 2NJ (7225 2501, www.beccacosmetics.com). South Kensington tube. Open 10am-6pm Mon-Sat.
Products from make-up artist favourite Becca are great for dewy, radiant skin. Barely-there mineral-base foundations cost from £30, while concealers come in a remarkable 34 shades.

HQ hair & beautystore
2 New Burlington Street, W1S 2JE (0871 220 4141, www.hqhair.com). Oxford Circus tube. Open 10am-6pm Mon, Sat; 10am-7pm Tue, Fri; 10am-8pm Wed, Thur.
A beauty junkie's dream, HQ is crammed with stellar products, from Bare Escentuals' mineral-based foundations to Terax's hair range – a firm favourite with the A-list.

Liz Earle Naturally Active Skincare
38-39 Duke of York Square, King's Road, SW3 4LY (7730 9191, www.lizearle.com). Sloane Square tube. Open 10am-7pm Mon-Sat; 11am-5pm Sun.
Packed with botanical ingredients, this streamlined range encourages a no-fuss

MOBILE BEAUTY

After a relaxing massage or facial, the last thing you want to do is trek home. The answer is a mobile beauty therapist, who'll come to your home and leave you perfectly pampered.

InParlour
7736 7713, www.inparlour.co.uk. Open appointments line 9am-7pm Mon-Fri.
Experts range from beauticians and yoga teachers to stylists and wardrobe experts, with a minimum fee of £60 per visit. The popular Heavenly Bodies fake tan (£60) is artfully applied with pashmina brushes, with darker areas on your shoulders and décolletage to mimic the real thing.

Return to Glory
7993 8063, www.returntoglory. co.uk. Open appointments line 9.30am-9.30pm daily.
Whatever the service (from Swedish massage to manicures), you'll pay a flat rate of £55 an hour, £70 for 90 minutes or £90 for two hours. On the website, click on profiles of experts in your area to check their qualifications, customer feedback and availability.

Tranquillity
07850 426387, www.tranquil-beauty.co.uk. Open appointments line 9am-7pm Mon-Sat.
Operating in north and east London, mobile beauty therapist Tracy offers everything from basic beauty maintenance (manicures, waxing) to luxurious massages, body wraps and Elemis facials. You could have an hour-long Swedish massage for £40, for example, or a bikini wax for £10.

Unlisted London
0845 225 5505, www.unlisted london.com. Open appointments line 9am-9pm Mon-Sat; 10am-6pm Sun.
Aimed at stressed-out high-flyers, Unlisted offers a huge menu of treatments and a team of therapists that work 'pretty much 24/7' and cover the whole of London. Facials, from £75 per hour, include REN, Rodial and Karin Herzog; the minimum call-out charge is £75.

---

regime of cleansing, toning and moisturising. Despite the quality, it's relatively inexpensive.

Lost in Beauty
117 Regent's Park Road, NW1 8UR (7586 4411, www.lostinbeauty.com). Chalk Farm tube. Open 10am-6.30pm Mon-Sat; noon-5.30pm Sun.
Kitted out with vintage shop fittings, this chic boutique stocks a well-edited array of beauty brands, including Phyto, Environ and REN.

Ortigia
55 Sloane Square, SW1W 8AX (7730 2826, www.ortigia-srl.com). Sloane Square tube. Open 10am-6.30pm Mon-Sat.
Sicilian brand Ortigia's exotically presented soaps, candles and skincare products make fantastic gifts. Plants indigenous to Sicily are used to create the luxurious but well-priced toiletries – and they smell all the better for it. Think pretty-as-a-picture lavender drawer sachets, orange blossom shower gel and geranium hand cream.
Other locations *23 Marylebone High Street, W1U 4PF (7487 4684).*

Pixi
22A Foubert's Place, W1F 7PW (7287 7211, www.pixibeauty.com). Oxford Circus tube. Open 11am-7pm Mon-Sat; noon-5pm Sun.
Pixi's goodies range from candy-hued glosses and blushers to light, sheer foundations and credit-card slim eyecolour kits (£26), packed with subtle, deliciously easy to wear shades.

GOING OUT

BEAUTY

FASHION

PARTIES

FOOD

HEALTH

ECO

OUTDOORS

HOME

CHILDREN

PETS

TRANSPORT

RESOURCES

Space NK

8-10 Broadwick Street, W1F 8HW (7734 3734, www.spacenk.com). Oxford Circus or Tottenham Court Road tube. Open 10am-7pm Mon-Fri, 11am-5.30pm Sat.

Attentive assistants are a blessing for those needing advice, while the constantly updated product range keeps beauty mavens hooked.

Other locations *across the city.*

Services

EYEBROW THREADING

For the uninitiated, threading is an Indian hair removal technique whereby the therapist twists a length of thread around stray hairs, whipping brows into shape at lightning-quick speed. In addition to the companies listed below, waxing queen **Arezzoo Kaviani** (*see p43*) also offers threading for £35, while the highly experienced **Rekha Joshi** offers Friday and Saturday appointments at **Lost in Beauty** (*see p37*) for £17. Topshop's **Powder Lounge** (*see p36*) is also recommended.

Apsara Herbal

249 Whitechapel Road, E1 1DB (7377 2004, www.apsaraherbal.co.uk). Whitechapel tube. Open 9.30am-7.30pm Mon-Sat; 11am-6pm Sun.

Threading costs from £6 and takes five to ten minutes at this no-nonsense East End beauty salon; they can generally fit you in without an appointment.

Blink Eyebrow Bar

Fenwick, 63 New Bond Street, W1A 3BS (7408 0689, www.blinkbrowbar.com). Bond Street tube. Open 10am-6.30pm Mon-Wed, Fri, Sat; 10am-8pm Thur.

Blink's innovative threading bars offer a speedy walk-in service, though appointments can be booked in advance. Eyebrows take 15 minutes and cost £17; the majority of therapists here were trained in India.

Other locations *throughout the city.*

Kamini Salon

14-16 Lancer Square, off Kensington Church Street, W8 4EP (7937 2411, www.kaminibeauty.com). High Street Kensington tube. Open 10am-7.30pm Tue-Fri; 10am-6pm Sat.

With over 25 years' experience, eyebrow obsessive and celebrity favourite Kamini Vaghela delivers a fast, relatively painless service and long-lasting results. She has an infallible eye for which arch will best suit your face shape, and prices start from £45 per session.

Malika

Toni & Guy, Canada Place, E14 5AH (7719 1369, www.malika.co.uk). Canary Wharf tube. Open 11am-7pm Mon; 10am-7pm Tue, Wed; 9am-8pm Thur; 9am-7pm Fri; 10am-5pm Sat; noon-6pm Sun.

Eyebrow shaping costs £15 here, and we've had great results with Ritu, head therapist and one of the company's founders. Other services include inexpensive Indian head massage, eyelash tinting and manicures.

Other locations *throughout the city.*

Vaishaly

51 Paddington Street, W1U 4HR (7224 6088, www.vaishaly.com). Baker Street tube. Open 9am-6pm Mon-Sat.

Threading with facials guru Vaishaly Patel costs £45 for an initial consultation, then £45 thereafter. Aficionados swear by her perfect results; if she's out of your price range, ask for one of her three assistants (£30).

GOING OUT
BEAUTY
FASHION
PARTIES
FOOD
HEALTH
ECO
OUTDOORS
HOME
CHILDREN
PETS
TRANSPORT
RESOURCES

BEAUTY

GOING OUT
FASHION
PARTIES
FOOD
HEALTH
ECO
OUTDOORS
HOME
CHILDREN
PETS
TRANSPORT
RESOURCES

MAKE-UP LESSONS

BECCA

For listings, see p36.
A pre-booked lesson costs £90, £45 of which is redeemable against purchases. Over a glass of champagne, you'll be shown how to create flawless skin and a polished day-to-evening look.

Cosmetics à la Carte

For listings, see p36.
A huge range of lessons is on offer at the Knightsbridge store, from 20-minute make-up recharge sessions (£25) or half-hour make-up MOTs (£45) to longer, more in-depth lessons.

Lost in Beauty

For listings, see p37.
Make-up artist Georgie Hamed (a regular on glossy fashion shoots) offers lessons and parties in an airy private room. Prices start from £30 for a mini-makeover.

MAC

109 King's Road, SW3 4PA (7349 0022, www. maccosmetics.com). Sloane Square tube. Open 10am-6.30pm Mon-Sat; noon-5.30pm Sun.
Expert staff offer hour-long makeover sessions for glamorous going-out looks (£25), or more hands-on 90-minute tutorials (£50) – both fully redeemable against purchases. At £8.50, professional lash application is a steal, false lashes included.

MANICURES

There's nothing like a quick manicure to leave you looking perfectly groomed: if you haven't got time to make a special trip to the nail bar, you can always have a mani/pedi while you're having your hair done at **Jo Hansford** (see p49), or call a mobile beauty therapist like Tracy at **Tranquillity** (see p37)

California Nail Bar

78 Heath Street, NW3 1DN (7431 8988, www.california-nail-bar.co.uk). Hampstead tube. Open 10am-7pm Mon-Sat; 11am-6pm Sun.
This reliable nail bar charges £12.50 for a simple manicure with polish; if you're faking it, a full set of gel nails costs from £30.
Other locations 219D Finchley Road, NW3 6LP (7625 1188). 20 Malcombe Street, NW1 6AH (7224 9998).

Hawkeye

5 Silver Place, off Beak Street, W1F 0JR (7287 1847, www.hawkeyehair.com). Oxford Circus tube. Open 10am-6pm Tue, Sat; 10am-8pm Wed-Fri.
Taking a different approach to express nail bars, the therapists here make sure you relax with a complimentary glass of wine. The hour-long 'Pure Indulgence Experience' (£34) includes a manicure and full arm massage, though you can just pop in for a speedy shape and paint (£13).

Iris Chapple ★

3 Spanish Place, W1U 3HX (07956 307392). Baker Street or Bond Street tube. Open by appointment 8am-5pm Tue-Sat. No credit cards.
Ever-popular with glossy beauty editors, Chapple is warm and friendly whoever you are. Forget express treatments: this expert takes a good hour to file and polish nails to

GOING OUT

BEAUTY

FASHION

PARTIES

FOOD

HEALTH

ECO

OUTDOORS

HOME

CHILDREN

PETS

TRANSPORT

RESOURCES

Pixi

For listings, *see p37*.
Pop in for a quick 'little black dress'
day-to-evening makeover (£20),
or bring your make-up bag for the
90-minute masterclass (£60): staff
will advise on what to clear out, as
well as going through colours and
techniques. After-hours parties are
a bargain: for £15 a head, you get
the shop to yourselves, a glass
of bubbly and the services of two
make-up artists.

Shu Uemura

*24 Neal Street, WC2H 9QU
(7240 7635). Covent Garden
tube. Open 10.30am-7pm Mon-Sat;
noon-6pm Sun.*
Shu Uemera offers all kinds of
lessons, from one-to-one 90-
minute classes (£40) to two-hour
masterclasses; alternatively, staff
will do your eye make-up for £10.

her trademark 'square with a bevelled edge'
perfection. It costs £35 – but you'd pay as
much for less in many a nail bar. Pedicures
are equally miraculous.

Liza Smith

*Patrick Ludde, 22 Maddox Street,
W1S 1PW (7495 9040, www.patrickludde.
com). Oxford Circus tube. Open 9am-6pm
Mon, Tue, Sat; 9am-7pm Wed; 9am-8pm
Thur-Fri.*
There was much excitement in beauty circles
when manicurist to the stars (including
Naomi Campbell, Sarah Jessica Parker,
Victoria Beckham and Kylie) Liza Smith set
up shop at Patrick Ludde in 2010. Book in for
a spa pedicure (£75) or try a speedy
lunchtime mani or pedi (£30-£40/30 mins).

Leighton Denny ★

*Urban Retreat, 5th Floor, Harrods, 87-135
Brompton Road, SW1X 7XL (7893 8333,*

*www.harrods.com). Knightsbridge tube.
Open 10am-8pm Mon-Sat; 11.30-6pm Sun.*
An expert when it comes to the perfectly
shaped nail, the ebullient Leighton Denny and
his crack team of manicurists can be found at
Harrods' Urban Retreat. Using his long-
lasting polishes, a mani costs £35, a pedi £50.

Wah Nails

*420 Kingsland Road, E8 4AA (7812 9889,
www.wah-nails.com). Dalston Junction or
Haggerston rail. Open noon-8pm Tue-Sat.*
Hip Dalston nail salon specialising in nail art.
Decorate your talons with Wah's signature
leopard print (£18) or go for all-over
rhinestones (£70) for maximum bling.
Whether you want your nails long, short,
square, round or pointy; stripy, spotty or
covered in Lichtenstein-style 'Pows'; black,
gold, orange, fuschia or grey... Wah has it
covered, with glitter on top.
Other locations *Topshop Basement, 214
Oxford Street, W1D 1LA (7927 7844).*

MASSAGE

City Beach

*28 Hanbury Street, E1 6QR (7247 7878,
www.citybeach.biz). Liverpool Street tube/rail
or Shoreditch High Street rail. Open 10am-
7pm Mon-Wed, Fri; 10am-8pm Thur;
10am-5pm Sat, Sun. No credit cards.*
The massages at this Spitalfields salon come
recommended and are great value: a full body
massage (for women only) costs £35, while a
half-hour back, neck and shoulder rub is £25.

Lavender Hill Siam Beauty

*119 Lavender Hill, SW11 5QL (7585 1222,
www.siambeauty.co.uk). Clapham Junction
rail. Open 9.30am-11pm daily. Massage
11am-11pm daily.*
We salute this no-frills gem for its long
opening hours and amazing value for money.
Thai or Swedish massage costs a mere £30
for an hour, while other treatments are
equally cheap: a brow shape is yours for a
paltry fiver, while hour-long Decleor or
Dermalogica facials cost from £38.
Other location *12 Lavender Hill, SW11
5RW (7924 1695).*

Make the most of London life

Pure Massage

3-5 Vanston Place, SW6 1AY (7381 8100, www.puremassage.com). Fulham Broadway tube. Open 11am-9pm Mon-Fri; 10am-9pm Sat; 11am-6pm Sun.

Pure offers a wide range of massages in tranquil surroundings. Drop in for a 15-minute, fully clothed 'chair' massage (£15), or indulge in 90 dreamy minutes with the Body Pure Massage (£97), combining deep tissue, Thai, Swedish and acupressure techniques. **Other locations** *Fenwick, 63 New Bond Street, W1A 3BS (7381 8100).*

Relax

65-67 Brewer Street, W1F 9UP (7494 3333, www.relax.org.uk). Piccadilly Circus tube. Open 10am-9pm Mon-Sat; noon-8pm Sun.

This Soho massage specialist offers a slick service at reasonable prices (generally £70/hr or £40/half hr). Therapists are extremely professional and the place has an unfussy vibe that makes it appealing to men as well as women. The menu includes aromatherapy, swedish, sports, deep tissue and pregnancy massages (among others) along with reflexology, reiki and various beauty treatments. For those high on stress but short on time, there are chair massages available to put you back on track without getting your kit off. Try the Relax Energiser (£17 for 15 minutes) or the longer (30 minutes) Relax Unwinder. **Other locations** *2-3 The Media Centre, BBC White City, W12 7TS (7087 9033).*

Shine Holistic

52 Stoke Newington Church Street, N16 0NB (7241 5033, www.shineholistic.co.uk). Stoke Newington rail or 73, 476 bus. Open 10am-9.15pm Mon-Fri; 10am-6pm Sat; 11am-6pm Sun.

Practitioners at this friendly holistic health centre offer all manner of massage specialists, from Thai to deep tissue, in the spacious, stylishly understated treatment rooms. Aromatherapy massages with Florentina (£50/hr) are blissful, easing out every tension with a bespoke blend of oils that's tailored to each client's needs.

WAXING

Hair removal expert **Kamini** (*see p39*) also offers waxing. Using aromatherapy wax, she promises silky-smooth results and no ingrown hairs.

For a waxing session in the comfort of your own home, *see p37*.

Arezoo Kaviani

Hans Crescent, Knightsbridge (7584 6868, www.arezoo.co.uk). Knightsbridge tube. Open 9am-9pm daily. No credit cards.

Celebrity favourite Arezoo Kaviani charges £65 for a Brazilian wax, £70 for a Playboy. Specify if you'd like to be waxed by Arezoo herself, and book well ahead.

Katie Young's

Unit 12, Hoxton Walk, Hoxton Street, N1 6RA (7739 9271). Old Street tube/rail. Open 10am-6pm Tue, Wed; 10am-7pm Thur, Fri; 9am-6pm Sat.

This cheap-and-cheerful Hoxton salon provides good quality waxing at bargain rates, charging from £12 for a half-leg wax.

Ki Mantra Urban Life Spa

5 Camden Passage, N1 8EA (7226 8860, www.kimantra.co.uk). Angel tube. Open 11am-8pm Mon; 10am-8pm Tue-Fri; 11am-6pm Sun.

Waxing prices are surprisingly reasonable at this Islington salon, located just off Upper Street: a half leg wax is £20, a bikini £14, and a full leg and bikini £36. Weekends tend to be busy, so try to book ahead. **Other locations** *Holiday Inn, Ozone Health and Fitness, 1 King's Cross Road, WC1X 9HX (7698 4039).*

Otylia Roberts ✦

23 Geroge Street, W1U 3QA (7486 5537, www.otyliaroberts.co.uk). Bond Street tube. Open 10am-6pm Mon; 10am-7pm Tue-Thur; 10am-5.30pm Fri; 9.30am-5pm Sat.

Queen of the Brazilian, Polish-born Otylia Roberts uses beeswax-based hot wax instead of strips. Less painful, and with better results, it is pricier: from £34 for a half leg (the Brazilian is £49, while a Hollywood is £51).

GOING OUT

BEAUTY

FASHION

PARTIES

FOOD

HEALTH

ECO

OUTDOORS

HOME

CHILDREN

PETS

TRANSPORT

RESOURCES

GOING OUT

BEAUTY

FASHION

PARTIES

FOOD

HEALTH

ECO

OUTDOORS

HOME

CHILDREN

PETS

TRANSPORT

RESOURCES

Strip
*112 Talbot Road, W11 1JR (7727 2754,
www.2strip.com). Westbourne Park tube.
Open 10am-8pm Mon-Fri; 10am-6pm Sat;
noon-6pm Sun.*
The therapists at Strip use Lycon wax, which
promises – and, according to our sources,
delivers – a less painful wax; treatment
rooms also feature distracting plasma screen
TVs. Prices aren't too steep, with a bikini
wax costing from £22. The lengthy menu
also has plenty of options for men, from back
waxes to 'Male Brazilians'.
Other locations *102 Fulham Road, SW3
6HS (7590 0050). 69 Berwick Street, W1F
8SZ (7434 4222).*

Spas

Best for…
Amazing facials

Adamina Day Spa
*276-280 Kensington High Street, W8 6ND
(7751 1611, www.adaminaspa.com). High
Street Kensington tube. Open 11am-8pm
Mon-Fri; 11am-7pm Sat; 11am-6pm Sun.*
Adamina offers superlative facials using
rarely seen Yon-ka products – beloved of
facialists and A-listers across the pond. The
collagen-boosting 'Adamina Glow' is a good
place to start: £105 for 90 blissful minutes.

Angel Therapy Rooms
*16B Essex Road, N1 8LN (7226 1188,
www.angeltherapyrooms.com). Angel tube or
Essex Road rail. Open noon-8pm Wed,
Thur; 11am-6pm Fri; 11am-6pm Sat;
11am-5pm Sun.*
Set in a lovely Victorian townhouse, Angel
Therapy Rooms offers a range of organic
treatments. The superb signature Holistic
Facial blends reiki, reflexology and intense
massage techniques (£95/75mins).

Eve Lom
*2 Spanish Place, W1U 3HU (7935 9988,
www.evelom.co.uk). Bond Street or Marble
Arch tube. Open 9am-5pm Tue-Sat. No
credit cards.*

The signature facial (£140/90mins) involves
a thorough cleanse, a pore-opening paraffin
wax mask, lymphatic drainage and an
acupressure massage; afterwards, even spa
cynics have admitted to seeing a visible
difference. To see Lom herself (£250), book
a couple of months ahead.

Fresh
*92 Marylebone High Street, W1U 4RD
(7486 4100, www.fresh.com). Baker Street
or Regent's Park tube. Open 10am-7pm
Mon-Wed, Fri, Sat; 10am-8pm Thur;
11am-5pm Sun.*
In an elegant treatment room, hidden away
at the back of this friendly shop, customised
facials take an hour (£65). While a face mask
works its magic, enjoy a neck, shoulder and
hand massage. Afterwards, therapists are
happy to apply a touch of Fresh make-up.

Best for…
Budget pampering

Porchester Spa
*The Porchester Centre, Queensway, W2
5HS (7792 3980, www.nuffieldhealth.
com/communityfitness). Bayswater or
Royal Oak tube. Open women only 10am-
10pm Tue, Thur, Fri; 10am-4pm Sun. Men
only 10am-10pm Mon, Wed, Sat. Mixed
couples 4-10pm Sun. Last admission 2hrs
before closing.*
The Grade II-listed Porchester's marble and
green-tiled relaxation room is an art deco
delight, while downstairs lies a warren of

City Secret

For the cheapest beauty treatments
in town, make for to the student-run
London School of Beauty (48
Margaret Street, W1W 8SE, 7580
0355). Here, supervised students will
beautify you for a fraction of the cost:
an hour-long French manicure will set
you back £9, for instance, while a 90-
minute stress-busting aromatherapy
massage costs just £25.

hot rooms, steam rooms and a sauna. Treatments include shmeise massages (£25), which are performed with a soapy raffia brush, and must be booked ahead. Admission is £23 for non-members, or £31 per couple on Sundays.

Spa London
York Hall Leisure Centre, Old Ford Road, E2 9PJ (8709 5845, www.spa-london.org). Bethnal Green tube. Open women only 10am-9.30pm Tue, Fri; 10am-4.30pm Wed; 9am-7.30pm Sat. Men only 11am-9.30pm Mon; 10am-9.30pm Thur. Mixed 5-9.30pm Wed; 9am-7.30pm Sun.

We didn't like losing the Turkish baths that made way for Spa London, but there's no denying it's good value for money – and rather slick to boot. After paying admission (£21.50 for non-members) you can relax in the steam rooms, Turkish hot rooms, sauna, monsoon showers and relaxation room, or book in advance for one of the reasonably priced face and body treatments or massages.

Best for...
Serious relaxation

Berkeley Spa ★
The Berkeley Hotel, Wilton Place, SW1X 7RL (7201 1699, www.the-berkeley.com). Knightsbridge tube. Open 8am-9pm Mon-Fri; 9am-7.30pm Sat, Sun.

If one were hopelessly rich, one just might move into the Berkeley and become a fixture at the spa. The facials, using Comfort Zone products, are excellent, eliminating every molecule of dirty city air (from £90/hr). To unwind seriously, take a dip in the ultra-glamorous rooftop pool afterwards – it's like being briefly but blissfully transported to a Côte d'Azur villa.

Body Experience
50 Hill Rise, Richmond, Surrey TW10 6UB (8334 9999, www. bodyexperience.co.uk). Richmond tube/rail. Open 10am-7.30pm Tue; 10am-8.30pm Wed, Thur; 10am-7pm Fri, Sat; 10am-6pm Sun.

The robes at Body Experience are the cosiest in London, and there's a wonderfully peaceful relaxation room and outdoor terrace where you can curl up with a complimentary post-treatment herbal tea and fresh fruit salad.

Floatworks
1 Thrale Street, SE1 9HW (7357 0111, www.floatworks.com). Borough tube or London Bridge tube/rail. Open 10am-10pm daily.

Flotation therapy involves lying in a dark, warm salt-water filled pod: the salt keeps you from sinking, while the watery suspension slowly unknots bad postural habits. After an hour-long session (£40; three sessions for £80), book a massage (from £45/hr) for the ultimate zone-out. There's a menu including aromatherapy, holistic, lymphatic drainage, pregnancy and shiatsu massages.

Best for...
A quick fix

Bliss
60 Sloane Avenue, SW3 3DD (7590 6146, www.blisslondon.co.uk). Sloane Square or South Kensington tube. Open 9.30am-8pm Mon-Fri; 9.30am-6.30pm Sat; noon-6pm Sun.

New York import Bliss shows the competition that speedy can also be special. Mani- and pedicures are the speciality and last for weeks. It's great for unchatty

GOING OUT
BEAUTY
FASHION
PARTIES
FOOD
HEALTH
ECO
OUTDOORS
HOME
CHILDREN
PETS
TRANSPORT
RESOURCES

GOING OUT

BEAUTY

FASHION

PARTIES

FOOD

HEALTH

ECO

OUTDOORS

HOME

CHILDREN

PETS

TRANSPORT

RESOURCES

Londoners, as you can don headphones and watch sitcoms as your tootsies are shaped, buffed and polished (from £30/30mins).

Cucumba

12 Poland Street, W1F 8QB (7734 2020, www.cucumba.co.uk). Oxford Circus tube. Open 10am-8pm Mon-Fri; 11am-7pm Sat; by appointment Sun.

Ten minutes is enough for a nifty head massage, threading or a foot spa (all £13.50) – and if it's just too good to call a halt to, a cheeky five minutes more is £3.50. Twenty-minute sessions, meanwhile, are £22.50.

Groom

Selfridges, 400 Oxford Street, W1A 1AB (7499 1199, www.groomlondon.com). Bond Street tube. Open 9.30am-9pm Mon-Sat; 11.30am-6pm Sun.

With two therapists working on you at once, Groom delivers fast results. Nippiest of all are the half-hour packages: the Zoom Groom (£65) incorporates a mini-facial and manicure or pedicure, while the Wax Works package (£60) includes a lightning-speed half leg, bikini and underarm wax.

Best for...
Men

Nickel Spa

27 Shorts Gardens, WC2H 9AP (7240 4048, www.nickelspalondon.co.uk). Covent Garden tube. Open noon-6pm Mon; 10am-7pm Tue, Wed, Sat; 10am-8pm Thur, Fri; noon-5pm Sun.

With fantastic, male-specific grooming products upstairs, the treatments happen downstairs, where the decor is New York boxing gym meets submarine. Hour-long massages can be teeth-grittingly hard if you wish, but the aesthetic side is not overlooked – an eye-watering 'back, sack and crack' wax can be yours for £45.

Refinery

60 Brook Street, W1K 5DU (7409 2001, www.the-refinery.com). Bond Street tube. Open 10am-7pm Mon, Tue; 10am-8pm Wed-Fri; 9am-6pm Sat; 11am-5pm Sun.

Gentlemen's club melds with contemporary spa at this reliable men-only venue. An hour-long sports therapy massage is suitably manly (£90), while traditional wet shaves are £40. For the office-bound chap, a (fake) sun-kissed face is £25.

Best for...
Sheer luxury

Spa at Brown's

Brown's Hotel, Albemarle Street, W1S 4BP (7518 4009, www.brownshotel.com). Green Park tube. Open 9.30am-8pm daily.

With lots of dark wood, low lighting and expensive fixtures, Brown's plush spa is a delight. Treatment rooms are sumptuously kitted out for treats such as Mellow Mama pampering pregnancy massages (from £95/75mins) and slimming mud wraps using Natura Bisse wonder products (from £110/75mins).

Spa InterContinental

InterContinental Park Lane, 1 Hamilton Place, W1J 7QY (7318 8691, www.spa intercontinental.com). Hyde Park Corner tube. Open 10am-9pm Mon; 9am-9pm Tue-Fri; 10am-6pm Sat, Sun.

In a spa where you find Elemis's gorgeous, hard-working products, you can be assured of a top-notch treatment in soothing, luxurious surroundings. An extensive menu of 15-minute booster treatments (£22.50), which can be added on to longer massages, facials or floats, are great for the time-poor. Packages include lunch.

Spa at Mandarin Oriental

Mandarin Oriental Hyde Park, 66 Knightsbridge, SW1X 7LA (7838 9888, www.mandarinoriental.com). Knightsbridge tube. Open 7am-10pm daily.

Arrive early to wind down in the wet rooms and relaxation areas of this most opulent of hotel spas, with its sleek, Eastern-inspired decor and 'Amethyst Crystal' steam room. If money's no object, the shiatsu-inspired ginger ritual offers two hours of heavenly massage, with two therapists working in unison (£360).

Hair

From bargain trainee cuts to swanky Mayfair glamour, below you'll find our pick of the city's hairdressers and salon services.

Blow-dry bars & lessons

There's nothing like a salon blow-dry for feeling super-groomed. Prices vary considerably, depending on how swish the salon is and how senior the stylist: we've come across anything from £15 to £40. The following offer blow-dry lessons, or a particularly special service.

Aveda Institute

174 High Holborn, WC1V 7AA (7759 7355,www.aveda.co.uk). Holborn tube. Open 9am-7pm Mon-Wed; 8am-8pm Thur, Fri; 9am-6.30pm Sat; 11am-5pm Sun.
Blow-dries range from £25 with an assistant to £64 with an artistic director, and are best booked a week in advance. One-on-one 75-minute lessons with Olivier are offered on Thursdays, Fridays and Saturdays.

Hari's

305 Brompton Road, SW3 2DY (7581 5211, www.harissalon.com). South Kensington tube. Open 9.30am-6.30pm Mon-Sat.
Head to this slick salon for the ultimate styling session – the Brazilian (or permanent) blow-dry. At £200, it's not cheap but the results last for up to four months – a godsend for the frizz-afflicted. A mix of natural ingredients (including cocoa oil, white and red clay, keratin and shea butter) is applied to the hair and sealed with straightening irons. After leaving the hair for three days, in which the treatment takes full effect, you wash it to reveal the smooth, shiny, perfect hair of your dreams.
Other locations *233 King's Road, SW3 5EJ (7349 8722).*

Headmasters Blo Out Bar

Fenwick, 63 New Bond Street, W1A 3BS (7629 9161, www.hmhair.co.uk). Bond Street tube. Open 10am-6.30pm Mon-Wed, Fri, Sat; 10am-8pm Thur.
Choose from a menu of six styles (£25), in this glassed-off area in the beauty hall. For added gloss, conditioning treatments are £7.50.

Hersheson's Blow Dry Bar

Topshop, 214 Oxford Street, W1W 8LG (7927 7888, www.hershesonsblowdrybar. com). Oxford Circus tube. Open 9am-9pm Mon-Sat; 11.30am-6pm Sun.
On Topshop's lower ground floor, a pink-and-white pod contains three blow-dry stations, with one reserved for walk-ins. Choose from eight catwalk-inspired styles, from the tousled Bardot up-do to the sleek Super Straight for £22: appointments last half an hour.
Other locations *Westfield, Ariel Way, W12 7GF (8743 0868).*

Pimps and Pin-ups ★

14 Lamb Street, E1 6EA (7426 2121, www.pimpsandpinups.com). Liverpool Street tube/rail. Open 10am-8pm Mon-Fri; 10am-6pm Sat, Sun.
If you really want to look the part at a '30s-style tea-dance or rockabilly night, use Pimps and Pin-ups' unique styling service. Bring in a picture of your favourite bygone starlet and your consultant will emulate their look – whether it's sleek, Veronica Lake-style bangs or Greta Garbo waves. Drop in for a consultation to find out if your chosen style involves a set (£40-£60) or just a blow-dry (£40). They'll do gent's quiffs for around £15.

Scissors Palace

122 Holland Park Avenue, W11 4UA (7221 4004). Holland Park tube. Open 9am-8pm

GOING OUT

BEAUTY

FASHION

PARTIES

FOOD

HEALTH

ECO

OUTDOORS

HOME

CHILDREN

PETS

TRANSPORT

RESOURCES

Mon, Wed, Thur; 9am-6pm Tue, Sat; 9am-7.30pm Fri; 11am-6pm Sun.

At £20 for an express blow dry, including a heavenly head massage, this west London walk-in service is a steal. After half an hour in the hands of an expert stylist, you can walk out with smooth, gleaming tresses.

Hairdressers

BUDGET

Clipso

35 Windmill Street, W1T 2JS (7580 3449, www.clipso.co.uk). Goodge Street or Tottenham Court Road tube. Open 10am-7pm Mon, Fri; 10am-9pm Tue-Thur; 9.30am-6pm Sat.

Regulars praise the friendly service and in-depth consultations about cuts and upkeep – plus you get a complimentary glass of wine. Prices for women's cuts range from £37-£90: Jack (£37) is highly recommended – 'the best cuts I've ever had', says one devotee.

Stamp Hair

139 Bethnal Green Road, E2 7DG (7613 3097, www.stamphair.com). Shoreditch High Street rail. Open 11am-8pm Mon-Wed, Fri; 11am-9pm Thur; 11am-6pm Sat; 11am-5pm Sun.

Thanks to Sicilian owner Vince's sharp, consummately stylish cuts, this is a destination salon for local fashion kids. Artwork by emerging local talent occupies one wall, while the vibe is über-friendly. Men's cuts cost £27, ladies' from £40.

Vision Hairdressers

8 Dray Walk, The Old Truman Brewery, 91 Brick Lane, E1 6QL (7247 6842, www.visionhair.co.uk). Liverpool Street tube/rail or Shoreditch High Street rail. Open 10am-7pm Mon-Wed, Sat; 11am-9pm Thur, Fri; 11am-6pm Sun.

Beloved of fashionable East Londoners, Vision offers sleek cuts and colour in slick surrounds. Free drinks and Japanese head massages are a bonus at these prices: ladies' cuts cost from £35, gents' from £30.

MODERATE

Fish

30 D'Arblay Street, W1F 8ER (7494 2398, www.fishweb.co.uk). Oxford Circus tube. Open 10am-7pm Mon-Wed, Fri; 10am-8pm Thur; 10am-5pm Sat.

Housed in a blue-tiled former fishmongers, Fish is part hip hairdresser, part laid-back barbershop. Gent's cuts cost from £34, women's from £41: Donna is a dab hand.

Taylor Taylor

137 Commercial Street, E1 6BJ (7377 2737, www.taylortaylorlondon.com). Liverpool Street tube/rail or Shoreditch High Street rail. Open 10am-8pm Mon-Wed; noon-9pm Thur; 10am-7pm Fri; 10am-6pm Sat, Sun.

Opulent decor (chandeliers, birdcages and gold tiling) and complimentary cocktails make a cut here blissfully pampering. Prices start from £52 for women, but it's worth spending a bit extra for the art director-level stylists: Drew (at the Cheshire Street branch) is great for cuts.

Other locations *12 Cheshire Street, E2 6EH (7033 0330).*

Unruly Studio

253 Portobello Road, W11 1LR (7727 7444, www.unrulystudio. co.uk). Ladbroke Grove or Westbourne Park tube. Open 10am-10pm Mon-Fri; 10am-7pm Sat; 10am-5pm Sun.

Unruly's director Michael specialises in curly hair, achieving miraculous results (from £35). Open until late, the salon has great customer service: free fringe trims are offered between cuts, PlayStations and Wi-Fi supplement the usual magazines, and if you spend over £60 the salon will pay your congestion charge.

Zoo N1

267 Upper Street, N1 2UQ (7226 1865). Angel tube. Open 10am-6.15pm Mon-Wed; 10am-7pm Thur, Fri; 10am-5.30pm Sat; 11am-5pm Sun.

This busy Islington salon offers ladies' cuts and restyles at £46 from a switched-on team of senior stylists, many of whom work on

BARGAIN CUTS

The cheapest way to get your tresses trimmed is to become a hairdressing model. Trainees' work is checked by a qualified supervisor, though that does mean it takes time – generally two to three hours for a cut. All of the salons listed below need models on a regular basis, though you need to call ahead.

The classic place for a bargain cut is the **Toni & Guy Training Academy** (71-75 New Oxford Street, WC1A 1DG, 7836 0606, www.toniandguy.com). Cuts cost a fiver (or free with a newspaper ad) and are closely supervised, with five to six students to one art director. Highlights are £25, tints £20 – but some more extreme, fashion-led cuts and colour are free (depending on what the students need to practise at the time).

Vidal Sassoon Creative Academy (56 Davies Mews, W1K 5AA, 7399 6902, www.sassoon.com) is equally well established, offering weekday appointments between 10am and 2pm. Cuts cost £12 (£5 for students) while highlights are £35, and there's a maximum student-teacher 12 to one.

Soho's **Fish Hairdressing** (see p48) offers Monday morning appointments as in-house training for salon juniors. There's close supervision from the stylists, and a some flexibility over styles. Cuts are £5, colour from £15. **Mahogany Academy** (22 Dering Street, W1S 1AN, 7629 4078, www.mahoganyhair.co.uk), meanwhile, doesn't charge a penny. Participants are qualified hairdressers looking to learn new techniques, so you're in safe hands. Finally, the **Aveda Academy** (7759 7355, see p47) holds a host of colour and cutting workshops and classes, and frequently needs models; call the academy to find out what's on.

---

magazine shoots and catwalk styling on the side. Our fashionista friends' favourite is Japanese stylist Taka.

EXPENSIVE

Daniel Hersheson
Harvey Nichols, 109-125 Knightsbridge, SW1X 7RJ (7201 8797, www.daniel hersheson.com). Knightsbridge tube. Open 10am-8pm Mon-Sat; noon-6pm Sun.
For perfect highlights book an appointment with head colourist Sibi Bolan, who's one of the best in London; a half-head with her costs £170. Cuts start at £71 (men's from £46), though you'll pay £307 to see Daniel himself: both branches also offer afro hair services.
Other locations *45 Conduit Street, W1S 2YN (7434 1747).*

Errol Douglas
18 Motcomb Street, SW1X 8LB (7235 0110, www.erroldouglas.com).
Knightsbridge tube. Open 9am-6pm Mon; 9am-7pm Tue-Sat.
Converts rave about the salon's relaxed atmosphere and beautifully sleek cuts and blow-dries. Its eponymous owner is charm itself: down to earth, and good at listening to what you want. A cut with him costs £200 for women and £100 for men, although prices drop considerably if you see another member of the team.

Jo Hansford ★
19 Mount Street, W1K 2RN (7495 7774, www.johansford.com). Bond Street or Green Park tube. Open 8.30am-6pm Tue-Sat.
Favourite of fashion editors and models alike, Jo Hansford is probably the best-known colourist in London – and much in demand for perfectly blended highlights or colour correction emergencies. A half-head costs from £140 to £400, tints from £85 to £150. Beauticians and manicurists are also on hand to complete the look.

GOING OUT

BEAUTY

FASHION

PARTIES

FOOD

HEALTH

ECO

OUTDOORS

HOME

CHILDREN

PETS

TRANSPORT

RESOURCES

GOING OUT

BEAUTY

FASHION

PARTIES

FOOD

HEALTH

ECO

OUTDOORS

HOME

CHILDREN

PETS

TRANSPORT

RESOURCES

Address Book Secrets
Sharmadean Reid
Owner of Wah Nails

I've never been keen on posh West End nail bars and I don't much like the downmarket options either. I set up **Wah Nails** (420 Kingsland Road, E8 4AA, 7812 9889, www.wah-nails.com) because I wanted something between the two. I've styled it like my living room so it looks more like a studio than a salon. There's art on the walls and great music – it's a bit of a hangout. We pride ourselves on being able to do whatever you want, whether that's two-inch long nails painted with pole-dancers or digits decorated with pictures of peas and carrots (really!). Whatever the art, I recommend **Seche Vite** top coat (www.seche.com) – it's the best and a real professional secret.

I love **Kiehl's** (29 Monmouth Street, WC2H 9DD, 7240 2411, www.kiehls.com) products, especially their Crème de Corps. My favourite place to shop for beauty products is **Heathrow Airport** (www.heathrowairport.com). In fact, any airport – I hate the excessive attention you get when you approach beauty counters in department stores.

For a great facial, I love the **Cowshed** spa at Shoreditch House (Ebor Street, E1 6AW, 7749 4531, www.cowshedonline.com). The products smell amazing and they do half price treatments for under-27s (members' only) on Monday.

I'm really into vintage American workwear and love hunting down great pieces at the **Vintage Showroom** (14 Earlham Street, WC2H 9LN, 7836 3964, www.thevintageshowroom.com). I also like the basement at **Dover Street Market** (7-18 Dover Street, W1S 4LT, 7518 0680, www.doverstreetmarket.com) for brands like Opening Ceremony and Supreme. It's great for jewellery too. Another shop I love is **Wilde Ones** (283 King's Road, SW3 5EW, 7352 9531, www.wildeones.com). It's a real one-off and packed with fab Native American jewellery and artefacts. For books I adore **Claire de Rouen** (1st Floor, 121-125 Charing Cross Road, WC2H 0EW, 7287 1813, www.claire derouenbooks.com). She has amazing fashion magazine archives and is the most glamorous, beautiful lady.

To keep fit I mostly go to the gym at Shoreditch House but I also love **Park Road Lido** (Park Road, N8 8JN, 8341 3567, www.haringey.gov.uk) in Muswell Hill. It's quieter than London Fields Lido and is great on a summery day.

I love Japanese food but, for a relaxing Sunday, you can't beat **Villiers Terrace** (120 Park Road, N8 8JP, 8245 6827, www.villiersterracelondon.com). It serves up a fantastic roast. I love the decor, the outdoor seating on sunny days and the relaxed feel.

To get away from it all, there's nowhere like **Highgate Wood** (www.cityoflondon.gov.uk). I walk my dog there every day and feel like I'm not even in London. Another great escape is the conservatory at the **Barbican** (Silk Street, EC2Y 8DS, 7638 4141, www.barbican.org.uk). I love the fact that, in the middle of all that concrete, you feel like you're in a tropical jungle.

Fashion

Accessories

Below we've focused on smaller boutiques and independent labels rather than well-known high street names and department stores (unless they offer a particular speciality). For the complete lowdown on London's shopping scene, invest in a copy of Time Out's *London's Best Shops* guide.

Bags

Both **Black Truffle** (*see p55*) and **Kate Kanzier** (*see p56*) are worth checking out for their desirable bags. **Lara Bohinc**'s (*see p55*) bags are also extremely covetable.

Ally Capellino ★
9 Calvert Avenue, E2 7JP (7613 3073, www.allycapellino.co.uk). Shoreditch High Street rail. Open noon-6pm Tue-Fri; 11am-6pm Sat; 11-5pm Sun.
Ally Capellino's cult accessories empire has been quietly bubbling away since 1980; her beautifully made, unisex leather, cotton and canvas bags are fashion classics.

J&M Davidson
97 Golborne Road, W10 5NL (7313 9532, www.jandmdavidson.com). Ladbroke Grove or Notting Hill Gate tube. Open 10am-6pm Mon-Sat.
Anglo-French couple John and Monique Davidson's bags and leather accessories have a slightly retro aesthetic that has stood them in good stead for over 20 years. Traditional craftsmanship – high-quality leather, hand-stitching – combined with constantly evolving design means bags that don't date but look fantastic. The company now does knitwear and clothing.

Lulu Guinness
3 Ellis Street, SW1X 9AL (7823 4828, www.luluguinness.com). Sloane Square tube. Open 10am-6pm Mon-Fri; 11am-6pm Sat.
Lulu Guinness's much-imitated signature style oozes femininity, matched with an irrepressibly playful streak. There's no mistaking her more extravagant handbag designs: bold, lip-shaped perspex or snakeskin clutches. Cheaper pieces are equally distinctive, running from retro-print laminated canvas vanity cases and make-up bags to gorgeously girly umbrellas. Look out too for the vintage-inspired sunglasses. **Other location** *23 Royal Exchange, EC3V 3LR (7626 5391).*

Mimi ★
40 Cheshire Street, E2 6EH (7729 6699, www.mimimika.com). Shoreditch High Street rail. Open 10.30am-6pm Mon-Fri; 11am-6pm Sat, Sun.
Central St Martin's graduate Mimi Berry designs simple, elegant leather bags and purses in beautiful hues. The satchel-style Elsie (£230) is a classic, while leather Oyster card holders come in at a mere £22.

Ollie & Nic
20 Foubert's Place, W1 7PL (7494 4214, www.ollieandnic.com). Oxford Circus tube. Open 10am-7pm Mon-Sat; noon-6pm Sun.
Refreshingly inexpensive, Ollie & Nic's sparkling new Carnaby Street flagship is ideal for credit-crunched style lovers. Designs are unique (rather than poor It-bag copies), with cute shoulder bags, clutches and retro-floral cotton shoppers.

Pickett
32-33 & 41 Burlington Arcade, W1J 0PZ (7493 8939, www.pickett.co.uk).

Green Park tube. Open 9am-6pm Mon-Fri; 10am-6pm Sat.

There's nothing too quirky at Pickett – it's the deliciously conservative styles that excite. Check out the men's attaché cases and A-lister-worthy leather and canvas holdalls.

Glasses & sunglasses

arckiv
Arch 67 Stables Market, NW1 8AH (07790 102204, www.arckiv.net). Camden Town or Chalk Farm tube. Open 1-6pm Tue-Fri; 11am-6pm Sat, Sun.

Supplying frames and lenses to the theatre, TV and film industries, arckiv specialises in beautiful and unusual designs, antique and modern: find monocles, flying and biking goggles, glam rock or space-age designs, as well as the usual suspects (Mikli, Ray-Ban, Persol) and a few high-end names too.

Cutler & Gross
16 Knightsbridge Green, SW1X 7QL (7581 2250, www.cutlerandgross.com). Knightsbridge tube. Open 9.30am-7pm Mon-Sat; noon-5pm Sun.

Established for three decades, this renowned opticians has over 600 frame styles in its archive (book a viewing appointment), plus a

---

---

regularly renewed selection of sunglasses. Styles vary hugely, but include a mixture of modern and retro shapes. Unique vintage frames are on sale in the sister shop at No.7. **Other locations** *7 Knightsbridge Green, SW1X 7QL (7590 9995).*

David Clulow at Selfridges
400 Oxford Street, W1A 1AB (0800 123400, www.selfridges.com). Bond Street or Marble Arch tube. Open 9.30am-9pm Mon-Sat; noon-6pm Sun.

The large sunglasses-only concession on the ground floor Wonder Room at Selfridges stocks all the big, blingy fashion names, from Prada and Robert Cavalli to Tom Ford and Oliver Peoples. Prices go from £89 to £2,000.

Eye Company
159 Wardour Street, W1F 8WH (7434 0988, www.eye-company.co.uk). Oxford Circus or Tottenham Court Road tube. Open 10.30am-6.30pm Mon-Wed, Fri; 10.30am-7.30pm Thur; 11am-6pm Sat.

Supplying the film and TV industry, Soho's Eye Company is a hip independent intent on challenging the mediocrity of the high-street chains. Its select range of mint-condition vintage frames (some dating back to the 18th century), its stylish own-brand frames and its selection of cherry-picked numbers from the likes of Cutler & Gross, Oliver Peoples and Dita make you positively want to have to wear glasses.

Mallon & Taub
35D Marylebone High Street, W1U 4QB (7935 8200, www.mallonandtaub.com). Baker Street or Regent's Park tube. Open 10am-6.30pm Mon-Wed, Fri, Sat; 10am-7pm Thur; 11am-5pm Sun.

The high-tech premises impress, while friendly opticians take time to talk to each customer. A fabulous range of brands includes Ørgreen, Oliver Peoples and Ray-Ban; prices go stratospheric, but start at a palatable £250.

McClintock ★
29 Floral Street, WC2E 9DP (7240 5055, www.mcclintock-eyewear.co.uk). Covent

GOING OUT
BEAUTY
FASHION
PARTIES
FOOD
HEALTH
ECO
OUTDOORS
HOME
CHILDREN
PETS
TRANSPORT
RESOURCES

GOING OUT
BEAUTY
FASHION
PARTIES
FOOD
HEALTH
ECO
OUTDOORS
HOME
CHILDREN
PETS
TRANSPORT
RESOURCES

Garden tube. Open 11am-7pm Mon-Sat; noon-5pm Sun.

Stylish McClintock is the world's biggest stockist of Kirk Originals (from £215). Also on offer are designs from unusual brands like Kilsgaard and Funk, as well as wooden frames from ethical brand MADE.

Spex in the City

1 Shorts Gardens, WC2H 9AT (7240 0243, www.spexinthecity.com). Covent Garden or Leicester Square tube. Open 11am-6.30pm Mon-Fri; 11am-6pm Sat; 1-5pm Sun.

Expect a well-chosen range of European and British frames, including Ørgreen, Reiz and Bruno Chaussignand. Prices start at £60, rising to around £280. Also stocks its own brand, Gillian Caplan (prices start at £120).

36 Opticians

36 Beauchamp Place, SW3 1NU (7581 6336,www.36opticians.co.uk). South Kensington or Knightsbridge tube. Open 10am-6pm Mon-Sat.

Prices at this relaxed but expert opticians start at an affordable £45 for no-frills, classic frames. Trendies may prefer pricier styles by the likes of Tom Ford and Barton Perreira.

Jewellery

For more playful, quirky lines, we love online retailer **Hannah Zakari** (www. hannahzakari.co.uk). A showcase for independent designers and crafty types,

---

City Secret

Looking for the perfect umbrella? Well look no further. **James Smith & Sons** (53 New Oxford Street, WC1A 1BL, 7836 4731, www. james-smith.co.uk) opened in 1830 and has been dealing in exquisite brollies ever since. Classic City umbrellas, parasols and high-tech folding models all feature.

---

it stocks a bewildering array of goodies, with prices as low as £4 for brooches. If you're prepared to pay for shipping, US crafts collective **Etsy** (www.etsy.com) is an unrivalled source of handmade pieces.

Ben Day ★

3 Lonsdale Road, W11 2BY (3417 3873, www.benday.co.uk). Ladbroke Grove tube. Open 10.30am-6pm Mon-Sat.

Ben Day has built up a loyal following for his exquisite creations and this fancy new Notting Hill shop is testament to his success. His work makes wonderful use of colour: think flawless South Sea pearls (blue, silver, gold and black), shimmering pink kunzite or heavy drops of vivid green chysoprase. Each piece is a handmade one-off; for those who want something even more personal, Day will undertake bespoke work.

Berganza

88-90 Hatton Garden (entrance on Greville Street), EC1N 8PN (7404 2336, www. berganza.com). Chancery Lane tube or Farringdon tube/rail. Open 10am-5pm Mon-Sat.

Specialising in antique rings, which come in beautifully tattered velvet boxes and with handwritten provenance labels, Berganza offers a gorgeous range of sparklers, many of them Victorian, with the odd art deco gem.

ec one

41 Exmouth Market, EC1R 4QL (7713 6185, www.econe.co.uk). Farringdon tube/ rail. Open 10am-6pm Mon-Wed, Fri; 11am-7pm Thur; 10.30am-6pm Sat.

Co-owner Jos Skeates' designs are for the bold (and affluent), but there are plenty of more modestly priced pieces, such as Alex Monroe's lovely bumblebee necklace (£130). New designers are introduced all the time, so there's always fresh temptation.

Other location 56 Ledbury Road, W11 2AJ (7243 8811).

Electrum Gallery

21 South Molton Street, W1K 5QZ (7629 6325). Bond Street tube. Open 10am-6pm Mon-Sat.

Exclusive pieces available in this gallery-cum-shop include work by up-and-coming designer Jo Hayes-Ward and more than a hundred other contemporary designers.

French's Dairy
13 Rugby Street, WC1N 3QT (7404 7070, www.frenchsdairy.com). Holborn or Russell Square tube. Open 11am-6pm Mon-Fri; 11am-4pm Sat.
With prices ranging from £20 to £2,000, this sweet little shop, housed in a former dairy, has something for all budgets. Pretty pieces from Anton Heunis are at the lower end of the price spectrum, while Phillipe Ferrandis' opulent handmade pieces are guaranteed show-stoppers.

Kabiri ★
37 Marylebone High Street, W1U 4QE (7224 1808, www.kabiri.co.uk). Baker Street tube. Open 10am-6.30pm Mon-Sat.
Kabiri's admirable mission statement is to showcase the best in jewellery, regardless of its price, provenance or how well known the designer is – though many of its unknowns go on to become very successful indeed. Collections change with dizzying speed, but there's always plenty for smaller budgets. Kabiri also has a concession in Selfridges. **Other location** *18 The Market, The Piazza, WC2E 8RB (7240 1055).*

Lara Bohinc
49F Sloane Street, SW1X 9BZ (7730 8194, www.larabohinc107.co.uk). Sloane Square tube. Open 10am-6pm Mon, Tue, Thur-Sat; 10am-7pm Wed; noon-5pm Sun.
Glamorous, Slovenian-born Bohinc is best known for her contemporary pieces that effortlessly fuse modernity with classic design. Her latest collections are inspired by cubism and rayonism. Luxurious, supremely stylish bags, belts, shoes and sunglasses are also on offer.

Lesley Craze Gallery
33-35A Clerkenwell Green, EC1R 0DU (7608 0393, www.lesleycrazegallery.co.uk). Farringdon tube/rail. Open 10am-5.30pm Tue-Sat.

Hidden away in Clerkenwell, this gallery houses the work of over 100 international jewellers, metalsmiths and textile designers. Its contemporary skew ensures a healthy dollop of emerging talent; perfect for one-off gifts for creative types.

Solange Azagury-Partridge
162 New Bond Street, W1S 2UG (7792 0197, www.solangeazagury partridge.com). Green Park tube. Open 10am-6pm Mon-Sat.
Following a move from Notting Hill to this high-end location, self-taught jewellery designer Solange Azagury Partridge is really going up in the world. The two-level boutique is a sight to behold in itself: red trinket-box walls, rainbow carpet, luxe fittings throughout. Her designs are striking and beautiful, with a distinctive rock 'n' roll edge. The 'Love' ring is particularly appealing, as are the sweet enamel ladybird and bee rings.

Shoes & trainers

Adidas Originals Store
9 Earlham Street, WC2H 9LL (7379 4042, www.adidas.com). Covent Garden tube. Open 10.30am-7pm Mon-Sat; noon-6pm Sun.
Retro trainer fiends should make a beeline for this Covent Garden shop to browse iconic Adidas designs to their heart's content. The Stan Smiths (£55) are an enduring classic and always popular.

Black Truffle
52 Warren Street, W1T 5NJ (7388 4547, www.blacktruffle.com). Warren Street tube. Open 11am-6.30pm Mon-Sat.
This sleek boutique is full of wearable but individual shoes, with footwear from Chie Mihara, Alberto Fermani and Roby & Pier. A fetching pair of Chie Mihara shoe boots come in at £205. The shop also stocks tasteful bags from the likes of Abro and some great accessories (tights, gloves, jewellery). **Other location** *4 Broadway Market, E8 4QJ (7923 9450).*

GOING OUT

BEAUTY

FASHION

PARTIES

FOOD

HEALTH

ECO

OUTDOORS

HOME

CHILDREN

PETS

TRANSPORT

RESOURCES

GOING OUT

BEAUTY

FASHION

PARTIES

FOOD

HEALTH

ECO

OUTDOORS

HOME

CHILDREN

PETS

TRANSPORT

RESOURCES

Georgina Goodman

44 Old Bond Street W1S 4GB (7493 7673, www.georginagoodman.com). Green Park tube. Open 10am-6pm Mon-Wed, Fri, Sat; 10am-7pm Thur.

Even Manolo Blahnik's a fan of Goodman's exquisitely made statement heels (from £300). They're surprisingly comfortable too – you can even run for a bus in them. The flat boots are always popular; prices start at £510. Goodman's personal touch remains key to the success of the brand: there's a 'Made in Love' inscription on the sole of every mainline shoe.

Kate Kanzier ★

67-69 Leather Lane, EC1N 7TJ (7242 7232, www.katekanzier.com). Chancery Lane tube. Open 8.30am-6.30pm Mon-Fri; 11am-4pm Sat.

Adored for great-value directional footwear, Kate Kanzier is the place to come for brogues (£30), ballerinas (£20-£25), and stylish boots in a huge range of colours. Sexy high-heeled pumps also feature strongly, in patent, suede, leather and animal prints, with vintage designs dominating. The range is attractively arranged alongside a line of straightforward handbags and clutches in the spacious Holborn shop.

Kazmattazz

39 Hoxton Square, N1 6NN (7739 4133, www.kazmattazz.com). Old Street tube/rail or Hoxton rail. Open 11am-6.30pm Mon-Thur; 10.30am-10pm Fri-Sun.

Nike, Adidas and Etnies are just some of the brands on sale at this lively, no-frills sneaker shop in Hoxton Square. Lesser-seen names include Ballerr, Showlove and Fila, and prices range from £30-£85.

Laura J

114 Islington High Street, N1 8EG (7226 4005, www.laurajlondon.com). Angel tube. Open 11am-5.30pm Mon; 11am-6pm Tue, Wed; 11am-6.30pm Thur, Fri; 11am-7pm Sat; noon-5pm Sun.

This petite boutique, previously called Lollipop London, has more girly charm than you can shake a stick at. Owner Laura Allnatt has sourced interesting lines from some of the world's best independent designers. Displays see newer labels such as Wilomena, Talie and London-based brand Esska sit alongside more established favourites, such as the Jackson Twins, Velvet Bee and Francesco Morichetti. The own-brand Laura J designs are also doing well.

Oliver Sweeney

66 Conduit Street W1S 2XD (7491 9126, www.oliversweeney.com). Oxford Circus tube. Open 10am-7pm Mon-Sat; noon-6pm Sun.

Sweeney makes some of the best-looking, most comfortable men's shoes around, and is a fashion editors' favourite. The classic Kamanchi loafer is £225, while a pair of daring stingray-skin Bells, made to order, costs £795.

Other location 133 Middlesex Street, E1 7JS (7626 4466).

The Other Side of the Pillow

61 Wilton Way, E8 1BG (07988 870508, www.theotherothersideofthepillow. blogspot.com). Hackney Central rail or 38, 242, 277 bus. Open 11am-6pm Thur-Sun. No credit cards.

At first the name may seem strange, but not if you're into original Vans skate shoes and trainers and vintage sportswear. Then you'll know why this shop, situated on whisper-quiet Wilton Way in Hackney, is mining a rich seam of cool. The Vans range from £25 to £150. Owners Henry Davies and Maurizio Di Nino have a passion for all kinds of collectables from the 1960s to the mid '90s.

Size?

33-34 Carnaby Street, W1F 7DW (7287 4016, www.size-online.co.uk). Oxford Circus tube. Open 10am-7.30pm Mon-Wed, Fri, Sat; 10am-8pm Thur; noon-6pm Sun.

Size? is a seemingly obvious inclusion on this list – but it remains a constant favourite with the sneak-obsessed. Lakai and DVS are some of the leftfield labels stocked alongside more common brands (Puma, Reebok, Nike et al).

Other locations *across the city.*

Address Book Secrets
Leesa Whisker
Personal stylist & director of Whisker Agency

There are many boutiques I love, especially **Austique** (330 King's Road, SW3 5UR, 7376 4555, www.austique. co.uk) and **Press** (3 Erskine Road, NW3 3AJ, 7449 0081, www.press primrosehill.com), but **Matches** (60-64 Ledbury Road, W11 2AJ, 7221 0255, www.matchesfashion.com) is my tried and trusted favourite for a well-chosen mix of established and up-and-coming designers.

For vintage shopping nowhere beats **Rellik** (8 Golborne Road, W10 5NW, 8962 0089, www.relliklondon.co.uk). I bought an amazing Sgt Pepper-style coat there about five years ago and I'm always stopped in the street when I wear it. A Savile Row tailor tried to buy it off me to sample, but it's a keeper. I also like **Palette London** (21 Canonbury Lane, N1 2AS, 7288 7428, www.palette-london.com), which also stocks amazing designs by my favourite milliner **Justin Smith Esquire** (www.jsmithesquire.com).

One of my favourite new designers is **Holly Fulton** (available at Browns Focus, 38-39 South Molton Street, W1K 5RN, 7514 0000, www.browns fashion.com). She does these amazing art deco shift dresses. The designer I always return to is **Diane Von Furstenberg** (www.dvf.com).

My bargain basics tip of the moment is online and mail order company **Kettlewell Colours** (www.kettlewell colours.co.uk). They produce good-quality basic camisoles and T-shirts in every colour of the rainbow. For designer gear at discount prices, **Billion Dollar Babes** (www.billiondollar babes.com) sample sales are the best.

Successful shopping is all in the planning ahead. When I need to source a capsule wardrobe for a client in one day, I either choose a department store and book a personal shopping suite or pinpoint an area with a good mix of independent designer boutiques and high street stores like the junction of **Ledbury Road** and **Westbourne Grove** or **Marylebone High Street**.

My energy levels received a massive boost when I discovered Jillian and Michael at the **London Meditation Centre** (www.londonmeditationcentre. com) – their simple meditation techniques really facilitate deep relaxation and improved clarity of thought. I also can't recommend more highly psychotherapeutic coach **Barbara Lindner** (barbara. lindner@yahoo.com 07963 961180).

I sell all my unwanted designer items on eBay through Jane Phipps at **Label Xchange** (www.labelxchange. com). She arranges collection from clients' homes.

As well as styling and shopping for individual clients, I also run interactive style workshops. My **Find Your True Style** workshop (0870 043 4126, www.whiskeragency.co.uk) is fantastic for anyone wanting to learn to look great every day, with a style that's all their own.

GOING OUT

BEAUTY

FASHION

PARTIES

FOOD

HEALTH

ECO

OUTDOORS

HOME

CHILDREN

PETS

TRANSPORT

RESOURCES

GOING OUT

BEAUTY

FASHION

PARTIES

FOOD

HEALTH

ECO

OUTDOORS

HOME

CHILDREN

PETS

TRANSPORT

RESOURCES

Bespoke

The best way to get a truly individual look and a perfect fit?
Simple: go bespoke.

Bikinis & underwear

Biondi
*55B Old Church Street, SW3 5BS (7349
1111, www.biondicouture.com). Sloane
Square tube. Open 10.30am-6.30pm
Mon-Sat.*
This luxury bikini boutique also offers a
great bespoke service. Made-to-measure
(from £350) designs are created using
existing shapes and materials, then tweaked
to a perfect fit before your eyes.

Buttress & Snatch
*7502 3139, www.buttressandsnatch.co.uk.
Open by appointment only.*
'Handmade in Hackney by honest hard-
working girls' is the company motto; sure
enough, prices are good and the quality's
great. Fully bespoke bikinis and lingerie cost
from £200 and take up to four weeks to make.

Jeans

Bodymetrics at Selfridges
*400 Oxford Street, W1A 1AB (0800
123400, www.selfridges.com). Bond Street
or Marble Arch tube. Open 9.30am-8pm
Mon-Wed, Fri, Sat; 9.30am-9pm Thur;
noon-6pm Sun.*
Bodymetrics' 3D scanner promises a perfect
fit; once your measurements have been taken,
choose your ideal fabric, fit and cut. Prices
start at £195.

Shirts

In addition to the following shirtmakers,
trusty **Marks & Spencer** (0845 609

0200, www.marksandspencer.com) now
offers an online made-to-measure service.
Choose your fit, detailing, monogram and
material, and the finished shirt will be
sent to you within 21 days (from £45).

Charlie Allen
*1 Coopers Yard, 181 Upper Street, N1
1RQ (7359 0883, www.charlieallen.co.uk).
Angel tube or Highbury & Islington tube/
rail. Open by appointment 10am-7pm
Mon-Sat.*
The made-to-measure shirt service, which
gives you the choice of over 1,000 fabrics,
takes from three to six weeks and costs from
£150. Charlie Allen is also known for
spectacular suits.

Ede & Ravenscroft
*8 Burlington Gardens, W1X 1LG
(7734 5450, www.edeandravenscroft.
co.uk). Green Park or Piccadilly Circus
tube. Open 9am-6pm Mon-Fri;
10am-6pm Sat.*
A bespoke shirt from Ede & Ravenscroft
makes a stylish gift. Your chosen length of
material is boxed up for the lucky recipient,
who then visits the shop to be measured up
and pick his collar and cuffs (from £125).
Other locations across the city.

New & Lingwood
*53 Jermyn Street, SW1Y 6LX (7493
9621, www.newandlingwood.com).
Piccadilly Circus tube. Open 9am-6pm
Mon-Fri; 10am-6pm Sat.*
For seriously smart gents (and Eton pupils:
official supplier status was granted in 1865),
New & Lingwood offer more than 700 fabrics,
plus optional embroidery. Note that there
is a minimum order of four shirts (from
£200 each).

GOING OUT

BEAUTY

FASHION

PARTIES

FOOD

HEALTH

ECO

OUTDOORS

HOME

CHILDREN

PETS

TRANSPORT

RESOURCES

Shoes & trainers

John Lobb
9 St James's Street, SW1A 1EF (7930 3664). Green Park tube. Open 9am-5.30pm Mon-Fri; 9am-4.30pm Sat.
One of the finest shoemakers in the world, the eponymous Mr Lobb was cobbler to King Edward VII. At £2,530, made-to-measure shoes might cost nigh-on a king's ransom, but will be the finest footwear you'll ever buy.

NIKEiD Studio London
NikeTown, 236 Oxford Street, W1W 8LG (7612 0990, http://nikeid.nike.com). Oxford Circus tube. Open 10am-8pm Mon-Sat; noon-6pm Sun.
Book a one-on-one session with a design consultant to create your dream pair of trainers; the service costs from £65 to £225.

Terry de Havilland
336 Kingsland Road, E8 4DA (7254 4445, www.terrydehavilland.com). Haggerston rail. Open by appointment only.
This shoemaker extraordinaire began making his gorgeous, vertigo-inducing wedge heels and platform shoes back in the 1960s. Bespoke show-stoppers can be created in two to three weeks and cost from £450-£850.

Suits

Chris Kerr
52 Berwick Street, W1F 8SL (7437 3727, www.chriskerr.co.uk). Oxford Circus tube. Open 9am-5.30pm Mon-Fri; 9am-1pm Sat.
Eddie Kerr has been making suits for celebs since the '60s. Now semi-retired, he's handed over the reins to son Chris, and they're still creating sharp bespoke suits, shirts and ties in their friendly, unostentatious shop. With full suits starting at around £1,200, it's an affordable way to indulge in real tailoring.

Gieves & Hawkes
1 Savile Row, W1S 3JR (7434 2001, www.gievesandhawkes.com). Green Park or Piccadilly Circus tube. Open 9.30am-6.30pm Mon-Wed, Fri; 9.30am-8pm Thur; 10am-6pm Sat.
Despite four centuries of bespoke supremacy, Gieves and Hawkes' approach to style can be surprisingly contemporary. Bespoke suits take about three fittings and cost from £3,000, while a made-to-measure suit will set you back around £695.

Kilgour
8 Savile Row, W1S 3PE (7734 6905, www.kilgour.com). Green Park or Piccadilly Circus tube. Open 9am-5.30pm Mon-Fri; 9.30am-6pm Sat.
Kilgour's sleek, modern store reflects its new design direction. A perfectly tailored bespoke suit costs upwards of £2,500, but prices are half that for 'entry level' suits (fitted and cut on Savile Row, but basted externally).

Mr Start
40 Rivington Street, EC2A 3BN (7729 6272, www.start-london.com) Old Street tube/rail. Open 10.30am-6.30pm Mon-Fri; 11am-6pm Sat, 1-5pm Sun.
Made-to-measure suits at this Rivington Street boutique cost from £750. The laid-back atmosphere and friendly staff will soon put nervous novice suit-buyers at their ease.

GOING OUT

BEAUTY

FASHION

PARTIES

FOOD

HEALTH

ECO

OUTDOORS

HOME

CHILDREN

PETS

TRANSPORT

RESOURCES

Clothes

All your fashion questions answered, from where to bag the best
charity shop bargains to places to hunt down the perfect pair of jeans.

Boutiques

Aimé
32 Ledbury Road, W11 2AB (7221 7070,
www.aimelondon.com). Notting Hill Gate
tube. Open 10am-6.30pm Mon-Sat.
Shoppers searching for a touch of Gallic chic
on London's streets should make Aimé their
first port-of-call. Inside you'll find the crème
de la crème of French designers, with labels
like APC, APC Madras, Isabel Marant and
Forte Forte. Bath products and seductive
home accessories, including Aimé's range of
scented candles, are equally attractive. Next
door, Petit Aimé stocks an adorable range of
clothes for babies and children.

b Store
24A Savile Row, W1S 3PR (7734 6846,
www.bstorelondon.com). Oxford Circus
tube. Open 10.30am-6.30pm Mon-Fri;
10am-6pm Sat.
One of London's trendiest clothes shops, b
store's reputation as a stockist of innovative
fashion labels remains unimpeachable —
where else can you pick up clothes designed
by this year's Saint Martin's graduates?
Choose from both emerging and more
established designers, including Ian Batten,
Opening Ceremony and Peter Jensen. The in-
house b Store label goes from strength to
strength too.

Browns
23-27 South Molton Street, W1K 5RD
(7514 0000, www.brownsfashion.com).
Bond Street tube. Open 10am-6.30pm
Mon-Wed, Fri, Sat; 10am-7pm Thur.
Famed as it is, we couldn't omit the grande
dame of London's boutiques. Browns stocks
a heady mix of established names and edgy

new talent; Erin Mullaney, formerly of
Selfridges, is the buyer casting her expert eye
over the international collections.

Diverse ★
294 Upper Street, N1 2TU (7359 8877,
www.diverseclothing.com). Angel tube.
Open 10.30am-6.30pm Mon-Wed, Fri,
Sat; 10.30am-7.30pm Thur; 11.30am-
5.30pm Sun.
Islington stalwart Diverse does a fine job of
keeping N1's style queens in fashion-forward
mode. You'll find a well-edited collection of
incredibly desirable garments (Marc by Marc
Jacobs, Vanessa Bruno, APC, Sonia Rykiel
and more), plus some original jewellery,
accessories and shoes thrown in for good
measure. Menswear is also stocked at this
branch now.

Hub
49 & 88 Stoke Newington Church Street,
N16 0AR (7254 4494, www.hubshop.co.uk).
Bus 73, 393, 476. Open 10.30am-6.30pm
Mon-Sat; 11am-5pm Sun.
No.49 houses the womenswear; over the road
at No.88, Hub Men stocks knits by John
Smedley and a selection of items from Folk,
Fred Perry, Barbour and more. An excellent
neighbourhood boutique.

KJ's Laundry ★
74 Marylebone Lane, W1U 2PW (7486
7855, www.kjslaundry.com). Baker Street
or Bond Street tube. Open 10am-7pm Mon-
Wed, Fri, Sat; 10am-8pm Thur; 11am-5pm
Sun.
Owners Jane Ellis and Kate Allden stock a
mix of lesser-known designers in their super-
chic and spacious Marylebone store. Figure-
hugging stripy tops from Humanoid are
currently selling out fast.

Labour of Love

193 Upper Street, N1 1RQ (7354 9333, www.labour-of-love.co.uk). Highbury & Islington tube/rail. Open 11am-6.30pm Mon-Sat; noon-5.30pm Sun.

Owner Francesca Forcolini combines her own Labour of Love label with a host of quirky smaller labels, plus shoes and accessories, temptingly arrayed in antique cabinets. Check out designs by the likes of Peter Jensen, Eley Kishimoto and Miriam Ocariz.

No-one

1 Kingsland Road, E2 8AA (7613 5314, www.no-one.co.uk). Shoreditch High Street rail. Open 11am-7pm Mon-Wed, Fri, Sat; 11am-8pm Thur; noon-5pm Sun.

This cool Shoreditch boutique stocks hip labels like Ryan Noon, Trainspotter and Cheap Monday (it was the first UK stockist). The shop also has counters brimming over with vintage sunglasses, knitted accessories, badges, jewellery, toiletries and cult magazines and books.

Start ★

42-44 Rivington Street, EC2A 3BN (7729 3334, www.start-london.com). Old Street tube/rail. Open 10.30am-6.30pm Mon-Fri; 11am-6pm Sat; 1-5pm Sun.

At Start's women's store, you'll find well-known brands such as Sonia by Sonia Rykiel alongside up-and-coming labels like Richard Nicoll and Jean Pierre Braganza. There's also a hugely covetable range of accessories such as sunglasses by Cutler & Gross, an expanding shoe section and jewellery by Lucy Hutchings. Across the road at the men's store enjoy browsing rails of Neil Barrett, Martin Margiela, Moncler, Acne and City Company.

Charity shops

British Red Cross

85 Ebury Street, SW1W 9QU (7730 2235, www.redcross.org.uk). Victoria tube/rail. Open 10am-5.30pm Mon-Sat.

Designer labels abound, thanks to moneyed locals: you could snap up a pair of Manolo Blahniks or a smart Armani skirt, and there are puffy '80s ballgowns galore. The Chelsea branch (67 Old Church Street, SW3 5BS, 7376 7300) is equally good.

Crusaid

19 Churton Street, SW1V 2LY (7233 8736, www.crusadeshop.co.uk). Victoria tube/rail. Open 10am-6pm Mon-Sat; 11am-3pm Sun.

An excellent all-rounder, Crusaid offers rich pickings among its vinyl, CDs, books and clothes: Nicole Farhi gems are often to be found on its crowded rails, as are unsold Urban Outfitters stock items.

Oxfam Goodge Street

52 Goodge Street, W1T 4LZ (7636 7311, www.oxfam.co.uk). Goodge Street tube. Open 10.30am-6pm Mon-Fri; noon-5pm Sat.

This branch of Oxfam has added extra spoils to its shelves of late thanks to a deal with Urban Outfitters where it sells on their unsold stock. Check it out for great blouses, knits and dresses and a mere snip of the price you'd pay in UO itself. There are also some H&M (and M&S) pieces and plenty of the usual wardrobe clear-out gems.

Oxfam Hampstead

61 Gayton Road, NW3 1TU (7794 4474, www.oxfam.co.uk). Hampstead tube. Open 10am-5.30pm Mon-Fri; 10am-5pm Sat.

Once again, charity shopping in a well-heeled neighbourhood pays dividends: expect quality separates, frocks, knits, shoes and accessories, along with a great books section.

Salvation Army

Princes Street, W1 2LQ (7495 3958, www2.salvationarmy.org.uk) Oxford Circus tube. Open 10am-6pm Mon-Sat.

This store stocks an eclectic array of clothes, from sparkly platforms to wool military jackets. It's popular with eagle-eyed London College of Fashion students, so arrive early to nab the bargains.

Traid

154 Camden High Street, NW1 0NE (7485 5253, www.traid.org.uk). Camden Town tube. Open 11am-7pm Mon-Sat; 11am-5pm Sun.

GOING OUT

BEAUTY

FASHION

PARTIES

FOOD

HEALTH

ECO

OUTDOORS

HOME

CHILDREN

PETS

TRANSPORT

RESOURCES

GOING OUT
BEAUTY
FASHION
PARTIES
FOOD
HEALTH
ECO
OUTDOORS
HOME
CHILDREN
PETS
TRANSPORT
RESOURCES

Follow the fashion stylists and journalists to Traid's flagship store, with its ethical reclaimed interior, superior labels and award-winning in-house recycled fashion label, TRAIDremade.

Jeans

Not only does **Selfridges** (*see p58*) offer a bespoke jeans service, it also has one of the best denim departments in town. Brix Smith's **Start** boutique (*see p61*) also has an excellent reputation for hot-looking denim.

Donna Ida
106 Draycott Avenue, SW3 3AE (7225 3816, www.donnaida.com). South Kensington tube. Open 10am-7pm Mon-Fri; 10am-6.30pm Sat; noon-6pm Sun.
This smart boutique showcases a changing array of hot labels (currently including Marrakesh by Made in Heaven, Rock & Republic and Siwy), while staff have a keen eye for which styles will best achieve a leggy, pert-of-bottom look.

Harvey Nichols
109-125 Knightsbridge, SW1X 7RJ (7235 5000, www.harveynichols.com). Knightsbridge tube. Open 10am-8pm Mon-Sat; noon-6pm Sun.
Sleek, slim-fitting beauties from Goldsign, bootcuts from Paige and classics from J Brand are among the multitude of hip labels in Harvey Nichols' expansive jeans section.

Trilogy
33 Duke of York's Square, King's Road, SW3 4LY (7730 6515, www.trilogystores. co.uk). Sloane Square tube. Open 10am-6.30pm Mon-Sat; noon-6pm Sun.
A veritable temple to cult denim brands, Trilogy's stock includes better-known labels (J Brand, Paige and Goldsign) and lesser-known finds such as Anlo's lovely, perfectly tailored trews. A new store was due to open in Kensington as this guide went to press.
Other location *63 Weymouth Street, W1G 8NU (7486 8085).*

Lingerie & swimwear

The ultimate indulgence is bespoke undies and bikinis (*see p58*) – a delicious extravagance. We're also smitten with the bow-bedecked silk knickers available online at **Sugarlesque** (www.sugarlesque.com), which also does a lovely line in burlesque nipple tassels and ostrich-feather fans.

Agent Provocateur
6 Broadwick Street, W1V 1FH (7439 0229, www.agentprovocateur.com). Tottenham Court Road tube. Open 11am-7pm Mon-Wed, Fri, Sat; 11am-8pm Thur; noon-5pm Sun.
Incredibly sexy cuts, gorgeous fabrics and friendly assistants make this place lingerie shopping heaven; bras cost from around £55.
Other locations *across the city.*

Apartment C ★
70 Marylebone High Street, W1U 5JL (7935 1854, www.apartment-c.com). Regent's Park tube. Open 10am-6pm Mon-Sat; noon-5pm Sun.
Kenya Cretegny's Marylebone lingerie emporium is all about 'hanging out in your knickers, drinking gin out of a teacup and reading *The Last Tango in Paris* out loud'. The list of designers is long – Afterwear and Aloe to Lounge Lover and Paperself – and the range of styles impressive.

Bordello
55 Great Eastern Street, EC2A 3HP (7503 3334, www.bordello-london.com). Old Street tube/rail or Shoreditch High Street rail. Open 11am-7pm Mon-Sat.
This decadent boutique stocks seductive corsets by Eternal Spirit, plus silky, frothy lingerie from the likes of Myla, Ayten Gasson, Ell & Cee and Mimi Holliday.

Heidi Klein
174 Westbourne Grove, W11 2RW (7243 5665, www.heidiklein.com). Notting Hill Gate tube. Open 10am-6pm Mon-Sat; noon-5pm Sun.

Head here for impeccably cut swimsuits, men's trunks and bikinis (from around £120). There's also an on-site beauty salon for all those last-minute grooming essentials and a fabulous array of beauty products.
Other location 257 Pavilion Road, SW1X 0BP (7259 9418).

Myla
74 Duke of York Square, King's Road, SW3 4LY (7730 0700, www.myla.com). Sloane Square tube. Open 10am-6.30pm Mon-Sat; noon-5pm Sun.
Myla's sumptuous silk, satin and lace designs are sexy but never tawdry, with bras from £60. Seasonally updated collections always include fashion-forward colours and designs. Lovely swimwear and nightwear too.
Other locations across the city.

Odabash
48B Ledbury Road, W11 2AJ (7229 4299, www.odabash.com). Notting Hill Gate tube. Open 10am-6pm Mon-Sat; noon-5pm Sun.
Expect sleek designs and a stylish spectrum of colour and print at Melissa Odabash's swimwear boutique; most bikinis cost around £140. A range of Odabash flip flops are also available. Watch out for the excellent late summer sale too.

Pistol Panties
75 Westbourne Park Road, W2 5QH (7229 5286, www.pistolpanties.com). Westbourne Park tube. Open 9.30am-6pm Mon-Fri; 11am-5pm Sun.
Bikinis are a mix of flirty, frilly, '50s-styles and super-glam gold numbers, plus cut-out swimsuits. Bright, oversized beach bags, attractive cover-ups, flip flops and beachy jewellery are also on offer.

Tallulah Lingerie
65 Cross Street, N1 2BB (7704 0066, www.tallulah-lingerie.co.uk). Angel tube. Open 9.30am-6pm Mon-Fri; 10.30am-6.30pm Sat; 12.30-5pm Sun.
This elegant boudoir has a dreamy selection of lingerie from the likes of Fleur T, Aubade and Lejaby – from everyday bras to silky smalls.

Menswear

Albam ★
23 Beak Street, W1F 9RS (3157 7000, www.albamclothing.com). Oxford Circus tube. Open noon-7pm Mon-Sat; noon-5pm Sun.
Albam focuses on high-quality, mainly British-made designs with a subtle retro edge. The airy store stocks timeless staples.
Other locations 286 Upper Street, N1 2TZ (7288 0835); 111a Commercial Street, E1 6BG (7247 6254).

Goodhood
41 Coronet Street, N1 6HD (7729 3600, www.goodhood.co.uk). Old Street tube/rail. Open 11am-7pm Tue-Sat.
Hoxton's glittering luxe streetwear specialist, stocking cult Australian brands PAM and Rittenhouse along with Copenhagen label Wood Wood and some excellent accessories.

Hideout
7 Upper James Street, W1F 9DH (7437 4929, www.hideoutstore.com). Oxford Circus tube. Open 11am-7pm Mon-Fri; 11am-6.30pm Sat; noon-5pm Sun.
This small but central streetwear store has a New York feel to it – unsurprising as much of the stock, such as Supreme, comes from the Big Apple and Japan. There are also cool labels from London and further afield popular with the city's skater contingent– such as Norse Projects, W Taps, Neighbourhood, NBHD denim and Original Fake too.

Interstate
17 Endell Street, WC2H 9BJ (7836 0421). Covent Garden tube. Open 11am-6.45pm Mon-Fri; 11am-6.30pm Sat; noon-6pm Sun.
Denim and workwear are the focus here, and it's packed with a decent range of sizes and well-chosen brands.

Sefton
196 Upper Street, N1 1RQ (7226 7076, www.seftonfashion.com). Highbury & Islington tube/rail. Open 10am-6.30pm Mon-Wed, Sat; 10am-7pm Thur, Fri; noon-6pm Sun.

Check out cult pieces by Comme des Garçons, Moncler and Barbour at this Islington boutique. Quality pieces from John Smedley, Marc Jacobs and Acne are on offer, as well as great accessories and tees.

Wholesome
47 Rivington Street, EC2A 3QB (7729 2899, www.wholesomelondon.com). Old Street tube/rail. Open 10am-7pm Mon-Sat; noon-6pm Sun.
Wholesome has young London labels like A.IN.T and Trapstar hanging next to cult US brands, such as Crooks & Castles, Mishka and Diamond. T-shirts start at a friendly £30.

Vintage

Beyond Retro
110-112 Cheshire Street, E2 6EJ (7729 9001, www.beyondretro.com). Shoreditch High Street rail. Open 10am-7pm Mon-Wed, Fri, Sat; 10am-8pm Thur; 10am-6pm Sun.
Packed with over 10,000 items, and great for classics like prom dresses, leather jackets and embroidered cowboy boots.

East End Thrift Store ★
Watermans Building Assembly Passage, E1 4UT (7423 9700, www.theeastend thriftstore.com). Stepney Green tube. Open 11am-6pm Mon-Wed, Sun; 11am-7pm Thur-Sat.
The clue's in the name: 'thrift' rather than 'vintage', which means you get yesteryear classics at prices around the £7-£10 mark.

Merchant Archive Boutique ★
320 Kilburn Lane, W9 3EF (8969 6470, www.merchantarchive.com). Queen's Park tube/rail. Open 10am-7pm Tue-Fri; 10am-6pm Sat; 11am-5pm Sun.
As a destination shop for both vintage and contemporary clothing, Merchant Archive takes pride of place in the address books of many a stylist. Owner Sophie Merchant's discerning eye is evident in the well-edited selection of beautiful one-off antique pieces for sale here.

Old Hat
66 Fulham High Street, SW6 3LQ (7610 6558). Putney Bridge tube. Open 10.30am-6.30pm Mon-Sat.
Fight off the stylists and designers from brands like Burberry and Dunhill who frequent this men's vintage boutique, and you might discover a Savile Row suit for £100, a pair of pristine moleskin trousers or the perfect pair of scuffed vintage brogues.

Palette London
21 Canonbury Lane, N1 2AS (7288 7428, www.palette-london.com) Highbury & Islington tube/rail. Open 11am-6.30pm Mon-Sat; noon-5.30pm Sun.
Owner Mark Ellis specialises in collectable designer vintage and avant-garde labels. He has a vast range of desirable vintage pieces from Pucci, Courrèges and Ossie Clark.

Shikasuki
67 Gloucester Avenue, NW1 8LD (7722 4442, www.shikasuki.com). Camden Town or Chalk Farm tube. Open 11am-7pm Mon-Sat; noon-7pm Sun.
Shikasuki stocks a well-edited (but not overpriced) array of clothes and accessories, with every item graded A to E, depending on its condition, and priced accordingly.

Vintage Hart
96 Church Road, SE19 2EZ (07982 184657, www.vintagehart.co.uk). Crystal Palace rail. Open noon-8pm Fri; noon-6pm Sat, Sun.
This diminutive boutique offers carefully chosen vintage finds from the '50s onwards. Unwilling partners can check out the White Hart pub – just next door– so everyone is happy.

What the Butler Wore
131 Lower Marsh, SE1 7AE (7261 1353, www.whatthebutlerwore.co.uk). Lambeth North tube. Open 11am-6pm Mon-Sat.
A colourful array of heels and impeccably clean 1960s and '70s frocks awaits at this charming little shop, presided over by owner Bridget Duffy and her resident cat, Binky.

GOING OUT

BEAUTY

FASHION

PARTIES

FOOD

HEALTH

ECO

OUTDOORS

HOME

CHILDREN

PETS

TRANSPORT

RESOURCES

GOING OUT

BEAUTY

FASHION

PARTIES

FOOD

HEALTH

ECO

OUTDOORS

HOME

CHILDREN

PETS

TRANSPORT

RESOURCES

Services

Keep your wardrobe in good repair with our recommended alterations and mending services, dry-cleaners and cobblers.

Alterations & repairs

British Invisible Mending Service
32 Thayer Street, W1U 2QT (7935 2487, www.invisible-mending.co.uk). Bond Street tube. Open 8.30am-5.30pm Mon-Fri; 10am-2pm Sat.
These miracle workers extract threads from a hidden section of a damaged garment, then reweave the fibres to blend in any holes or tears. It costs from £48 per hole, plus VAT.

Designer Alterations ★
220A Queenstown Road, SW8 4LP (7498 4360, www.designeralterations.com). Queenstown Road rail. Open 9am-6pm Mon-Wed, Fri; 9am-8pm Thur; 10am-4pm Sat.
Repairs and alterations are reasonably priced at this well-established company – it's around £40 to shorten the hem on a dress.

First Tailored Alterations
85 Lower Sloane Street, SW1W 8DA (7730 1400). Sloane Square tube. Open 9am-6pm Mon-Sat.
This traditional tailor is particularly good at working with delicate fabrics such as chiffon and silk, as well as sheepskin and tweed.

KS Tailoring Services
Lower Ground Floor, 13 Savile Row, W1S 3NE (7437 9345). Piccadilly Circus tube. Open 9.30am-5.30pm Mon-Fri; 10am-2pm Sat. No credit cards.
Quite appropriately, given the location, KS is known for its excellent alterations of suits and shirts. As a sample indicative price, shortening a pair of jacket sleeves comes in at £21 plus VAT.

Manuela Alterations
Oriel Court, Heath Street, NW3 6TE (7431 9283). Hampstead tube. Open 10am-6pm Mon-Fri; 10am-5pm Sat. No credit cards.
Regulars are full of praise for Manuela Alterations' speedy, good value shortening, hemming and taking in; to have a pair of trousers taken up costs from £16.

Dry-cleaning

The **Textile Services Association** (8863 7755, www.tsa-uk.org) lists a network of dry-cleaners and launderers that comply to its code of practice.

Blossom & Browne's Sycamore
73A Clarendon Road, W11 4JF (7727 2635, www.blossomandbrowne.com).

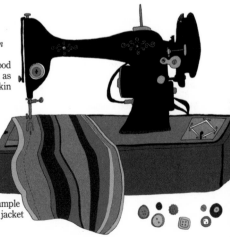

Holland Park tube. Open 8.30am-5.30pm Mon-Wed, Fri; 8.30am-4.30pm Thur; 8.30am-3pm Sat.

With Royal warrants aplenty, you know your dry-cleaning is in safe hands. Prices aren't too steep (a two-piece suit costs from £12.95) and if you set up an account, clothes can be picked up and delivered back with minimum hassle. **Other locations** *across the city.*

Celebrity Cleaners

9 Greens Court, W1F 0SS (7437 5324). Piccadilly Circus tube. Open 8.30am-6.30pm Mon-Fri.

Thanks to its regular work with West End theatres, this place knows how to shift make-up or sweat stains from pretty much anything, whether it be a common or garden men's shirt or your favourite LBD.

James of London

32 Upper Tachbrook Street, SW1V 1SW (7630 6596). Victoria tube/rail. Open 8.30am-7.30pm Mon-Fri; 9am-7pm Sat.

James offers a highly recommended invisible mending service as well as pristine dry-cleaning, at very reasonable prices; two men's suits can be done for £12.

Jeeves of Belgravia

8-10 Pont Street, SW1X 9EL (7235 1101, www.jeevesofbelgravia.co.uk). Knightsbridge or Sloane Square tube. Open 8.30am-7pm Mon-Fri; 8.30am-6pm Sat.

It's not cheap, but you get what you pay for at Jeeves. Precious designer pieces and delicates are a speciality, while pick-up and delivery are free. Two-piece suits cost from £33.25, and shirts from £6.25. Repairs, laundry washes and alterations are also available at Jeeves.
Other locations *across the city.*

Lewis & Wayne

13-15 Elystan Street, SW3 3NU (7589 5075,www.lewiswayne.co.uk). South Kensington tube. Open 8am-5pm Mon-Fri; 8.30am-12.30pm Sat.

Fifty years of experience ensure a quality service at this South Kensington dry-cleaners. Staff at Lewis & Wayne are

confident tackling anything from skiwear to haute couture gowns and wedding dresses.

Master Cleaners

189 Haverstock Hill, NW3 4QG (7431 3725). Belsize Park tube. Open 8am-7pm Mon-Wed, Fri; 8am-6pm Thur, Sat; 10am-4pm Sun.

Eco-warriors with grubby suits take note: Master Cleaners offer a greener, more gentle wash. Dry-cleaning a day dress costs from £12.50 at standard prices; using the gentler F-clean process is £18.50.

Parkers

28 Goodge Street, W1T 2QQ (7636 6373). Goodge Street tube. Open 8am-6.30pm Mon-Fri; 9am-5pm Sat.

This unpretentious dry-cleaners offers a friendly service, reasonable prices and expert advice on how best to tackle whatever stain your garment has acquired on its latest adventure.

Valentino

56B New Oxford Street, WC1A 1ES (7436 1660). Tottenham Court Road tube. Open 8.30am-6pm Mon-Fri; 9am-1pm Sat.

Specialising in cleaning and de-staining delicate designer pieces, suede and leather, Valentino offers great value for money, charging a mere £38.50 to spruce up a suede jacket. On orders over £40, collection and delivery are free.

Village Klean

1-20 St Johns Hill, SW11 1SA (7350 2562, www.villageklean.com). Clapham Junction rail. Open 7am-8pm Mon-Fri; 9am-6pm Sat.

City Secret

If you've got a watch in need of repair, **WJ Jenkins** (81A Rochester Row, SW1P 1LJ, 7834 4305) could be just what you're looking for. The traditional watchmaker and jeweller can repair watches and also has some great value watches for sale.

GOING OUT

BEAUTY

FASHION

PARTIES

FOOD

HEALTH

ECO

OUTDOORS

HOME

CHILDREN

PETS

TRANSPORT

RESOURCES

Hand-finished shirts are £1.99 and a silk blouse £5.25 at this smart, eco-friendly dry-cleaning chain. It also offers alterations and re-heeling, along with dry-cleaning pick-ups. **Other locations** *across the city.*

Shoe repair

Broadway Shoe Repairs
2 Bank Chambers, Tooting High Street, SW17 0SU (8682 0618, www.broadway-engraving.co.uk). Tooting Broadway tube. Open 8am-7pm Mon-Fri; 9am-6pm Sat.
Reasonable prices are matched by speedy efficiency at Broadway, with cobblers who'll take on well-worn shoes most other shoe-menders would write off.

Chelsea Green Shoe Company
31 Elystan Street, SW3 3NT (7584 0776). South Kensington tube. Open 8am-5.30pm Mon-Fri; 9am-1pm Sat.
Regulars love this reliable cobblers, where staff are happy to attend to cracked heels and frayed straps. Re-heeling costs from £7.50.

Fifth Avenue Shoe Repairs
41 Goodge Street, W1T 2PY (7636 6705). Goodge Street tube. Open 8am-6.30pm Mon-Fri; 10am-6pm Sat.
This traditional cobblers handles shoe repairs, bag repairs and key cutting in an old-fashioned shop that also stocks a small range of traditional men's shoes and accessories such as shoe polish and luggage.

City Secret

Beloved but battered cashmere can be posted (rather than taken) to the **Cashmere Clinic** (Flat 5, 53 Redcliffe Gardens, SW10 9JJ, 7584 9806) to be magically returned to its former glory. Repairing pesky moth holes costs from £15, while basic cleaning is from £20.

Well Heeled
443 Bethnal Green Road, E2 9QH (7739 3608). Bethnal Green tube. Open 7am-5pm Mon-Fri; 8am-4pm Sat.
Ken Holmes is the man in charge of your favourite strappies and brogues – and he's a safe pair of hands. You won't catch him solving problems with a slick of glue; this East End cobbling institution is strictly a needle and thread man.
Other locations *across the city.*

Specialist services

Bobbi Specialist Dyer
Winchmore Hill, N21 1NG (8360 6148, www.bobbispecialistshoedyer.com). Open by appointment only.
With 20 years' experience, Bobbi dyes shoes, gloves and bags to match special occasion outfits. A self-confessed perfectionist, she's coloured heels from the likes of Christian Louboutin, Emma Hope and Jimmy Choo.

Chalfont Dyers & Cleaners
222 Baker Street, NW1 5RT (7935 7316). Baker Street tube. Open 8.30am-6.30pm Mon-Fri; 9.30am-1pm Sat.
Bored of that white shirt? As long as it's made from natural fibres, the expert dyers here will do the rest, with prices from £40. Disastrous colour runs can also be dealt with.

Hand & Lock
86 Margaret Street, W1W 8TE (7580 7488, www.handembroidery.com). Oxford Circus tube. Open 9am-5.30pm Mon-Fri.
The crème de la crème of bespoke hand embroidery since 1767, Hand & Lock have honed their skills on film costumery and the Royal family. Shirt monogramming, beading and custom embroidery are all possible.

Julia Taylor
7289 3966. Open by appointment only.
If you've stained your favourite silk or satin shoes or need to dye bridesmaids' shoes to match their frocks, Taylor's your woman. She can also sew beads or appliqué lace on to shoes.

Parties

Caterers

Of *course* you made it all yourself.

Delis

Atari-ya
20 James Street, W1U 1EH (7491 1178, www.atariya.co.uk). Bond Street tube. Open 11am-8pm daily.
Delicious and well-presented sushi and sashimi platters are made to order (collection only) at this takeaway branch of the Japanese grocery chain. An extensive list of fish and seafood includes eel, squid, surf clam and, at the pricier end, sea urchin and snow crab leg meat.

Flavours ✦
For listings, see p82.
Former *Masterchef* winner Julie Friend creates a great range of dishes using produce from her two north London delis. Menus often have a Mediterranean slant, but British classics –

CELEBRATION CAKES

Bea's of Bloomsbury
44 Theobald's Road, WC1X 8NW (7242 8330, www.beasofbloomsbury. com). Holborn or Chancery Lane tube. Open 8am-7pm Mon-Fri; 10am-7pm Sat; noon-7pm Sun.
Pastry chef Bea Vo's masterpieces range from hearty carrot cakes to sumptuous vegan chocolate mousse cakes. Better still, 'build-a-cake' allows you to design your dream cake. Gold leaf on top? Passionfruit or praline buttercream? It's entirely up to you. An array of tempting brownies, meringues and cookies are also available.

Cake Boy
Unit 2, Kingfisher House, Juniper Drive, SW18 1TX (7978 5555, www.cake-boy.co.uk). Wandsworth Town rail. Open 8am-6pm Mon-Fri; 9am-6pm Sat.
Master pâtissier Eric Lanlard creates the most glamorous gateaux in town: the A-list celebs wouldn't buy their wedding cakes anywhere else. Options range from the simple

sachertorte or cheesecake (from £24) to elaborate bespoke creations (from £6 per serving).

Hummingbird Bakery
133 Portobello Road, W11 2DY (7229 6446, www.hummingbirdbakery.com). Notting Hill Gate tube. Open 10am-6pm Mon-Sat; 11am-5pm Sun.
As well as sweet-treat-of-the-moment whoopie pies (*see right*), they bake a mean birthday cake; the Red Velvet (a red-hued vanilla sponge with a hint of chocolate, covered with cream cheese) always goes down a treat. Messages can be iced on to cakes or cupcakes, if you order ahead.
Other locations 155A Wardour Street, W1F 8WG (7434 3003); 47 Old Brompton Road, SW7 3JP (7584 0055).

Lola's Kitchen
7483 3394, www.lolas-kitchen.co.uk. The giant 'showgirl' cupcakes on offer here make excellent party centrepieces (£45), as do the more traditional birthday cakes in chocolate,

such as shepherd's pie followed by trifle – are popular too. A finger-food buffet for ten starts at £7.50 per head.

Hand Made Food
40 Tranquil Vale, SE3 OBD (8297 9966, www.handmadefood.com). Blackheath rail. Open 9am-5pm Mon, Wed-Sat; 9am-2pm Tue; 9am-4pm Sun.
Fergus and Vicky Clague cater events of all sizes, making party food for as few as 25 people. Canapés are a speciality, with an international menu that includes Jamaican beef patties, parmesan gnocchi and spanakopita (£1.50 each). For larger events their jerk chicken tent is a winner (from £20 a head). Ingredients are sourced as locally as possible, and meat is organic.

carrot, banana and red velvet varieties (among others). Lola's signature cupcakes (try the peanut butter, lemon or rocky road versions) are a cut above too.

Konditor & Cook
10 Stoney Street, SE1 9AD (7407 5100, www.konditorandcook.com). Borough tube or London Bridge tube/rail. Open 7.30am-6pm Mon-Fri; 8.30am-5.30pm Sat.
This celebration cake stalwart continues to make delicious traditional birthday cakes in a range of pleasing flavours: dark chocolate, curly wurly, lemon chiffon, frosted carrot (from £21.20). You can have your choice of cake iced with a birthday message for just £4 extra. K&C's famous mini 'magic cakes' are another popular choice: a letter can be iced on to each fondant-covered biscuit, spelling out a birthday message. The cake hotline is 0800 319 6767.
Other locations across the city.

Melrose & Morgan
42 Gloucester Avenue, NW1 8JD (7722 0011, www.melroseandmorgan.com). Camden Town tube. Open 8am-7pm Mon-Fri; 8am-6pm Sat, Sun.
This lovely deli has answered many a disorganised local's dinner party prayers with its divine, daily-changing menu of savoury tarts (£20, serves eight), huge chicken or mushroom pies (£24.95, serves five) and delicious apple crumbles (£15, serves eight). For a larger (and less spontaneous) do, there are fabulous seasonal sharing menus (M&M will supply staff to prepare, serve and clear up).

Mimosa
16 Half Moon Lane, SE24 9HU (7733 8838, www.mimosafoods.com). Herne Hill rail. Open 9am-6pm Mon-Fri; 9am-5.30pm Sat; 9.30am-3pm Sun.
Friendly and flexible Mimosa offers Moroccan- and French-themed spreads alongside the more usual finger food; you can borrow Moroccan dishes for perfect presentation. A buffet for ten costs from £15.75 a head.

Mr Christian's
11 Elgin Crescent W11 2JA (7229 0501, www.mrchristians.co.uk). Notting Hill Gate tube. Open 7.30am-6.30pm Mon-Fri; 7.30am-6pm Sat; 8am-3pm Sun.
Pop into this beautifully presented deli and you might spot a local A-lister making arrangements for a dinner party, or planning catering for up to 200 guests. An enormous menu runs from tempting canapés to à la carte menus, along with sumptuous salads

City Secret

It's all over for the cupcake. Anyone who's anyone is tucking into a whoopie pie (two slabs of cookie-cake deliciousness with a cream filling) with their afternoon cuppa these days. Try **Hummingbird Bakery's** (*see left*) pumpkin (with cream cheese filling), chocolate and red velvet versions (from £2).

GOING OUT
BEAUTY
FASHION
PARTIES
FOOD
HEALTH
ECO
OUTDOORS
HOME
CHILDREN
PETS
TRANSPORT
RESOURCES

COCKTAIL HOUR

Endlessly refilling your guests' glasses is no way to spend a party: instead, think about investing in a barman for the evening, or even hiring a mobile bar.

At Your Service (7610 8610, www.ays.co.uk) provides bar staff, while sister company Bamboo has experienced cocktail 'mixologists'. Prices start from £25 per hour. Alternatively, **High Society** (7228 0333, www.high-society.co.uk) charges £59 per barman for four hours, then £12.75 an hour.

London's Mobile Bar (07788 822326, www.eventcocktails.com) offers mobile bars and mixologists, charging from £145. Or you can just hire the equipment, from mixers and blenders to strainers, tumblers, flutes and tongs.

Shaker Events (0870 720 2877, www.shaker-events.com) supplies all manner of bars, including a bamboo-clad tiki version, from which its professional bartenders will mix up a storm of cocktails. Prices start at £350 for a four-hour service, plus stock and VAT.

Wedding Trikes (07958 722251, www.weddingtrikes.com) offers the Cocktail Camper: a VW camper converted into a cocktail bar (hire from £600 for a 12-hour dry hire, with one helper), complete with its own sound system. More low key (and cheaper) is its Pimm's Trike. Also on offer are mojito bars or organic ice-cream on trikes and a posh dogs hotdog cart.

Rent a Keg (0800 977 5113, www.rent-a-keg.com) has a good range of ice-cold lager kegs (88 pints of Becks, delivery, set-up and tap hire for £235), plus ales and cider. Proper pint glasses and a bar are also available.

(butternut squash, shaved parmesan and baby spinach, for example) and quiches (the emmental and tomato is delicious).

Pie Man

16 Cale Street, SW3 3QU (7225 0587, www.thepieman.co.uk). South Kensington or Sloane Square tube. Open 6.30am-5pm Mon-Fri; 6.30am-2pm Sat.
If you've ever tried Murray Tollemache's deli, you'll know you're in for a treat with his catering service. A canapé selection (minimum ten guests) starts at £12 per head and ranges from simple shots of gazpacho to the more elaborate likes of seared scallops with pea purée. Children's parties are catered for.

Independent caterers

Amaze in Taste

0844 800 1655, www.amazeintaste.com.
If you want your guests to fill up on proper food but still be able to mingle, serve 'bowl food': mushroom risotto with parmesan and parsley, perhaps, or mini sausage and mash. More traditional party food includes finger-food buffets (thai sesame beef skewers, mini yorkshire puddings with roast beef and such like), from £10 per head for 25 people.

Gorgeous Gourmets

8944 7771, www.gorgeousgourmets.co.uk.
This Wimbledon-based stalwart deals in tried and trusted menus – from stilton and walnut scones with parma ham and red onion confit to filo tartlets of devilled crab salad – and offers a range of catering options, including a finger-food buffet for ten from £16.25 per head (plus VAT and delivery).

El Vergel

7401 2308, www.elvergel.co.uk.
Stella de Garcia and Kiko Sanhueza blend Latin American and Mediterranean influences to create fabulous fusion food. Canapés (from £8 a head) might include Chilean village bread with refried bean spread or smoked salmon and guacamole. Vegetarian finger buffets served on fresh banana leaves cost around £15 per person, dinners from £25.

London
Captured

Stunning photography through the ages.

GOING OUT

BEAUTY

FASHION

PARTIES

FOOD

HEALTH

ECO

OUTDOORS

HOME

CHILDREN

PETS

TRANSPORT

RESOURCES

Party shops

From balloons to Batman costumes.

Fancy dress

Angels ✱
*119 Shaftesbury Avenue, WC2H 8AE
(7836 5678, www.fancydress.com). Leicester
Square or Tottenham Court Road tube.
Open 9.30am-5.30pm Mon, Tue, Thur,
Fri; 10.30am-7pm Wed.*
The undisputed doyenne of London fancy
dress hires out an unparalleled array of
outfits, with prices from £80 plus VAT. The
website is devoted to cheaper costumes to
buy, from trolley dolly and Zorro outfits to
Wonder Woman costumes for dogs.

Contemporary Wardrobe
*The Horse Hospital, Colonnade, WC1N 1HX
(7713 7710, www.contemporarywardrobe.
com). Russell Square tube. Open viewings
10am-6pm Mon-Fri. Hire by appointment.*
This specialist hire company has some gems
among its 15,000-strong collection, including
vintage Dior and Biba pieces, and outfits
worn by pop icons such as David Bowie and
the Beatles. Weekly hire prices for outfits are
around £85, plus VAT.

Escapade
*45-46 Chalk Farm Road, NW1 8AJ (7485
7384, www.escapade.co.uk). Chalk Farm
tube. Open 10am-7pm Mon-Fri; 10am-6pm
Sat; noon-5pm Sun.*
The shop is always crammed with folk trying
on wigs or peeking through sequin-encrusted
masks. There are cheaper ensembles to buy
outright, or higher-quality costumes to hire.

Mad World
*69-85 Tabernacle Street, EC2A 4BA (0800
783 6582, www.madworldfancydress.com).
Old Street tube. Open 9.30am-7pm Mon-
Wed, Fri; 9.30am-8pm Thur; 10am-5pm Sat.*

There's a staggering array of costumes to hire,
from pantomime horse two-parters to sequin-
studded basques. There are masks aplenty for
masked balls and an impressive selection of
children's dressing up gear (from navity
angels to full-on regal king and queen get-ups).

Pantaloons
*119 Lupus Street, SW1V 3EN (7630 8330,
www..pantaloons.co.uk). Pimlico tube. Open
noon-5pm Mon; 11am-6pm Tue, Wed;
11am-7pm Thur, Fri; 10am-7pm Sat.*
Choose from more than 4,000 hire costumes,
from Uma Thurman's yellow *Kill Bill* get-up
to a similarly yellow (but rather less cool)
giant banana suit. A week's hire starts at
£25. For a unique look, splash out on the
'haute couture' service, where your costume
is custom-designed and fitted.

Prangsta Costumiers
*304 New Cross Road, SE14 6AF (8694
9869, www.prangsta.com). New Cross Gate
rail. Open 11am-7pm Mon-Sat.*
Discerning dresser-uppers adore Prangsta's
extravagant, beautifully made costumes.
Burlesque-style basques and gowns are a
forte, but you'll also find circus ringmaster
suits, silky 1930s frocks and more.

Party supplies

Circus Circus
*176 Wandsworth Bridge Road, SW6 2UQ
(7731 4128, www.circuscircus.co.uk).
Fulham Broadway tube. Open 10am-6pm
Mon-Sat; 10am-1pm Sun.*
Head here for bargain-priced supplies, from
multicoloured balloons to bosoms (of the fake
plastic variety). There's a great selection of
fancy dress costumes and accessories too,
including luxuriant stick-on moustaches.

PRESENTS BY POST

A monthly delivery of little luxuries has to be the ultimate gift.

Neal's Yard Dairy
7500 7653, www.nealsyarddairy shop.co.uk.
What cheese lover wouldn't covet a subscription to Neal's Yard Dairy's Cheese of the Month service? Each delivery comprises four superb cheeses – often unusual, small-scale, artisan affairs – which are sent out with tasting notes and information on the cheesemakers. Options range from one-off deliveries (£55) to quarterly (£198) and monthly boxes (£550), while a more modestly sized bi-monthly four-cheese box is £275.

Real Ale Beer Club
8894 1114, www.realale.com.
Make a beer drinker very happy indeed with a monthly case of 12 unusual and delicious real ales, plus tasting notes (£28.30 per month). A 13th case is delivered free at the end of the year. To keep costs down you could go for three or six months of deliveries.

Real Flower Company
01730 818300, www.realflowers. co.uk.
What could be more romantic than receiving a hand-tied bouquet of seasonal, headily scented roses every month for a year? True love doesn't come cheap, though, with prices starting at £480 per year for the posy-sized option, not including postage.

The Spicery
01255 426309, www.thespicery.com.
Budding chefs will love a monthly spicebox delivery from the Spicery. Choose from a Friday Night Curry box (vegetarian and carnivorous recipe options are available for all boxes) or Season & Spice box and each month your recipient will receive a beautifully packaged array of spices to create a delicious meal for four. A year's deliveries come in at £79.95 (three-and six-month gifts are available for a cheaper option) and includes rare ingredients such as Tahitian vanilla and long pepper that more than justify the cost.

Stone, Vine & Sun
01962 712351, www.stonevine. co.uk.
Wine merchants can seem offputtingly stuffy – but not the friendly Stone, Vine & Sun. One-off gift boxes are available, or you can opt for a gift that keeps on giving with the Doorstep Dozen (from £75/month). This brings a monthly (or bi-monthly) case of reds and whites, mixing classic buys with notable new discoveries and with tasting notes included.

Oscar's Den
127-129 Abbey Road, NW6 4SL (7328 6683, www.oscarsden.com). Swiss Cottage tube/West Hampstead tube/rail. Open 9.30am-6pm Mon-Sat; 10am-3pm Sun.
This balloon specialist also does a fine line in everything from paper plates and fireworks, to bubble machines and bouncy castles for hire. Also hires out smoke machines, disco lights and the like.

Party Party
9-13 Ridley Road, E8 2NP (7254 5168, www.ppshop.co.uk) Dalston Kingsland rail/67, 76, 149 bus. Open 9am-5.30pm Mon-Thur; 9am-6.30pm Fri, Sat.
A local favourite that's filled to the brim with party paraphernalia – cake-baking trays and cakestands, balloons, wigs, fancy dress costumes – and all at bargain-basement prices.

GOING OUT

BEAUTY

FASHION

PARTIES

FOOD

HEALTH

ECO

OUTDOORS

HOME

CHILDREN

PETS

TRANSPORT

RESOURCES

Venues

Fabulous venues to suit your budget. For children's parties, *see p174*.

CENTRAL

Carpenter's Arms

68-70 Whitfield Street, W1T 4EY (7580 3186). Goodge Street tube. Available for hire venue noon-midnight Sat, Sun; 1st floor noon-midnight Mon-Wed, Sat, Sun. Capacity venue 200 standing; 1st floor 70 standing. Minimum spend venue from £2,500; 1st floor from £600.

This boho boozer has three areas for hire. Downstairs, the backroom has a kitsch, working men's club feel thanks to its '70s-style floral wallpaper and bench seating; for more intimate gatherings, there's a smaller front-of-bar space. The real gem is upstairs, where a second bar leads on to one of Fitzrovia's prettier outdoor drinking spots: a small, wooden-decked terrace with four tables, fairy light-draped bird cages and a back wall decorated with bird prints.

Cellar Door

Zero Aldwych, WC2R 0HT (7240 8848, www.cellardoor.biz). Covent Garden tube. Available for hire 4pm-1am daily. Capacity venue 60 standing; private room 60 standing. Minimum spend venue from £750-£4,000; private room from £750-£4,000.

Once a gentlemen's public convenience, this place has been transformed into a suitably louche bar, often host to jazz and cabaret nights. Lipstick-red walls and racy toilets (the clear glass turns opaque when the door's locked) add risqué appeal, while clever design makes the space feel intimate rather than claustrophobic. An SMS jukebox allows you to choose tunes without leaving your seat, and the cocktails are inspired.

Positively 4th Street

119 Hampstead Road, NW1 3EE (7388 5380, www.positively4thstreet.co.uk).

Warren Street tube/ Euston tube/rail. Available for hire 5-1am Fri; 7pm-1am Sat. Capacity 120. Hire charge £135. Minimum spend £1,500.

Just a few minutes' walk from Warren Street tube, Positively 4th Street is a little-known gem. Part Prohibition-style speakeasy, part Japanese diner, it serves inventive cocktails and Japanese food in seductive surrounds: think deep red decor, art deco mirrors and sultry lighting. Bring your own decks or simply plug in the iPod; there's also a mic and projector for more arty entertainment.

NORTH

Barrio North

45 Essex Road, N1 2SF (7688 2882, www.barrionorth.com). Angel tube. Available for hire noon-midnight Mon-Thur; noon-2am Fri, Sat; 3pm-midnight Sun. Capacity Venue 175 standing. Private areas 4: 8-70 standing. Minimum spend Venue £2,000. Private areas free-£500.

For a small gathering with hip novelty appeal, book out the fairy-lit caravan at this narrow Essex Road

DJ bar (it seats 15). Larger groups can go for the caravan and the whole mezzanine at the back (the whole venue is also available for hire). Think dancing in the aisles, icy bottles of Brahma, platters of nachos and an excessive tequila shot session for the road.

Harrison
28 Harrison Street, WC1H 8JF (7278 3966, www.harrisonbar.co.uk). King's Cross tube/ rail. Available for hire noon-11.30pm Sat. Capacity 100 standing. Minimum spend £300.
A stone's throw from King's Cross and in fine fettle after a 2008 refurbishment, the Harrison is a warm, inviting place to throw a party. You can rent out the entire pub on Saturday nights and make full use of the DJ decks, PA and stage at no extra charge – or just connect up your iPod. The pub can get an extended licence a few times a year, so ask nicely and you may get lucky.

Old Queen's Head
44 Essex Road, N1 8LN (7354 9993, www.theoldqueenshead.com). Angel tube. Available for hire noon-midnight Mon-Wed, Sun; noon-1am Thur. Capacity private room 170 standing, 100 seated. Minimum spend from £1,000.
The elegantly proportioned upstairs room offers a vast parquet dancefloor, professional sound system and proper DJ booth, along with a well-stocked bar and artfully battered chesterfields. If that's beyond your means, smaller private areas (with a capacity of up to 20 people each) can be booked either upstairs or in the downstairs bar for a minimum preorder.

Paradise by Way of Kensal Green
19 Kilburn Lane, W10 4AE (8969 0098, www.theparadise.co.uk). Kensal Green tube/ Kensal Rise rail. Available for hire noon-midnight Mon-Wed, Sun; noon-1am Thur; noon-2am Fri, Sat. Capacity reading room 14 seated, 40 standing; dining room 20 seated, 70 standing; music room 50 seated, 150 standing. Minimum spend music room £3,000 Fri, call for details other days; dining room £1,000; reading room £300.

This deliciously theatrical gastropub offers three different rooms. Downstairs, the book-lined reading room hosts private dinners or 'host a roast' three-course feasts (£29 a head). Upstairs there's a more secluded and opulently decorated dining room, with a door leading on to the roof terrace. Finally, there's the spacious music room, complete with deer antlers, a stuffed peacock and professional-quality sound system and decks.

Rosemary Branch
2 Shepperton Road, N1 3DT (7704 2730, www.rosemarybranch.co.uk). Old Street tube/ rail, then 21, 76, 141 bus. Available for hire noon-11pm Mon-Thur; noon-midnight Fri, Sat; noon-10.30pm Sun. Capacity venue 200 standing; private room 80 standing; theatre 80 seated. Hire charge venue from £5,000; private room £200-£500; theatre £200.
This mellow pub and theatre offer a beautifully decorated function room, with startling pink-flowered wallpaper, stripped floors and an ornate bar. With a proper sound system, film-screening facilities and decks on request, it's well set up for celebrations. If you're feeling ambitious you can hire out the theatre and put on your own production; the hire price includes technical support, lighting and use of the battered grand piano.

EAST

dreambagsjaguarshoes
34-36 Kingsland Road, E2 8DA (7729 5830, www.dreambagsjaguarshoes.com). Old Street tube/rail. Available for hire noon-midnight Mon; noon-1am Tue-Sat; noon-12.30am Sun. Capacity private room 100 standing. Minimum spend £500.
This former shoe shop-turned bar remains a cornerstone of the East End's drinking scene. Changing art exhibitions hang against the white and turquoise wallpaper, while trendy regulars lounge on slouchy couches. The brick-walled basement can be hired out for parties (mainly Monday to Wednesday). You can't choose the music, though, so only those who like electro and alt-rock need apply.

GOING OUT
BEAUTY
FASHION
PARTIES
FOOD
HEALTH
ECO
OUTDOORS
HOME
CHILDREN
PETS
TRANSPORT
RESOURCES

GOING OUT
BEAUTY
FASHION
PARTIES
FOOD
HEALTH
ECO
OUTDOORS
HOME
CHILDREN
PETS
TRANSPORT
RESOURCES

PARTY PIECES

Special services to make sure your party is remembered for all the right reasons.

Boothnation

7613 5576, www.boothnation.com. Always forget to take party pictures in the heat of the moment? Hire a mobile photo booth for the evening and watch as your guests squeeze in to strike a pose. The Classic Booth is a 1950s US import, but for sheer glamour it's hard to beat the sparkly, silver-clad Glitterbox, complete with silver lamé curtains. Prices include on-the-day prints, and start at £1,545 for four hours.

London Jukeboxes

8318 2852, www.london-jukeboxes.com. Personalise your party soundtrack by hiring out a cool retro jukebox. Options range from the 50-CD Wurlitzer-shaped Rockola Bubbler (£245) to the boxy, all-vinyl Jakovich (£160); you can choose the tunes you want loaded. Delivery is charged outside SE postcodes.

Oyster Boys

07792 868502, www.oysterboys.co.uk
Colin Thwaites and Robin Dunlop's Oyster Boys have proved a rousing success at hip parties across the UK since 2005. They offer impressive cocktail and canapé (all with a unique Scottish flavour) services, but a pair of tartan-clad oyster shuckers working the room at your soirée remains the real winner. Perfect for injecting some serious energy into your guests.

Drunken Monkey

222 Shoreditch High Street, E1 6PJ (7392 9606, www.thedrunkenmonkey.co.uk). Shoreditch High Street rail. Available for hire noon-midnight daily. Capacity venue 250 standing; private rooms (2) 28-35 standing, 12-15 seated. Minimum spend venue £2,000-£7,000; private rooms free.
Lit by glowing paper lanterns and serving dim sum as well as drinks, the Drunken Monkey is a raucous, rollicking party venue. Your options include a quieter private dining area, plus 'concubine rooms' along the sides that seat 12. For serious partying, the entire venue can be hired out. Music is loud and varied but tends towards housey, while stellar staff do their utmost to accommodate special party requests.

Exit

174 Brick Lane, E1 6RU (7377 2088). Shoreditch High Street rail. Available for hire 4pm-1am Tue-Thur; 4pm-2am Fri; 10am-2am Sat; 9am-1am Sun. Capacity Private areas 40. Minimum spend call for details.

Large areas for up to 40 guests can be reserved at this cosy Brick Lane bar. The vibe is relaxed and the simple set-up works a treat – there's a long, narrow room with plenty of distressed leather seating, a bar up one side and a bit of floor space for dancing at the back. Perfect for a low-key (or last-minute) party where you want the music taken care of by someone else.

Gramaphone

60-62 Commercial Street, E1 6LT (7377 5332, www.thegramaphone.co.uk). Aldgate East tube. Available for hire noon-2am Mon-Thur; noon-3am Fri, Sat. Capacity private room 200 standing. Hire charge £200-300.
Popular with band and club promoters, the Gramaphone's basement is also perfect for big birthday bashes. The decks are set up so you can bring your own DJs; if you'd prefer a band to play, the hire fee includes full PA and an engineer. The battered wooden floor and furniture and low-level lighting are worn-in but welcoming; best of all, you have your own bar.

SOUTH

Balham Bowls Club

7-9 Ramsden Road, SW12 8QX (8673 4700, www.antic-ltd.com). Balham tube/rail. Available for hire 4-11pm Mon-Thur; 4pm-1am Fri; noon-1am Sat; noon-11pm Sun. Capacity private rooms (2) 80-150 standing. Hire charge £75-£100.

Once home to Balham's Bowls Club, this charming venue still brims with original fixtures, from the old wooden scoreboard and framed rosettes on the wall to the wonky seating. The entire right-hand side is available for hire, and perfect for anything from a quirky wedding reception to a proper birthday knees-up. The smaller front room can hold 50 people, but for larger dos the doors open up and the room extends into the snooker hall. Dancing to tunes from your iPod is encouraged, while food can be arranged on request. *See also p33.*

Bar du Musée

17 Nelson Road, SE10 9JB (8858 4710, www. bardumusee.com). Cutty Sark DLR. Available for hire 7pm-1am Mon-Fri, Sun; 7pm-2am Sat. Capacity venue 80 seated, 250 standing; private room 20 seated, 50 standing. Hire charge varies; call for prices.

This Greenwich bistro and late-night bar has a sophisticated party space in the shape of the adjoining George Room. Despite not having its own bar (an obliging waiter takes the drinks orders), it's a charming room, with a lofty ceiling, granite-topped tables (which can be arranged or removed as you please), walls adorned with etchings and paintings, and welcoming

leather sofas. Music can be provided courtesy of your own iPod (just plug it in and you're good to go), while canapés can be arranged. Perfect for more elegant gatherings.

Harrison's

15-19 Bedford Hill, SW12 9EX (8675 6900, www.harrisonsbalham.com). Balham tube/rail. Available for hire noon-midnight Mon-Wed, Sun; noon-1am Thur-Sat. Capacity private room 15 seated, 40 standing. Minimum spend £400 Mon-Wed, Sun; £800 Thur-Sat.

Hidden away at the bottom of a spiral staircase leading off the plush main restaurant lies Harrison's private bar. Lined with leather banquettes, and with its own *Barbarella*-ish bar, it's totally separate from the rest of the venue and provides a sophisticated setting for a really special occasion. Music comes in the form of an MP3 connection, the cocktails are mixed to perfection, and food can be arranged to suit your needs.

Hide Bar ★

39-45 Bermondsey Street, SE1 3XF (7403 6655, www.thehidebar.com). London Bridge tube/rail. Available for hire 4.30pm-midnight Mon, Tue; 4.30pm-1am Wed, Thur; noon-2am Fri, Sat. Capacity venue 100 standing; private room 50 standing. Minimum spend venue £5,000; private room free.

Known for its stellar cocktails (*see p30*), Hide is also nicely set up for parties. Behind the main bar there's a low-lit lounge with leather seating, beautiful wallpaper and a chandelier made from crystal decanter tops, available for private hire. Alternatively, enquire about hiring the whole place out. The cocktail-making classes are especially popular with discerning hen parties.

GOING OUT

BEAUTY

FASHION

PARTIES

FOOD

HEALTH

ECO

OUTDOORS

HOME

CHILDREN

PETS

TRANSPORT

RESOURCES

WEST

Amuse Bouche

*51 Parsons Green Lane, SW6 4JA (7371
8517, www.abcb.co.uk). Parsons Green tube.
Available for hire 4-11pm Mon; 4pm-
midnight Tue-Thur; 4pm-12.30am Fri-Sat;
4-10.30pm Sun. Capacity Private room 38
seated, 70 seated. Seated terrace 20
seated, 40 standing. Hire charge £100.
Minimum spend £1,000.*

The smaller sibling to Amuse Bouche Soho
makes a versatile party venue. There's an
upstairs function room with a relaxed, shabby
chic feel that's great for birthday dinner
parties. It has a decent sound system and
space for a dancefloor too. Catering is provided
in-house and there's an inviting roaring fire for
cold, winter nights. Small summer parties can
be hosted on the lovely outdoor terrace.

Defectors Weld

*170 Uxbridge Road, W12 8AA (8749 0008,
www.defectors-weld.com). Shepherd's Bush
tube. Available for hire noon-midnight daily.
Capacity 50 seated, 70 standing. Minimum
spend £300-£600 Mon-Thur, Sun; £600-
£800 Fri, Sat.*

Hidden away from the after-work throng
crowding the bar below, the private room has
become a hip photo-shoot location of late,
thanks to its muted colour palette and country
house-style decor. By night, it becomes a cosy
party venue, probably better suited to dining
and conversation than raving (the bar menu is
top-notch, and party food can be arranged on
request). That said, you can bring your own
DJs or plug in an iPod, or music can be piped
up from downstairs. Attentive staff and
stylish surrounds give this place the feel of a
private members' club, at a fraction of the cost.

Grand Union

*45 Woodfield Road, W9 2BA (7286 1886).
Westbourne Park tube. Available for hire
noon-11pm Mon-Thur; noon-midnight Fri,
Sat; noon-10.30pm Sun. Capacity private
room 60 standing (minimum 20). Minimum
spend call for details.*

The Grand Union is ideal for a low-key
summer celebration – although if you hire the

downstairs room, you may have to share the
outside canalside space with the pub's
regulars. For a price, however, it can all be
yours. In summer, there's no better spot to
tuck into a jug of Pimm's and make the most
of the outdoor barbecue grill (even if the
views are more urban than idyllic, thanks to
the bus depot opposite). As night draws in,
retire into the snug indoor space, which has
its own bar and a selection of board games.

Idlewild

*55 Shirland Road, W9 2JD (7266 9198,
www.ruby.uk.com/idlewild). Warwick
Avenue tube. Available for hire 4-11pm
Mon-Thur; 4pm-midnight Fri; noon-
midnight Sat; noon-10.30pm Sun. Capacity
private room 80 standing. Minimum spend
£1,500-£3,000.*

This modish Maida Vale pub has bookable
booths on the ground floor, but the real gem
is on the first floor. Head straight up the
magnificent staircase (lined with cases of
framed insects and butterflies) to the grand,
petrol-blue cocktail lounge. Here, stately
Murano glass chandeliers and floor-to-ceiling
draped windows will wow even the most
jaded gastropub-goer. There's a fierce sound
system, along with decks, and canapés are
available on request. As you'd expect, there's
a sizeable minimum spend.

Westbourne House

*65 Westbourne Grove, W2 4UJ (7229 2233,
www.westbournehouse.net). Bayswater or
Royal Oak tube. Available for hire 10.30am-
11.30pm Mon-Thur; 10.30am-midnight Fri;
9.30am-midnight Sat; 9.30am-10.30pm
Sun. Capacity private areas (3) 25-40
standing. Hire charge £100 Mon-Thur, Sun;
£200 Fri, Sat.*

This handsome venue is part cosy
gastropub, part sleek cocktail bar – and it
works. Expert Italian bar staff mix cracking
cocktails from a list designed by drinks
supremo Mat Perovetz, with treats like the
dangerous 'martini with a spot': Plymouth
gin with vermouth and a spot of Pernod
absinthe. Rather than private rooms, there
are three mid-sized areas that can be
reserved, including a mezzanine space.

Food

GOING OUT
BEAUTY
FASHION
PARTIES
FOOD
HEALTH
ECO
OUTDOORS
HOME
CHILDREN
PETS
TRANSPORT
RESOURCES

Cafés & restaurants

From brilliant brunches to the best places for BYO, the capital is brimming with great places to dine.

Breakfast & brunch

CENTRAL

Dehesa
25 Ganton Street, W1F 9BP (7494 4170, www.dehesa.co.uk). Oxford Circus tube. Meals served noon-11pm Mon-Sat; noon-5pm Sun. ££.
Head here for a Spanish-Italian brunch of Tuscan sausages, scrambled duck eggs with morcilla, or churros with thick hot chocolate, served weekends only.

Fernandez & Wells
73 Beak Street, W1F 9SR (7287 8124, www.fernandezandwells.com). Oxford Circus or Piccadilly Circus tube. Open 7.30am-6pm Mon-Fri; 9am-6pm Sat; 10am-6pm Sun. £.
Indulge in a breakfast bun brimming with pancetta and egg mayonnaise, washed down with a perfect cappuccino.

City Secret

Appease mid-week cravings for a roast with a visit to **Fuzzy's Grub** (6 Crown Passage, SW1Y 6PP, 7925 2791, www.fuzzysgrubcrown passage.co.uk). Here, takeaway lunchtime roasts are served Monday to Friday – in traditional and sarnie form. Choose your meat, add some potatoes and trimmings (sage and onion stuffing or crackling), then select a relish: own-made red onion marmalade, perhaps, or a dollop of sweet chilli jam.

Fleet River Bakery
71 Lincoln's Inn Fields, WC2A 3JF (7691 1457, www.fleetriverbakery.com). Holborn tube. Open 7am-6pm Mon-Fri; 9am-4pm Sat. £.
The brie and tomato croissants here are good for those on the go, while hot options for sit-ins include scrambled eggs on sourdough or sausage baguettes. Brunch on Saturdays includes indulgences such as pancakes with berry compôte and mascarpone.

Lantana
13 Charlotte Place, W1T 1SN (7637 3347, www.lantanacafe.co.uk). Goodge Street tube. Open 8am-6pm Mon-Wed; 8am-9pm Thur, Fri; 9am-3pm Sat, Sun. £££.
Antipodean café Lantana serves up some impressive breakfast plates (think the opposite of a greasy fry-up) and quality coffee. The eggs are free-range and meat is sourced from ethical suppliers.

NORTH

Banners ✦
21 Park Road, N8 8TE (8348 2930, www.bannersrestaurant.com). Hornsey rail. Open 9am-11.30pm Mon-Fri; 10am-midnight Sat; 10am-11pm Sun. £.
This family-friendly restaurant serves up a brunch menu that encompasses bacon baguettes, scrambled eggs, fruit salads, fry-ups and deliciously indulgent Banners' potatoes (new potatoes fried with onion, chilli and bacon topped with two fried eggs).

Flavours
9-10 Campdale Road, N7 0EA (7281 6565, www.delibelly.com). Tufnell Park tube. Meals served 8.30am-5pm Tue-Fri; 9am-5pm Sat; 10am-4pm Sun. £.

This modest little café-deli tempts with its overflowing baskets of artisan breads and delicious (and immense) almond croissants.

Ottolenghi
287 Upper Street, N1 2TZ (7288 1454, www.ottolenghi.co.uk). Angel tube. Meals served 8am-10pm Mon-Wed; 8am-10.30pm Thur-Sat; 9am-7pm Sun. £.
Heaped plates of scrambled eggs and salmon or moreish cinnamon french toast with fruit compôte are served at communal tables at this cool, white-painted deli and bakery. **Other locations** *across the city.*

EAST

Albion
2-4 Boundary Street, E2 7DD (7729 1051, www.albioncaff.co.uk). Shoreditch High Street rail. Open 8am-midnight daily. £.

NO BOOKING? NO PROBLEM

Forgotten to make that all-important reservation? Here's the solution.

Anchor & Hope
36 The Cut, SE1 8LP (7928 9898). Southwark tube or Waterloo tube/rail. Meals served 6-10.30pm Mon; noon-2.30pm, 6-10.30pm Tue-Sat; 2pm sitting Sun. ££
The pared-down, daily-changing menu at this foodie favourite offers inviting gastropub fare; rich chicken pithivier, perhaps, or a classic cassoulet.

Barrafina
54 Frith Street, W1D 4SL (7813 8016, www.barrafina.co.uk). Leicester Square or Tottenham Court Road tube. Meals served noon-3pm, 5-11pm Mon-Sat; 1-3.30pm, 5.30-10.30pm Sun. £.
Once you've scored a coveted seat at the broad, L-shaped bar, relax and enjoy the sensational tapas.

Busaba Eathai
8-13 Bird Street, W1U 1BU (7518 8080, www.busaba.com). Bond Street tube. Meals served noon-11pm Mon-Thur; noon-11.30pm Fri, Sat; noon-10pm Sun. ££.
Low lighting, stylish decor and a well-priced menu of soups, salads, stir fries and curries keep Busaba buzzing. **Other locations** *across the city.*

Dehesa
For listings see p82. ££.
Sumptuous charcuterie boards and Italian-influenced tapas are the draw at Dehesa; don't miss the Monte Enebro-stuffed courgette flowers.

Providores & Tapa Room
109 Marylebone High Street, W1U 4RX (7935 6175, www.the providores.co.uk). Baker Street tube. Meals served noon-10.30pm Mon-Fri; 4-10.30pm Sat; 4-10pm Sun. £-££.
Upstairs is the more grown-up Providores restaurant; below, the Tapa Room offers a delightfully fresh, eclectic menu. Traditional tapas dishes rub shoulders with unexpected delights: fig and buffalo mozzarella salad with Marcona almonds and basil oil, perhaps.

Vinoteca
7 St John Street, EC1M 4AA (7253 8786, www.vinoteca.co.uk). Farringdon tube/rail. Meals served noon-2.45pm, 5.45-10pm Mon-Fri; noon-3.45pm, 5.45-10pm Sat. ££.
A simple menu complements the stellar wine list, which boasts over 275 bottles. Options range from Spanish meat or cheese platters to robust, seasonal mains, such as pan-fried halibut with Jersey royals or steak with sorrel butter.

Terence Conran's take on a traditional caff offers a nostalgic, fancy-free, all-day menu that includes breakfast baps, devilled kidneys and a cracking full English.

Caravan ✈

11-13 Exmouth Market, EC1R 4QD (7833 8115, www.caravanonexmouth.co.uk). Farringdon tube/rail or 19, 38, 341 bus. Open 8am-10.30pm Mon-Fri; 10am-10.30pm Sat; 10am-4pm Sun. ££.
This hip all-day café serves a cracking breakfast. The weekend brunch menu has fry ups, eggs on sourdough toast and fruity porridge among the offerings. The house fry-up is divine (crisp streaky bacon, sweet roasted tomatoes, two eggs, sourdough or wholegrain toast and mushrooms).

Clerkenwell Kitchen

27-31 Clerkenwell Close, EC1R 0AT (7101 9959, www.theclerkenwellkitchen.co.uk). Angel tube or Farringdon tube/rail. Meals served 8am-5pm Mon-Fri. £.
Full English breakfasts, made with free-range and organic produce, or porridge with fruit compôte are prepared in the open kitchen; pancakes may be on the menu too.

E Pellicci ✈

332 Bethnal Green Road, E2 0AG (7739 4873). Bus 8, 388. Meals served 7am-4.30pm Mon-Sat. £.
A legend, famed for its fry-ups, Grade II-listed '50s interior and Cockney-Italian charm.

Little Georgia

87 Goldsmiths Row, E2 8QR (7739 8154). Hoxton rail. Meals served 9am-5pm Mon; 7am-11pm Tue-Sat; 9am-10pm Sun. £.
The hearty 'Full Georgian' breakfast (served weekends only) is a treat, with its handmade sausages and herby baked beans.

St John Bread & Wine ✈

94-96 Commercial St, E1 6LZ (7251 0848, www.stjohnbreadandwine.com). Liverpool Street tube/rail. Meals served 9-11am, noon-4pm, 5-10.30pm Mon-Fri; 10-11am, noon-4pm, 6-10.30pm Sat; 10-11am, noon-4pm, 6-9pm Sun. £-££.

St John in Farringdon's more informal sister restaurant serves up excellent quality breakfast fare. Choose from a short list of well-selected options: porridge with prunes, brioche or a Gloucester Old Spot bacon sandwich, for example. Great tea, coffee and fruit juice too.

SOUTH

Dosa n Chutny

68 Tooting High Street, SW17 0RN (8767 9200, http://dosanchutny.co.uk). Tooting Broadway tube. Meals served 10am-10.30pm daily. £.
Scoff superb dosas (lentil and rice flour cakes) with accompanying sambhar (a spicy vegetable and lentil 'soup') at this early-opening South Indian caff.

French Café

16-18 Ritherdon Road, SW17 8QD (8767 2660, www.the-french-cafe.co.uk). Balham tube/rail or Tooting Bec tube then 155 bus. Open 11am-10pm Mon-Fri; 10am-10pm Sat; 10am-8.45pm Sun. £-££.
Fry-ups here are the business. Indulge in a full English with fat, herby sausages and crisp hash browns, or go vegetarian which includes a sweetcorn crêpe. Lighter options include muesli or a simple croissant.

Maggie's Café

322 Lewisham Road, SE13 7PA (8244 0339, www.maggiesrestaurant.co.uk). Lewisham rail/DLR. Meals served 7am-8pm Mon-Fri; 7am-3pm Sat. £.
This Lewisham institution is known for its Irish charm, bargain all-you-can-eat brekkies and bottomless cups of tea and coffee.

WEST

Harp

304 Uxbridge Road, W12 2LJ (8723 2820). Shepherd's Bush tube. Meals served 7am-3.30pm Mon-Sat. £. No credit cards.
This cheery greasy spoon on the Uxbridge Road is known to serve the best bacon and egg butties in the neighbourhood.

Regency Café
17-19 Regency Sreet, SW1P 4BY (7821 6596). Pimlico tube. Meals served 7am-2.30pm, 4-7pm Mon-Fri; 7-11.45am Sat. £.
Declared the 'prince of caffs' by locals, the iconic Regency serves perfectly fluffy chips alongside its superb fry-ups.

202 Café
202-204 Westbourne Grove, W11 2RH (7727 2722). Notting Hill Gate tube. Meals served 10am-6pm Mon; 8.30am-10pm Tue-Sat; 10am-5pm Sun. ££.
The superlative breakfasts and brunches at this boutique's café fuel Notting Hill's finest; maple syrup-drizzled French toast with chargrilled bacon is heavenly.

BYO eateries

CENTRAL

Ali Baba
32 Ivor Place, NW1 6DA (7723 7474). Baker Street tube or Marylebone tube/rail. Meals served noon-midnight daily. Corkage no charge. £.
From street-food staples (fuul, falafels) to fusion favourites such as macarona (macaroni in béchamel sauce), Ali Baba covers the full spectrum of Egyptian cuisine.

Café Below ⚔
St Mary-le-Bow, EC2V 6AU (7329 0789, www.cafebelow.co.uk). St Paul's tube or Bank tube/DLR. Meals served 7.30am-9pm Mon-Fri. Corkage £6.75. £
Dine in the cool crypt, or in the charming courtyard of St Mary-le-Bow, on fresh, satisfying mainly vegetarian dishes (though meat is now on the menu too), plus sandwiches, soup and salads.

Patogh
8 Crawford Place, W1H 5NE (7262 4015). Edgware Road tube. Meals served 12.30-11pm daily. Corkage no charge. £. No credit cards.
Competition is fierce for the half-dozen or so tables, where the lucky few devour sesame-

studded flatbread and superb kebabs, prepared over the smoky charcoal grill.

NORTH

Jai Krishna ⚔
161 Stroud Green Road, N4 3PZ (7272 1680). Finsbury Park tube/rail. Meals served noon-2pm, 5.30-11pm Mon-Sat. Corkage £1.75. £.
This modest little South Indian fends off the competition from nearby Turkish cafés and pizzerias: most dishes from the delicious, all-vegetarian menu only cost around £3.

19 Numara Bos Cirrik I
34 Stoke Newington Road, N16 7XJ (7249 0400). Dalston Kingsland rail or 76, 149, 243 bus. Meals served noon-midnight daily. Corkage £1-£5. £.
Dalston's original Turkish grill continues to impress with its succulent kebabs and spare ribs, cooked to perfection on the ocakbasi grill.

SOUTH

Amaranth
346-348 Garratt Lane, SW18 4ES (8874 9036). Wandsworth tube. Meals served 6.30-11.30pm Mon-Sat. Corkage £2.50. £.
Booking is essential at this buzzing, no-frills little Thai restaurant in Earlsfield, thanks to its freshly made food and budget prices.

GOING OUT
BEAUTY
FASHION
PARTIES
FOOD
HEALTH
ECO
OUTDOORS
HOME
CHILDREN
PETS
TRANSPORT
RESOURCES

Cah Chi ★

34 Durham Road, SW20 0TW (8947 1081). Raynes Park rail or 57, 131 bus. Meals served noon-3pm, 5-11pm Mon-Fri; noon-11pm Sat, Sun. Corkage 10% of bill. £.

This friendly Korean serves honest, authentic fare at reasonable prices – the yukkaejang (spicy beef soup) is outstanding.

Nouvelle Spice

315 New Cross Road, SE14 6AS (8691 6644, www.nouvellespice.co.uk). New Cross or New Cross Gate rail. Meals served noon-11.30pm daily. Corkage no charge. £.

Top-notch Indian food at fair prices in comfortable surrounds (they also deliver); interesting vegetarian options include pumpkin massala.

EAST

Lahore Kebab House

2 Umberston Street, E1 1PY (7488 2551). Aldgate East or Whitechapel tube. Meals served noon-midnight daily. Corkage no charge. £.

Delicious Pakistani fare makes an early arrival essential at this basic, brightly lit BYO. The mixed grill starters are superlative, and the kulfis a must-try.

Rochelle Canteen

The Canteen, Old School Building, Arnold Circus, E2 7ES (7729 5677, www.arnold andhenderson.com). Shoreditch High Street rail. Meals served noon-3pm Mon-Fri. Corkage £5. £.

Set in an old school bike shed, this charming little eaterie attracts fashionistas and foodies alike. A pleasingly concise, daily-changing menu includes Mediterranean-inspired delights alongside modern British dishes; sorrel and pea soup, perhaps, or jellied ham.

Tay Do Café

65 Kingsland Road, E2 8AG (7729 7223). Hoxton rail. Meals served 11.30am-3pm, 5-11.30pm daily. Corkage £1 per person. £.

This tiny Vietnamese canteen is packed to the rafters every night with hungry Hoxtonites;

order the refreshing chao tom (prawn paste on sugar cane) or crunchy, shrimp-filled bo bia summer rolls.

Tayyabs

83 Fieldgate Street, E1 1JU (7247 9543, www.tayyabs.co.uk). Aldgate East tube. Open noon-midnight daily. Corkage no charge.

This modern Pakistani café attracts students, locals and City types, with its tasty curries, puffy flatbreads and excellent lamb chops. Service is swift and friendly too.

WEST

Adam's Café

77 Askew Road, W12 9AH (8743 0572, www.adamscafe.co.uk). Hammersmith tube, then 266 bus. Meals served 7-11pm Mon-Sat. Corkage £3. £.

Adam's delivers superb North African food in laid-back surroundings; the Tunisian-style starter of brik au thon (crisp, light ouarka pastry stuffed with egg, tuna and herbs) and grilled merguez are stellar staples. Service is amiable and efficient.

Alounak

10 Russell Gardens, W14 8EZ (7603 7645). Kensington (Olympia) tube/rail. Open noon-midnight daily. Corkage no charge. ££.

Iranian stalwart Alounak offers meltingly tender lamb and chicken kebabs, accompanied by own-made doogh (a salty yoghurt drink), fluffy Persian rice and piping-hot taftoon bread, fresh from the oven.

Miraggio

512 Fulham Road, SW6 5NJ (7384 9774, www.miraggio.co.uk). Fulham Broadway tube. Meals served noon-3pm, 6-11pm daily. Corkage £3. £.

Charming Italian staff serve impressive pizzas to share and classic home-made pasta (risotto ai funghi, spaghetti carbonara, linguine alle vongole) at this small, family-run restaurant near Parson's Green.

Polanka

258 King Street, W6 0SP (8741 8268, www. polanka-rest.com). Ravenscourt Park tube.

Meals served noon-8pm Mon-Fri, Sun; noon-10pm Sat. Corkage £2 wine, £5 spirits. £.
Located in the heart of west London's Polish community, Polanka serves up honest-to-goodness traditional Polish cooking: pierogi (dumplings), herring, golabki (cabbage rolls) and other traditional fare. For those with room, there's a fine array of cakes, including Polish cheesecake.

Cafés

CENTRAL

In addition to the cafés listed below, **Bea's of Bloomsbury** (*see p70*) offers expertly made coffees and Valrhona hot chocolate alongside an inspired selection of cakes, salads and sarnies. **Fernandez & Wells** and **Lantana** (for both *see p82*) are also sterling operations.

Flat White
17 Berwick Street, W1F 0PT (7734 0370). Leicester Square tube. Meals served 8am-7pm Mon-Fri; 9am-6pm Sat, Sun. £.
This Antipodean-run café specialises in its namesake brew, a coffee made with a large shot of espresso and generous slosh of milk (frothed slightly less than in a cappuccino).

Kastner & Ovens ★
52 Floral Street, WC2E 9DA (7836 2700). Covent Garden tube. Meals served 8am-4pm Mon-Fri. £.
This little café attracts hordes of hungry office workers during weekday lunchtimes, eager to chow down on the fresh and tasty home-made salads, hot mains, quiches and cakes made by owners Sue and Ann-Marie.

La Fromagerie ★
2-6 Moxon Street, W1U 4EW (7935 0341, www.lafromagerie.co.uk). Baker Street or Bond Street tube. Open 8am-7.30pm Mon-Fri; 9am-7pm Sat; 10am-6pm Sun. £.
A delightful place to sip coffee, tuck into breakfast or enjoy a full-on leisurely lunch. Naturally, anything involving cheese (the ploughman's, for example) is a cut above.

London Review Cakeshop
14-16 Bury Place, WC1A 2JL (7269 9030, www.lrbshop.co.uk). Tottenham Court Road tube. Meals served 10am-6pm Mon-Sat; noon-5.30pm Sun. £.
This charming bookshop café is run by Terry Glover, formerly of Maison Blanc. Literary types can sip Jing teas and enjoy superb cakes and well-filled baguettes while perusing their purchases.

FREE WI-FI

Free Wi-Fi is spreading fast in London's café culture; these are some dependable central hotspots.

Apostrophe
9 Tottenham Court Road, W1T 7PT (7436 6688, www.apostropheuk.com). Goodge Street tube. Open 7.30am-6pm Mon-Fri; 9.30am-5pm Sat.
Tucked away behind Tottenham Court Road, this branch tends to be nice and peaceful, so you should get a seat at the long communal tables.

Benugo Bar & Kitchen
BFI Southbank, Belvedere Road, SE1 8XT (7401 9000, www.benugo.com). Waterloo tube/rail. Open 9.45am-11pm Mon-Fri; 11am-11pm Sat; 11am-10.30pm Sun.
During the daytime, Benugo's plush couches are a supremely comfy spot to check your emails.

Hummus Brothers
88 Wardour Street, W1F 0TJ (7734 1311, www.hbros.co.uk). Oxford Circus tube. Meals served 11am-10pm Mon-Wed; 11am-11pm Thur, Fri; noon-11pm Sat; noon-10pm Sun.
Perfect for laptop-toting houmous lovers. After the lunch rush, you can linger over a fresh mint tea.

City Secret

In the heart of Mayfair, **Postcard Teas** (9 Dering Street, W1S 1AG, 7629 3654, www.postcardteas. com) is a labour of love, run by tea enthusiast Timothy d'Offay. Primarily a tea boutique selling top-quality Indian, Japanese, Chinese, Taiwanese and Sri Lankan blends, it also has a tasting table where you can sample the wares – including the unique coffee blossom tea – for a mere £1.75 per pot.

Nordic Bakery ✗
14a Golden Square, W1F 9JG (3230 1077, www.nordicbakery.com). Piccadilly Circus tube. Meals served 8am-8pm Mon-Fri; 9am-7pm Sat; 11am-6pm Sun. £.
Clean lines and modern Scandinavian design make this café a standout. Open-faced rye sandwiches feature typical Finnish toppings such as gravadlax with sweet mustard.

Ray's Jazz Café
1st floor, Foyles, WC2H 0EB (7440 3205). Tottenham Court Road tube. Meals served 8.30am-9pm Mon-Sat; 10am-8pm Sun. £.
Ray's offers a laid-back jazz soundtrack, generous hunks of cake and fresh mint tea and fresh juices.

Sacred
13 Ganton Street, W1F 9BL (7734 1415, www.sacredcafe.co.uk). Oxford Circus tube. Meals served 7.30am-8pm Mon-Wed; 7.30am-9pm Thur, Fri; 8am-8pm Sat; 10am-7pm Sun. £.
Excellent fairtrade coffees are matched by an extensive loose-leaf tea menu at this cosy, two-floor Soho café.

NORTH

Café Mozart
17 Swains Lane, N6 6QX (8348 1384). Gospel Oak rail or 214, C2, C11, C12 bus.

Meals served 9am-6pm Mon; 9am-10pm Tue-Sun. £.
Savouries at this Austrian café include borscht, sausages and schnitzel, but most customers are here to eye up the sweets: rich chocolate tortes, plum tarts and cheesecakes.

Lemon Monkey
188 Stoke Newington High Street, N16 7JD (7241 4454, www.lemon-monkey.co.uk). Stoke Newington rail. Meals served 9am-6pm Mon-Sat; 10am-6pm Sun. £.
This French café and deli delivers top-notch cheese, charcuterie and coffee; sweet tooths will adore the own-made macaroons.

Louis Pâtisserie
32 Heath Street, NW3 6TE (7435 9908). Hampstead tube. Meals served 9am-6pm daily. £. No credit cards.
After admiring the alluring window display, take a seat in the wood-panelled tearoom for an unhurried pot of tea and a chestnut slice.

Tea Rooms
153-155 Stoke Newington Church Street, N16 0UH (7923 1870). Stoke Newington rail or 73, 476. Meals served 11am-6pm Tue-Fri; 11am-6.30pm Sat, Sun. £.
This lovely '50s-style tearoom makes all its cakes and pastries. Afternoon tea, with delectable scones, is £12.50.

EAST

Jones' Dairy Café
23 Ezra Street, E2 7RH (7739 5372, www. jonesdairy.co.uk). Hoxton rail. Meals served 9am-3pm Fri; 9am-4.30pm Sat; 8am-3pm Sun. No credit cards. £.
Located just off Columbia Road Flower Market, this boho café welcomes an influx of shoppers on Sundays, so you'll have to queue to sample the own-baked cakes and bagels. Cooked dishes are offered Fri-Sat.

Tea Smith
6 Lamb Street, E1 6EA (7247 1333, www teasmith.co.uk). Liverpool Street tube/rail or Shoreditch High Street rail. Meals served 11am-6pm daily. £.

GOING OUT

BEAUTY

FASHION

PARTIES

FOOD

HEALTH

ECO

OUTDOORS

HOME

CHILDREN

PETS

TRANSPORT

RESOURCES

Unusual teas can be sipped at the counter at this airy, architect-designed shop and tearoom.

Venetia

55 Chatsworth Road, E5 0LH (8986 1642). Homerton rail or 242, 308 bus. Meals served 8am-5pm Mon-5pm Sun. £.
Cake stands at this elegant little eatery groan with chunky brownies, almond croissants and own-made victoria sponge. A heated garden area makes a great spot to relax in whatever the weather.

SOUTH

Café Crema

306 New Cross Road, SE14 6AF (8320 2317). New Cross or New Cross Gate rail. Meals served 9.30am-6.30pm Mon-Fri. £. No credit cards.
Goldsmiths students flock here for the vegetarian food and creamy hot chocolate. There's a little back garden complete with chickens, a piano and a screen for films.

Café St Germain

16-17 Crystal Palace Parade, SE19 1UA (8670 3670). Crystal Palace rail. Meals served 8am-5pm daily. £.
Go continental with a croque monsieur and potent black coffee at south-east London's answer to a Parisian café.

Petitou

63 Choumert Road, SE15 4AR (7639 2613). Peckham Rye rail. Meals served 9am-5.15pm Tue-Sat; 10am-5.15pm Sun. £.
There's a 1940s charm to Petitou, with its brown earthenware teapots, mismatched china and moist slabs of own-made cake.

WEST

Books for Cooks

4 Bleinheim Crescent, W11 1NN (7221 1992, www.booksforcooks.com). Ladbroke Grove tube. Meals served noon-2pm Tue-Sat. £.
Arrive before 12.30pm if you want to lunch at this bijou culinary bookshop. The kitchen

cooks up a three-dish set menu (a steal at £7) every day, but there's only a handful of tables.

Lisboa Pâtisserie

57 Golborne Road, W10 5NR (8968 5242). Ladbroke Grove or Westbourne Park tube, or 23, 52 bus. Open 7am-7.30pm daily. £.
Queues often form at the weekend, thanks to the café's famed freshly made pasties de nata (custard tarts) and bicas (espressos).

Late-opening cafés & restaurants

CENTRAL

Automat

33 Dover Street, W1S 4NF (7499 3033, www.automat-london.com). Green Park tube. Open 7am-midnight Mon-Fri; 10am-midnight Sat; 10am-10pm Sun. ££.
Automat's American comfort cooking (think macaroni and cheese, ribeye steaks, apple pie) is served until midnight from Monday to Saturday. Decor is sleek US brasserie-style and service is charming, but prices reflect the Mayfair location.

Balans

60 Old Compton Street, W1D 4UG (7439 2183, www.balans.co.uk). Leicester Square or Piccadilly Circus tube. Meals served 8am-5am Mon-Thur; 8am-6am Fri, Sat; 8am-2am Sun. ££.
This slightly retro Soho brasserie attracts the post-clubbing crowd with amazing spiced scrambled egg burritos for vegetarians, as well as substantial mains such as shrimp thai curry and the Balans burger (with bacon and cheese).

Café TPT

21 Wardour Street, W1D 6PN (7734 7980). Leicester Square or Piccadilly Circus tube. Meals served noon-1am daily. £.
Often filled with weary students in need of late-night sustenance, this clean, modern Chinatown caff offers great value for money; try the barbecue pork or soy sauce chicken.

HK Diner

*22 Wardour Street, W1D 6QQ (7434
9544). Leicester Square or Piccadilly
Circus tube. Meals served 11am-4am
daily. £.*

Take note: go for the specials menu, not the
unexceptional stir-fries. Cheery surrounds,
semi-private booths and hangover-curing
bubble teas and juices make this a popular
pitstop for young Chinese Londoners.

Joe Allen

*13 Exeter Street, WC2E 7DT (7836 0651,
www.joeallen.co.uk). Covent Garden tube.
Meals served 8am-12.30am Mon-Fri;
11.30am-12.30am Sat; 11.30am-11.30pm
Sun. ££.*

A classic post-show stopover, Joe Allen's is a
theatreland institution. It's all about the
buzzing atmosphere, with a thespian crowd
gathering to toast that night's performance
and devour grilled tuna, ribs and steaks.

Wolseley ★

*160 Piccadilly, W1J 9EB (7499 6996,
www.thewolseley.com). Green Park tube.
Open 7am-midnight Mon-Fri; 8am-midnight
Sat, Sun. ££-£££.*

Stylish grand café the Wolseley serves up an
appealing array of dishes (eggs, burgers,
seafood, steaks and desserts) until midnight.
Service is faultless and the high ceilings and
huge space make this the perfect spot for
some low-key post-prandial people-watching.

Woo Jung

*59 St Giles High Street, WC2H 8LH (7836
3103). Tottenham Court Road tube. Meals
served noon-1am Mon-Sat; 5pm-midnight
Sun. ££.*

We can't think of better late-night food than
a hearty bowl of bibimbap (rice topped with
meat and vegetables), or warming beef stew.
Filling, homestyle Korean cooking and low
prices mean it's always busy.

Yalla Yalla ★

*1 Green's Court, W1F 0HA (7287 7663,
www.yalla-yalla.co.uk). Piccadilly Circus
tube. Open 10am-midnight Mon-Sat;
10am-10pm Sun. £-££.*

This appealing café dishes up excellent
Beiruti street food, mezedes and skewers of
lamb, chicken and prawns cooked on a wood-
burning grill. Pickled turnips and chillies are
complimentary. Drinks include fresh juices,
mint tea and Lebanese wines and beer.

NORTH

Gilgamesh

*Stables Market, Chalk Farm Road, NW1
8AH (7428 4922, www.gilgameshbar.com).
Chalk Farm tube. Meals served Bar noon-
2am Mon-Thur; noon-2am Fri-Sun.
Restaurant noon-midnight daily. ££.*

Unashamedly over-the-top decor and DJs
matched by pan-Asian food ranging from
elegant sushi to smart little dim sum.

Mangal II

*4 Stoke Newington Road, N16 8BH
(7254 7888, www.mangal2.com). Dalston
Kingsland rail. Meals served 3pm-1am
Mon-Thur, Sun; 2pm-2am Fri, Sat. ££*

Grilled fish and good-quality kebabs satisfy
late-night hunger pangs at this cheery blue-
and yellow-painted Turkish eaterie. If you're
merely peckish, order pide and delicious dips.

EAST

Somine

*131 Kingsland High Street, E8 2PB (7254
7384). Dalston Kingsland rail. Meals served
24hrs daily. £. No credit cards.*

Many come to this brightly lit 24-hour café
purely for the tasty lentil soup (£3.50), served
with soft, squidgy bread. Otherwise, choose
from the ever-changing selection of hearty,
no-nonsense stews at the counter.

Tinseltown

*44-46 St John Street, EC1M 4DT (7689
2424, www.tinseltown.co.uk). Farringdon
tube/rail. Meals served 11am-5am. £.*

This chilled-out Hollywood-themed diner
sees clubbers slurping phenomenal peanut
butter milkshakes and chomping burgers
alongside insomniacs and cabbies on a break.
Other locations 104 Heath Street, NW3
1DR (7435 2396).

GOING OUT

BEAUTY

FASHION

PARTIES

FOOD

HEALTH

ECO

OUTDOORS

HOME

CHILDREN

PETS

TRANSPORT

RESOURCES

Meze Mangal
245 Lewisham Way, SE4 1XF (8694 8099, www.meze-mangal.co.uk). Lewisham DLR/rail or St John's rail. Meals served noon-1am daily. £.
Lewisham locals head here for flavoursome, traditional Turkish fare; start with nutty, rough-textured kisir, then order a dish of tender çop sis (marinated chunks of lamb) and salad.

Vingt-Quatre
325 Fulham Road, SW10 9QL (7376 7224, www.vingtquatre.co.uk). South Kensington tube. Meals served 24hrs daily. ££.

LATE-NIGHT TAKEAWAYS

Forget limp pizzas and lurid yellow fries, there's a world of fine takeaway food out there.

Brick Lane Beigel Bake
159 Brick Lane, E1 6SB (7729 0616). Shoreditch High Street rail. Meals served 24hrs daily. £. No credit cards.
This 24-hour East End institution has the best freshly baked bagels in the capital. Service is brisk but charming, and the bagels top-notch.

Fishcotheque
79A Waterloo Road, SE1 8UD (7928 1484). Waterloo tube/rail. Meals served 11am-midnight Mon-Sat; noon-10pm Sun. £. No credit cards.
Don't let the unenticing exterior and boozy regulars deter you: the fish here is fresh, the portions generous. Chicken kebabs, doused with own-made chilli sauce, are also delicious.

Kebab Kid
90 New King's Road, SW6 4LU (7731 0427). Parson's Green tube. Meals served noon-midnight daily. £. No credit cards.
A foodie crowd (including off-duty chefs) are among the regulars queuing for fresh houmous- or taramosalata-topped chicken shawarma.

Kurz & Lang
1 St John Street, EC1M 4AA (7253 6623, www.kurzandlang.com).
Farringdon tube/rail. Meals served 11.30am-midnight Mon-Wed; 11.30am-1am Thur; 11am Fri-7am Sun; noon-7pm Sun. £.
This cheerful caff does a roaring trade in bratwurst sausages, topped with lashings of mustard, ketchup and sauerkraut. On weekends, it's open nonstop from Friday night until Sunday morning, to feed the post-party crowds.

Maoz
43 Old Compton Street, W1D 6HG (7851 1586). Leicester Square, Piccadilly Circus or Tottenham Court Road tube. Meals served 11am-1am Mon-Thur; 11am-2.30am Fri, Sat; 11am-midnight Sun. £.
Maoz offers much-needed sustenance to the late-night prowlers of Soho's bars and clubs. It's surprisingly healthy fare: falafels, houmous and flavoursome couscous salad – though there are chunky chips as well.

Ranoush Juice
43 Edgware Road, W2 2JR (7723 5929). Marble Arch tube. Meals served 8am-3am daily. No credit cards. £.
Watch as staff assemble lamb or chicken shawarma at lightning speed: the result, oozing garlic sauce at every bite, is sublime. There are plenty of vegetarian snacks available too, and the juices are excellent.

The short but classic menu at Vingt-Quatre ranges from grilled club sandwiches to baby back ribs: if you're feeling decadent, wash it all down with a bottle of Krug.

WEST

Cecconi's
5A Burlington Gardens, W1S 3EP (7434 1500, www.cecconis.co.uk). Green Park or Piccadilly Circus tube. Meals served 7am-1am Mon-Fri; 8am-1am Sat; 8am-midnight Sun. ££-£££.
One of the only restaurants in London to serve Italian tapas (cichetti), Cecconi's is perfect for sophisticated late-night nibbles in stylish art deco surrounds. Delicacies might range from quail eggs, to artichoke crostini and warm octopus.

High Road Brasserie ★
162-166 Chiswick High Road, W4 1PR (8742 7474, www.highroadhouse.co.uk). Turnham Green tube. Meals served 7am-midnight Mon-Thur; 7am-1am Fri; 8am-1am Sat; 8am-11pm Sun. ££.
This chic offshoot of Nick Jones' Soho House impresses with its classic brasserie menu, catering for all appetites until late.

O Fado
49-50 Beauchamp Place, SW3 1NY (7589 3002, www.ofado.co.uk). Knightsbridge or South Kensington tube. Meals served noon-3pm, 6.30-11pm Mon-Sat. ££.
Incongruously set in showy Knightsbridge, this homely little restaurant is one of London's oldest Portuguese eateries. Expect classics such as pastéis de bacalhau (salt cod fritters) and clam ameijoa a bulhao pato (clams poached in garlic and white wine).

Rossopomodoro ★
214 Fulham Road, SW10 9NB (7352 7677, www.rossopomodoro.co.uk). South Kensington tube, then 14 bus. Meals served noon-11pm daily. £-££.
The busy open kitchen at Rossopomodoro churns out consistently delicious antipasti, pizza and pasta dishes. For a calorific treat, try the deep-fried pizza.

Other locations *50-52 Monmouth Street, WC2H 9EP (7240 9095); 184A Kensington Park Road, W11 2ES (7229 9007).*

Romantic restaurants

CENTRAL

Andrew Edmunds ★
46 Lexington Street, W1F 0LW (7437 5708). Oxford Circus or Piccadilly Circus tube. Meals served noon-3pm, 6-10.45pm Mon-Fri; 1-3.15pm, 6-10.45pm Sat; 1-3.15pm, 6-10.30pm Sun. ££.
The snug tables here are perfect for romantic tête-à-têtes – though to avoid becoming too intimate with your neighbours, reserve on the marginally more spacious ground floor. Classic Modern European dishes are quietly satisfying: in-season asparagus or chicken liver parfait, perhaps, followed by rib-eye steak or wild halibut. The wine list is good value, with champagne at £5.50 a glass.

Aurora
49 Lexington Street, W1F 9AP (7494 0514). Oxford Circus or Piccadilly Circus tube. Meals served noon-10.30pm Mon-Sat; noon-9.30pm Sun. £-££.
With seating for 50 and a few tables in the garden, Aurora is delightfully intimate. There are sometimes two sittings an evening: make sure you're on the later one, so you can linger over dessert. Food is unfussy, with generous portions of modern British fare.

Le Comptoir Gascon ★
61-63 Charterhouse Street, EC1M 6HJ (7608 0851, www.comptoirgascon.com). Farringdon tube/rail. Meals served noon-2.30pm, 7-10pm Tue, Wed; noon-2.30pm, 7-11pm Thur, Fri; 11.30am-3pm, 7-10pm Sat. ££.
This French bistro focuses on cooking from the south-western provinces – much of it unashamedly carnivorous. The blackboard-scrawled specials might include roast suckling pig, while menu fixtures include a 'piggy treats' charcuterie board. Prices are reasonable, the atmosphere relaxed.

GOING OUT

BEAUTY

FASHION

PARTIES

FOOD

HEALTH

ECO

OUTDOORS

HOME

CHILDREN

PETS

TRANSPORT

RESOURCES

Shaka Zulu

Shaka Zulu is the newly launched £5.5m authentic South African restaurant & lounge bar

Shaka Zulu boasts a Seafood restaurant and Oyster bar on the mezzanine level as well as an authentic Braai restaurant, serving traditional South African dishes including fine cuts of game meat and Red Poll beef steaks fresh from the Queen's Estate in Sandringham.

The perfect late night venue for an exclusive dining, drinking & entertainment experience, set against a dramatic Zulu inspired backdrop.

To book, call 020 3376 9911
or visit www.shaka-zulu.com

Crazy Bear

26-28 Whitfield Street, W1T 2RG (7631 0088, www.crazybeargroup.co.uk). Goodge Street or Tottenham Court Road tube. Meals served noon-2.45pm, 6-10.45pm Mon-Sat; noon-2.45pm, 6-10pm Sun. ££.

Despite the zany name, Crazy Bear surprises with its belle époque-style decor and Eastern influenced menu. The moodily lit dining room is lined with leather banquettes and art deco lamps, while the menu ranges from dim sum to wok-fried lobster. Downstairs, the bar's padded alcoves are equally seductive.

Hakkasan ★

8 Hanway Place, W1T 1HD (7907 1888). Tottenham Court Road tube. Meals served noon-3pm, 6pm-midnight Mon-Fri; noon-5pm, 6pm-midnight Sat; noon-5pm, 6pm-midnight Sun. £££.

With its sultry good looks, dim lighting and underground location, it doesn't matter what time of day you eat here – Hakkasan's always romantic. Arrive early to quaff saké-infused cocktails at the long, back-lit bar before sampling the impressive menu.

NORTH

Almeida

30 Almeida Street, N1 1AD (7354 4777, www.danddlondon.com). Angel tube. Open 5.30pm-10.30pm Mon; noon-2.30pm, 5.30-10.30pm Tue-Sat; noon-3.30pm Sun. ££-£££.

This sleek, grown-up French restaurant makes a fine place for a date (tables are well-spaced and there's no music to hinder conversation). Dishes are sophisticated (poached langoustines, rock oysters, terrine of foie gras are among the starters on offer) and well executed. There's an appealing list of meat and fish mains, great desserts and a cheeseboard to die for.

Green Room

182 Broadhurst Gardens, NW6 3AY (7372 8188). West Hampstead tube/rail. Meals served 6pm-12.30am Mon-Sun. ££.

This Hampstead bistro's deliciously pretty chandelier-lit dining room is perfect for more

intimate soirées. An inviting Modern European menu sticks to the classics, cooked with real flair, while the interesting but inexpensive wine list adds to the appeal.

EAST

Bistrotheque

23-27 Wadeson Street, E2 9DR (8983 7900, www.bistrotheque.com). Bethnal Green tube/rail. Meals served 6.30-10.30pm Mon-Thur; 6.30-11pm Fri; 11am-4pm, 6.30-11pm Sat; 11am-4pm, 6.30-10.30pm Sun. ££.

Housed in a lofty warehouse space, Bistrotheque walks the line between street and sophistication. Cooking is unpretentious and punchy: braised ox tail, lentils, carrots and turnips, say, or garlicky roast chicken. After dinner retire to the Cabaret Room; pre-book tickets.

Les Trois Garçons

1 Club Row, E1 6JX (7613 1924, www.loungelover.co.uk). Shoreditch High Street rail. Meals served 6-10pm Mon; 6-10.30pm Tue-Thur; 6-11pm Fri, Sat. £££.

Generously gilded and crammed with bizarre *objets trouvés*, the dining room at Les Trois Garçons defiantly flouts the modern less-is-more aesthete. The food is equally artistically presented, with elaborate menu descriptions: more importantly, cooking is spot on.

SOUTH

Tentazioni

2 Mill Street, SE1 2BD (7237 1100, www.tentazioni.co.uk). Bermondsey tube or London Bridge tube/rail. Meals served noon-2.45pm, 6.30-10.45pm Tue-Fri; 6.30-10.45pm Sat. £££.

With its opulent plum-and-red decor and hidden-away location, Tentazioni is ideal for illicit rendezvous. Dishes are ambitious but accomplished, with bold flavours and polished presentation.

Upstairs

89B Acre Lane, entrance on Branksome Road, SW2 5TN (7733 8855). Brixton

GOING OUT

BEAUTY

FASHION

PARTIES

FOOD

HEALTH

ECO

OUTDOORS

HOME

CHILDREN

PETS

TRANSPORT

RESOURCES

tube. Meals served 6.30-9.30pm Tue-Thur; 6.30-10.30pm Fri, Sat. £££.

An unmarked door adds an air of exclusivity to this discreet little gem, where diners must ring a bell to gain admittance. Up the winding stairs lies a chilled out bar area, with another set of stairs leading to the Lilliputian dining room. The prix fixe menu offers three starters and three mains, with a strong seasonal focus. A chef's six-course tasting menu is also available (£38 per person).

WEST

Angelus ✖

4 Bathurst Street, W2 2SD (7402 0083, www.angelusrestaurant.co.uk). Lancaster Gate tube. Meals served 10am-11pm daily. £££.

Chef Olivier Duret offers a modern take on classic brasserie fare – notably with his famed foie gras crème brûlée. The art nouveau surrounds are as elegant as the food, with dark wood fittings and burgundy leather banquettes, and service is charming.

La Poule au Pot

231 Ebury Street, SW1W 8UT (7730 7763). Sloane Square tube. Meals served 12.30-2.30pm, 6.45-11pm Mon-Fri; 12.30-4pm, 6.45-11pm Sat; 12.30-4pm, 6.45-10pm Sun. ££.

This rustic, dimly lit French bistro is one of London's classic romantic hotspots. Things don't change much here, including the menu: expect robust dishes such as coq au vin or rabbit in creamy mustard sauce. Fairly priced house wines help conversation flow.

Saigon Saigon

313-317 King Street, W6 9NH (0870 220 1398). Ravenscourt Park or Stamford Brook tube. Meals served noon-3pm, 6-11pm Mon-Thur; noon-3pm, 6-11.30pm Fri, Sat; noon-3pm, 6-10pm Sun. £££.

Bamboo screens, dark wood flooring and photos of '40s Saigon evoke the glamour of a bygone age at this chic Vietnamese restaurant. Sophisticated dishes such as chargrilled quail and buttered frogs' legs won't fail to impress.

Sunday lunch

There's no shortage of gastropubs offering Sunday lunch, but only a select few truly shine: the following serve a roast that's second only to your mum's.

Charles Lamb

16 Elia Street, N1 8DE (7837 5040, www.thecharleslambpub.com). Angel tube. Meals served 4-11.30pm Mon, Tue; noon-11.30pm Wed-Sat; noon-10.30pm Sun.

It's well worth getting lost in the backstreets of Angel to stumble across the diminutive, wooden-floored Charles Lamb. There's a glorious array of world beers, ales and wines, while food is hearty and accomplished: the Sunday roast with all the trimmings is £13.50. Get there early to snag a seat.

Duke of Cambridge

30 St Peter's Street, N1 8JT (7359 3066, www.dukeorganic.co.uk). Angel tube. Meals served noon-3pm, 6.30-11pm Mon-Fri; 12.30-3.30pm, 6.30-11pm Sat, Sun. ££.

The original organic gastropub, the Duke of Cambridge dishes up a hearty Sunday lunch, made with seasonal, local and, of course, organic ingredients. The roast changes weekly, and arrives generously anointed with gravy and accompanied by crisp, fluffy-centred spuds.

Gipsy Moth

60 Greenwich Church Street, SE10 9BL (8858 0786, www.thegipsymoth greenwich.co.uk). Cutty Sark DLR or Greenwich rail. Meals served noon-10pm Mon-Sat; noon-9pm Sun. £.

The Gipsy Moth's huge beer garden is perfect for sunny Sunday lunches. Choose from roast pork belly with generous slabs of crackling and textbook-perfect mash and leeks, or half a roast chicken. A fine selection of draught beers, ales and ciders is another plus.

Gun ✖

27 Coldharbour, E14 9NS (7515 5222, www.thegundocklands.com). Blackwall or

Address Book Secrets
Guy Dimond
Time Out Group Food & Drink Editor

Breakfast or brunch should be relaxed and hassle-free, so that means local in my opinion. But let's assume you're in central London, and meeting friends? **The Wolseley** (160 Piccadilly, W1J 9EB, 7499 6996, www.thewolseley.com) takes some beating for posh, while **Lantana**'s (13 Charlotte Place, W1T 1SN, 7637 3347, www.lantanacafe.co.uk) good for a more casual brunch.

London has every conceivable cuisine, and competes well with other great international cities at most of them. But I think London's good Indian restaurants compare well with the best anywhere, and that's including India (where I lived for a while). Among them are **Veeraswamy** (Mezzanine Floor, Victory House, 99-101 Regent Street, W1B 4RS, 7734 1401, www.veeraswamy.com), **Moti Mahal** (45 Great Queen Street, WC2B 5AA, 7240 9329, www.motimahal-uk.com) and **Chutney Mary** (535 King's Road, SW10 0SZ, 7351 3113, www.chutney mary.com) – to name just a few. Oh, and you get pretty good British food in London too.

I recommend heading to Soho for lunch, where you're spoiled for choice. **Hummus Bros** (88 Wardour Street, W1F 0TH, 7734 1311, www.hbros.co.uk) is great; so is **Princi** (135 Wardour Street, W1F 0UT, 7478 8888, www.princi.co.uk) for the buzz, though it's dearer. **Fernandez & Wells** (73 Beak Street, W1F 9RS, 7287 8124, www.fernandez andwells.com) is great too.

Five years ago I could have counted London's great coffee shops on one hand. Now, there are scores. We've produded a good **coffee map of London** (www.timeout.com/london/gallery/243/best-coffee-in-london), so you can be sure you're never far from a decent brew.

My biggest bugbear about dining out in London is definitely the cost. It's an expensive city, and we need more good, affordable dining. Also, there are still a lot of places serving indifferent food, which clearly think being 'cool' is an adequate substitute. It's not.

The first really, really amazing restaurant I ate at when I just started reviewing restaurants was **Le Gavroche** (43 Upper Brook Street, W1K 7QR, 7408 0881, www.le-gavroche.co.uk). It was utterly sensational, and I'd never been anywhere like that in my life before. Nothing will ever compare with that astonishing first impression – which is why I've never been back.

For a great Sunday lunch, I like **Hix** (66-70 Brewer Street, W1F 9UP, 7292 3518, www.hixsoho.co.uk), **Modern Pantry** (47-48 St John's Square, EC1V 4JJ, 7250 0833, www.themodernpantry.co.uk) or **Great Queen Street** (32 Great Queen Street, WC2B 5AA, 7242 0622) – to name just a few. But don't forget dim sum – it's a great option for Sunday afternoon dining and so much more fun than roasts, I feel.

SECRET SUPPER CLUBS

Pop-up bistros, underground restaurants, guerrilla dining: whatever you want to call it, secret supper clubs have taken London by storm. Great for anyone feeling too jaded (or just too skint) for mainstream high-end restaurants – these low-key events offer a sense of occasion, the thrill of the unknown and, of course, a decent meal (often for a snip of the price you'd pay somewhere 'official').

Supper clubs and their locations are constantly changing, with new projects starting up as fast as old ones close down (or get too popular for their own good).

Check out Lady Gray's **Hidden Tea Room** (www.hiddentearoom.com), which serves up swanky afternoon teas at different secret locations. Or try MsMarmitelover's **Underground Restaurant** (marmitelover.blogspot.com) in Kilburn (yes, there has been a Marmite-themed meal) on for size.

The **Savoy Truffle Club** (www.savoytrufflesupperclub.com) was one of the scene's pioneers and continues to serve up multi-course feasts of locally sourced food.

For the latest places to dine in secret, check out www.timeout.com.

Canary Wharf DLR. Meals served noon-3pm, 6-10.30pm Mon-Fri; noon-4pm, 6-10.30pm Sat; noon-4pm, 6-9.30pm Sun. ££.
The terrace overlooking the Thames is a lovely spot for a leisurely Sunday lunch, if you can score a table; enormous Yorkshire puddings are the star of the show.

Herne Tavern
2 Forest Hill Road, SE22 0RR (8299 9521, www.theherne.net). Peckham Rye rail. Meals served noon-2.30pm, 6.30-9.45pm Mon-Fri; noon-4pm, 6.30-9.45pm Sat; noon-2.30pm, 6.30-9.30pm Sun. ££.
Gorge yourself on a groan-inducing roast for £11.50 at this welcoming, oak-panelled pub. Chef David Fegan uses organic and free-range produce, and there's a beer garden out back for the children to let off steam in.

Marquess Tavern ★
32 Canonbury Street, N1 2TB (7354 2975, www.marquesstavern.co.uk). Angel tube or Essex Road rail. Meals served 6-10pm Mon-Fri; noon-5pm, 6-10pm Sat; noon-5pm, 6-8.30pm Sun. ££.
Free-range and traditionally reared meat is on the menu at this superior gastropub,

where a roast beef Sunday dinner or pork belly with black pudding and apple sauce round off the weekend in style.

Norfolk Arms
28 Leigh Street, WC1H 9EP (7388 3937, www.norfolkarms.co.uk). Euston tube/rail. Meals served noon-3pm, 6-10.15pm Mon-Sat; noon-10.15pm Sun. ££.
Best known for its sterling selection of tapas, the Norfolk Arms is no slouch when it comes to inventive mains. You might find basque fish stew or marinated octopus on the menu, but Sunday brings traditional roasts: Gloucester Old Spot pork belly, perhaps, or a leg of Welsh lamb.

Royal Oak
73 Columbia Road, E2 7RG (7729 2220, www.royaloaklondon.com). Hoxton rail or 26, 48, 55 bus. Meals served 7-11pm Tue-Thur; 7pm-midnight Fri, Sat; noon-4pm Sun. ££.
Sunday lunch here means a whopping plate, filled to the brim with succulent roast. Veggie options are well thought out, and no-nonsense puddings round things off nicely. It's also very handily placed for the weekly Sunday flower market.

Shopping

A culinary tour of the capital's markets and specialist food shops.

Markets

The capital's markets scene continues to thrive, with farmers' markets cropping up across town and street-food markets serving lip-smackingly good, hot and cold food to hungry passers-by. Traditional markets still get a look in, with stallholders shouting their bowl-for-a-pound bargains. Fifteen of the city's farmers' markets are officially verified by **London Farmers' Markets** (www. lfm.org.uk), which means they must adhere to strict guidelines, including only selling produce from farms located within 100 miles of the M25.

CENTRAL

Berwick Street Market

Berwick Street, Rupert Street, W1. Oxford Circus tube. Open 9am-6pm Mon-Sat.
This is one of London's oldest street markets and remains a great place to head for bargain fruit and veg, fish and other comestibles.

Borough Market

Southwark Street, SE1 1TL (7407 1002, www.boroughmarket.org.uk). London Bridge tube/rail. Open 11am-5pm Thur; noon-6pm Fri; 8am-4pm Sat.
London's oldest food market is guaranteed to bring out your piggish side. Free samples abound, as do all manner of enticing lunch options: Brindisa's barbecued chorizo rolls are a standout. Take-home goodies range from fruit and veg to rare-breed meats, bread and cakes.

Cabbages & Frocks

St Marylebone Parish Church Grounds, Marylebone High Street, W1 (7794 1636,
www.cabbagesandfrocks.co.uk). Baker Street tube. Open 11am-5pm Sat.
Fashionistas and foodies happily mingle at this Saturday-only market. Pick up bread, olives, cupcakes and homemade preserves along with the eponymous frocks, then recover with a cream tea, served from 4pm.

Marylebone Farmers' Market

Cramer Street car park, off Marylebone High Street, W1 (7833 0338, www.lfm. org.uk). Bond Street or Baker Street tube. Open 10am-2pm Sun.
Just off chi chi Marylebone High Street, this farmers' market is brimming with fresh produce – from bounteous displays of fruit and veg to quality meats and excellent breads. A sneaky slice from Downland Produce's whole hog roast is a must-buy.

Whitecross Food Market

Whitecross Street, EC1Y 8JH (7527 1761, www.whitecrossstreet.co.uk). Barbican tube. Open 11am-4pm Thur, Fri.
This buzzing market attracts droves of hungry office workers, thanks to its enticing spread of takeaway vans and stalls. Options include Thai food, salads and bratwurst, with Luardo's burritos always attracting a queue.

NORTH

Chapel Market

Chapel Street, N1 0RW (7289 4371). Angel tube. Open 9am-6pm Tue-Sat; 8.30am-4pm Sun.
This lively street market in the heart of Angel sells fresh fruit and veg for a song, alongside cheap toiletries, knickers and other bits and bobs. The French cheese stall and fish stalls (complete with jellied eels) are worth a visit; if you're in need of refuelling, pop into Manze's pie and mash shop at no.74.

GOING OUT

BEAUTY

FASHION

PARTIES

FOOD

HEALTH

ECO

OUTDOORS

HOME

CHILDREN

PETS

TRANSPORT

RESOURCES

A world of experience on your doorstep

From £11.99/$19.95 at all good bookshops

Islington Farmers' Market

Chapel Street, N1 0RW (7833 0338, www.lfm.org.uk). Angel tube. Open 10am-2pm Sun.

This popular farmers' market was the first to begin operating in London, back in 1999, and continues to thrive at its Chapel Market location (since March 2010). There's a wealth of seasonal produce, from asparagus and broad beans in spring to pheasant, apples and native oysters in the autumn. Other goodies include specialist cheeses, organic meat and seafood.

Stoke Newington Farmers' Market

William Patten Primary School, Stoke Newington Church Street, N16 0NX (7502 7588, www.growingcommunities. org). Stoke Newington rail or 393, 476 bus. Open 10am-2.30pm Sat.

This modestly proportioned local farmers' market features some top-notch producers, selling organic greens and fruits, seafood, cakes, cheeses and meat. Once a month, look out for the Stour Valley Organic Lavender Company's wonderfully fragrant honey.

EAST

Brick Lane Sunday UpMarket

91 Brick Lane, E1 6QL (7770 6028, www. sundayupmarket.co.uk). Shoreditch High Street rail. Open 10am-5pm Sun.

The takeaway food court keeps expanding, with more and more interesting vendors pitching up alongside the fashion and art stalls. At the market's Brick Lane end you can try homestyle Moroccan dishes and piping-hot Japanese takoyaki (battered octopus) or quaff Ethiopian coffee, brewed in clay pots.

Broadway Market

London Fields, E8 (www.broadway market.co.uk). London Fields rail or 236, 394 bus. Open 9am-5pm Sat.

Delectably whiffy cheeses, charcuterie and artisanal desserts are among the wares at this charming East End market. Highlights include the Ghanaian food from Spinach & Agushi and dainty cupcakes from Violet.

SOUTH

Blackheath Farmers' Market

Station car park, 2 Blackheath Village, SE3 0ZH (7833 0338, www.lfm.org.uk). Blackheath rail or 54, 89, 108, 202 bus. Open 10am-2pm Sun.

In operation since late 2000, Blackheath is a veteran among the city's farmers' markets. Fresh, in-season fruit and vegetables all come from within 100 miles of the M25, and stallholders change from Sunday to Sunday. Keep an eye out for the excellent goat's cheeses from Nut Knowle Farm in Sussex.

Brixton Market

Electric Avenue, Pope's Road, Brixton Station Road, SW9. Brixton tube/rail. Open 8am-6pm Mon, Tue, Thur-Sat; 8am-3pm Wed.

This sprawling market is the best place in London to find African and Caribbean produce, from custard apples to yams and exotic fish. It can be overwhelming for the novice shopper, but take your time to peruse the stalls and ask the traders for cooking tips.

Northcote Road Market

Northcote Road, SW11 (www.northcoterd. co.uk). Clapham Junction rail. Open 10am-6pm Mon-Sat. Antiques 10am-6pm Mon-Sat; noon-5pm Sun.

This busy local market offers an impressive array of fresh fruit and veg, bread, fish, olives, cakes and stalls selling huge wedges of fresh pizza to hungry rummagers.

Wimbledon Farmers' Market

Wimbledon Park Primary School, Havana Road, SW19 8EJ (7833 0338, www.lfm. org.uk). Wimbledon Park tube/rail or 156 bus. Open 9am-1pm Sat.

Wimbledon's market is an unhurried, enjoyable affair. Some stalls rotate monthly, others fortnightly.

WEST

Notting Hill Farmers' Market

Car park behind Waterstone's, access via Kensington Place, W8 (7833 0338,

GOING OUT
BEAUTY
FASHION
PARTIES
FOOD
HEALTH
ECO
OUTDOORS
HOME
CHILDREN
PETS
TRANSPORT
RESOURCES

*www.lfm.org.uk). Notting Hill Gate tube.
Open Sat 9am-1pm.*
In the opposite direction to the infinitely more
touristy Portobello Road lies this gem of a
market. There's a great range of organic
produce stalls, mostly manned by farmers
from Kent, Surrey and Sussex.

Partridges Food Market
*Outside Duke of York Square, SW3 4LY
(www.partridges.co.uk/foodmarket). Sloane
Square or South Kensington tube. Open
10am-4pm Sat.*
Myriad stalls set up camp here each week,
with high-quality foods to tempt well-heeled
locals: look out for the artisanal pâtés and
darling cupcakes from Crumbs and Doilies.

Shepherd's Bush Market
*East side of railway viaduct, between
Uxbridge Road & Goldhawk Road, W12
(8749 3042, www.shepherdsbushmarket.
co.uk). Goldhawk Road or Shepherd's Bush
tube. Open 10.30am-6.30pm Mon-Sat.*
There's an impressive array of ethnic foods at
this lively local market, including Indian and
Polish grub. Follow your nose to the stalls
selling fragrant spices and juicy mangoes.

Specialist shops

CENTRAL

The top-notch bread and baked goods at
St John Bread & Wine (*see p84*) can
be bought to take away. For cheese fans,
La Fromagerie (*see p87*) is another
address-book essential.

Green Valley
*36-37 Upper Berkeley Street, W1H 5QH
(7402 7385). Marble Arch tube. Open
8am-midnight daily.*
Green Valley has a comprehensive mezedes
counter offering myriad possibilities for
quick, after-work suppers. You'll also find a
fantastic array of fruit and veg (lebanese
pears, aubergines, cucumbers, guava,
coconuts), freshly prepared juices and an eye-
catching display of baklava.

Japan Centre
*14-16 Regent Street, SW1Y 4PH (7255
8255, www.japancentre.com). Piccadilly
Circus tube. Open 10am-9pm Mon-Sat;
11am-7pm Sun.*
Japan Centre's basement grocery has taken
over next door's premises, allowing for the
expansion of the grocery and fresh meat, fish
and vegetable ranges, plus the addition of a
new bakery. With over 1,000 Japanese food
items in stock, this bustling store has
everything from *nori* seaweed and spices to
wasabi peas and fabulously packaged sweets
to snack on.

Lina Store
*18 Brewer Street, W1R 3FS (7437 6482).
Piccadilly Circus tube. Open 8am-6.30pm
Mon-Fri; 8am-5.30pm Sat.*
Beyond the 1950's green ceramic frontage at
this Italian family-run deli lies a wealth of
quality products – wooden crates full of dried
pastas, plus a deli counter filled with excellent
antipasti and (in season) truffles.

NORTH

Andreas Michli & Son
*405-411 St Ann's Road, N15 3JL
(8802 0188). Harringay Green Lanes
rail. Open 10am-7pm Mon-Sat; 11am-
3.30pm Sun.*

City Secret

For ice-cream with a difference,
check out **Chin Chin Laboratorists**
(50 Camden Lock Place, NW1 8AF,
www.chinchinlabs.com) – London's
first nitro ice-cream parlour. It looks
like a mad scientist's lab and the
ice-creams made on-demand using
liquid nitrogen taste divine. Try
Valrhona chocolate, vanilla or lemon
cheesecake. There are also colourful
sauces (salted caramel, raspberry
or blueberry) and toppings (orange-
flavoured sugar or gold-dusted
chocolate-coated popping candy).

Charming proprietor Mr Michli oversees operations at this Cypriot store, where staff will happily answer questions about the stock – from fresh yellow dates to hollyhock leaves, and seasonal fruit and veg from Cyprus or Mr Michli's Hertfordshire farm.

Food Hall

22-24 Turnpike Lane, N8 0PS (8889 2264). Turnpike Lane tube. Open 9am-7pm Mon-Sat; 9.30am-5pm Sun.
The speciality at this Ethiopian food shop is the freshly milled flour (including rice, millet and maize flour) used for making traditional breads such as soft, slightly sour injera. Other finds include aged spice butter (used to flavour stews) and the pungent, peppery West African 'grains of paradise' spice.

Le Péché Mignon

6 Ronalds Road, N5 1XH (7607 1826, www.lepechemignon.co.uk). Holloway Road tube. Open 8am-7pm Mon-Fri; 9am-6pm Sat; 9am-5pm Sun.
Set on a quiet residential side street, this impressive deli and café stocks plentiful supplies of cheese, charcuterie and products from all over Europe, from french tarte to paella rice.

Polsmak

39 Balls Pond Road, N1 4BW (7275 7045, www.polsmak.co.uk). Dalston Junction rail or 30, 56, 277 bus. Open 9am-8pm Mon-Fri; 9am-6pm Sat, Sun.
This little shop is so authentic, everything is labelled in Polish; happily, staff are at hand to explain. There's also a small café area where you can enjoy delicious Polish packzi (cream buns) and drozdzowka (yeast cake).

Steve Hatt ★

88-90 Essex Road, N1 8LU (7226 3963). Angel tube. Open 8am-5pm Tue-Thur; 7am-5pm Fri, Sat. No credit cards.
Expect first-class fresh fish from this long-established fishmonger and you won't be disappointed. A wet fish display stretching along the wide front window affords queuing customers plenty of opportunity to check out what's available and once you've made your selection, you can have your fish skinned, boned and filleted on request.

EAST

Leila's

15-17 Calvert Avenue, E2 7JP (7729 9789). Shoreditch High Street rail. Open 10am-6pm Wed-Sat; 10am-5pm Sun.
Leila McAlister's eclectic store has the nous to distinguish between crusty and gooey brownies and offer customers the choice. There are also fresh, seasonal fruit and vegetables, bread, cheese and Chegworth farm juices on offer.

London Star Night Supermarket & Video

203-213 Mare Street, E8 3QE (8985 2949). Hackney Central or London Fields rail, or bus 26, 48, 55. Open 10am-10pm daily.
Even the Vietnamese restaurants down the road rely on this place for the occasional ingredients run. Stock includes aromatic herbs such as Asian basil and saw-tooth herb, as well as staples such as rice noodles, fish sauce and bundles of morning glory.

Ginger Pig

99 Lauriston Road, E9 7HJ (8986 6911, www.thegingerpig.co.uk). Mile End tube then 277, 425 bus or London Fields rail. Open 9am-5.30pm Tue; 9am-6.30pm Wed-Fri; 9am-6pm Sat; 9am-3pm Sun.
The east London outlet for the celebrated farm-based butcher of rare meats that came to national attention via Borough Market in the late 1990s. You'll find cuts from Swaledale, Tamworth and Gloucester Old Spot pigs, plus own-made bacon, sausages, pies and terrines. There's also an excellent deli downstairs.

Taj Stores

112-114A Brick Lane, E1 6RL (7377 0061, www.tajstores.co.uk). Aldgate East tube or Liverpool Street tube/rail. Open 9am-9pm daily.
This Bangladeshi grocer does a brisk trade in halal meat, exotic herbs and fish. Freshly prepared naan and samosas are stocked, as

GOING OUT

BEAUTY

FASHION

PARTIES

FOOD

HEALTH

ECO

OUTDOORS

HOME

CHILDREN

PETS

TRANSPORT

RESOURCES

are more unusual vegetables such as lata and danga, pulses, grains, spices and tiffin tins.

Turkish Food Centre

89 Ridley Road, E8 2NT (7254 6754). Dalston Kingsland rail or 30, 56, 236 bus. Open 8am-9pm Mon-Sat; 8.30am-9pm Sun.
A formidable purveyor of Turkish foodstuffs, this Dalston stalwart has been in operation for more than 20 years. Fresh fruit and veg are flown in from Turkey, Greece and Cyprus, while pomegranate syrup is a bargain buy.

SOUTH

Cheese Block

69 Lordship Lane, SE22 8EP (8299 3636). East Dulwich rail. Open 9am-6.30pm Mon-Fri; 9am-6pm Sat.
With hundreds of cheeses, this is a haven for fromage lovers. Choosing can be tough, but staff are always happy to help; the mature Old Amsterdam gouda is a favourite.

Deepak Cash & Carry

953-959 Garrat Lane, SW17 0LW (8767 7819). Tooting Broadway tube. Open 8.45am-8pm Mon-Sat; 10am-4pm Sun.
If you're looking for a South Indian product and can't find it here, you're unlikely to find it anywhere. For dried goods and spices, this place has no peer. Best buys are pulses such as malawi toor dahl and channa dahl.

Gennaro Delicatessen

23 Lewis Grove, SE13 6BG (8852 1370, www.italianfoodexpress.co.uk). Lewisham rail/DLR. Open 9am-6pm Mon-Sat.
This family-run deli, passed down through generations, sells anything an Italian food aficionado could desire: quality prosciutto, fresh buffalo mozzarella, coffee and more. The own-brand Sicilian olive oil is top-notch.

Persepolis ★

28-30 Peckham High Street, SE15 5DT (7639 8007). Peckham Rye rail. Open 10.35am-9pm daily.
Owner Sally Butcher, author of the acclaimed *Persia in Peckham* cookbook, is often on hand to answer queries about the Iranian produce

available in her corner shop, from fresh herbs and pomegranates to saffron and sumak.

Talad Thai

326 Upper Richmond Road, SW15 6TL (8789 8084, www.taladthai.co.uk). Putney rail. Open 9am-8pm Mon-Sat; 10am-8pm Sun.
Talad Thai crams plenty in to its modest premises. Fresh fruit and vegetables are imported from Thailand, with hard-to-find delights such as mangosteens, the 'queen of fruits', as well as essentials such as kaffir lime leaves and Asian holy basil. There's a formidable range of curry pastes too.

WEST

R Garcia & Sons

248-250 Portobello Road, W11 1LL (7221 6119). Ladbroke Grove or Westbourne Park tube. Open 9am-6pm Mon-Fri; 9am-7pm Sat; 10am-6pm Sun.
A one-stop shop for all things Spanish, R Garcia stocks a comprehensive range of sherries, and a feast of cheeses and jamon. Even the tinned olives, imported from Spain, are excellent. The shop also sells clay cookware and dishes for entertaining at home.

Natural Natural

20 Station Parade, Uxbridge Road, W5 3LD (8992 0770, www.natural-natural.co.uk). Ealing Common tube. Open 9am-8pm Mon-Sat; 10am-7pm Sun.
This quaint Japanese store offers an excellent range of groceries, from saké and fresh fruit to ready-packaged and marinated cod and mackerel. Prime picks include mentaiko (spicy cod roe), jars of yamamomo (Japanese mountain peaches) and yuzu salad dressing.

VB & Sons

147 Ealing Road, Wembley, Middlesex HA0 4BU (8795 0387). Alperton tube. Open 9.30am-6.30pm daily.
Head here for a wealth of Gujarati products: cobra saffron, soapnuts, mango-ginger, malucca nuts, freshly made pickles, own-made paneer cheese and Indian noodles.

Health

All the key contacts you need – plus our pick of the capital's alternative practitioners.

Alternative health

Individual practitioners' working hours vary, so we've only listed opening hours for centres with set times.

GENERAL CLINICS

Hale Clinic
7 Park Crescent, W1B 1PF (7631 0156, www.haleclinic.com). Regent's Park tube. Open 8.30am-8.30pm Mon-Fri; 9am-5pm Sat.
If you're unsure about alternative health treatments, the Hale, with its focus on integrating conventional medicine with complementary techniques, is a good place to start. In total, there are around 100 treatments on offer, from homeopathy to hypnotherapy.

Inside Out Retreats
9 Brewers Lane, Richmond, Surrey TW9 1HH (8332 6566, www.insideoutretreats. com). Richmond tube/rail. Open 10am-6pm Tue-Sat; 11am-5pm Sun.

City Secret

If you're on a tight budget, check out the **Polyclinic** (115 New Cavendish Street, W1W 7UW, 7911 5041, www.westminster.ac.uk). Here, students from the University of Westminster's School of Integrated Health offer the public supervised, low-cost alternative treatments, with everything from acupuncture and herbal medicine to osteopathy, for a flat-rate £20 charge.

Familiar treatments such as homeopathy and reflexology sit alongside colour therapy, primordial sound meditation and ayurvedic facial rejuvenation at this chic centre, owned by life coach and energy healer Alison Pothier.

Neal's Yard Remedies Therapy Rooms
2 Neal's Yard, WC2H 9DP (7379 7662, www.nealsyardremedies.com). Covent Garden tube. Open 9am-9pm Mon-Thur; 9am-7pm Fri; 10am-6.30pm Sat, Sun.
The therapy rooms here offer an array of beauty treatments and alternative therapies, all using natural ingredients. Facials (£55 for 60 minutes) are excellent value and there are massages (from £35 for 30 minutes) to suit all requirements (aromatherapy, pregnancy, sports). Also on offer are acupuncture, cranial osteopathy, reflexology and reiki, as well as counselling, cognitive behavioural therapy and even tarot card readings. Also worth a visit is the NYR Organic Beauty Spa on King's Road.

SPECIALISTS

Eastern Clinic (Ayurvedic Medical Centre)
1079 Garratt Lane, SW17 OLN (8682 3876, www.easternclinic.co.uk). Tooting Broadway tube. Open 10.30am-7.30pm Mon-Fri; 10.30am-4pm Sat.
Ayurveda ('science of life' in Sanskrit) is an intriguing field; its medical practitioners train for a minimum of five years at university, followed by a year's hospital internship in India and Sri Lanka. As well as founding the Ayurvedic Medical Association of the UK, Dr Moorthy Sathiya consults for the NHS. Ayurveda is famed for its massage treatments, but clinical diagnosis of your ayurvedic body type and dietary advice are fundamental.

The Keet Clinic

62-70 Shorts Gardens, WC2H 9AB (7240 1438, www.keetclinic.com). Covent Garden tube. Open 10am-7pm daily.

Podiatrist Michael Keet is principal of the London College of Reflexology, which is based at this clinic. Hour-long sessions with a newly qualified reflexologist start at £35 and rise according to the therapist's experience and expertise.

London College of Shiatsu ★

95 Grays Inn Road, WC1X 8TX (7603 1191, www.londoncollegeofshiatsu.com). Russell Square tube. Open varies; phone for details. No credit cards.

At this training college for shiatsu there are Saturday student clinics every three weeks (£20 for one hour), where supervised third-year students offer treatments to members of the public. They are very popular so do book in advance. Treatments from fully qualified practioners are also available: call for further details and locations.

Milton Natural Health Centre

33 Milton Avenue, N6 5QF (8340 7062). Highgate tube. Open by appointment only.

A treatment at highly qualified Mark Mordin's home clinic may comprise everything from magnetic therapy to shiatsu. Wife Linda specialises in aromatherapy, with particular emphasis on mothers-to-be.

Paul Lennard Energy Healer

Ella Clinic, 106 Harley Street, W1G 7JE (7935 5281, www.theellaclinic.co.uk). Baker Street or Regent's Park tube. Open by appointment only.

One-hour sessions with energy healer Paul Lennard vary widely according to the needs of the client, but may incorporate craniosacral therapy, *chi nei tsang* (a Thai deep massage technique) and discussion of past traumas.

West London Osteopaths

65 Vespan Road, W12 9QG (8749 0581, www.westlondonosteopaths.com). Shepherds Bush or Stamford Brook tube. Open 8am-5.30pm Mon, Tue, Thur, Fri; 8am-7pm Wed; 9am-1pm Sat.

In addition to running this innovative clinic, owner David Tatton is Chairman of the London Osteopathic Society. Holistic massage and Pilates matwork sessions are offered to assist osteopathy sessions, which can benefit back pain, respiratory function, arthritis and accident trauma, among other conditions.

Yoga Biomedical Trust

1 Teesdale Street E2 6GF (7689 3040, www.yogatherapy.org). Bethnal Green tube. Open by appointment only.

Asthma, diabetes, cancer, mild MS and Parkinson's are just some of the medical conditions that can be helped with yoga therapy. After a consultation with a therapist (a yoga teacher who has undertaken two years of specialised training), you then undertake prescribed classes and home practice. Yoga therapy is now also offered at the NHS Kentish Town Health Centre (2 Bartholomew Road, NW5 2AJ).

Zita West Clinic

37 Manchester Street, W1U 7LJ (7224 0017, www.zitawest.com). Baker Street tube. Open 9am-6pm Mon-Thur; 9am-5pm Fri, Sat.

Fronted by renowned midwife Zita West, this is the place to come if you're having trouble getting pregnant or want to boost your chances for successful IVF. Nutritional therapy, hypnotherapy and acupuncture are among the complementary techniques used – and the clinic is integrated, so you also have access to a wide variety of medical tests.

Key contacts

NHS Direct (0845 4647, www.nhs direct.nhs.uk) is a one-stop-shop for free health advice, and should be your first port of call if you're feeling unwell, or need to find your nearest doctor, A&E, minor injuries unit, pharmacist, dentist or support group. Alternatively, the main NHS website at www.nhs.uk has a good range of search criteria that will enable you to find the best service for your condition, whether it be a sports and fitness injury or a dental emergency.

GOING OUT
BEAUTY
FASHION
PARTIES
FOOD
HEALTH
ECO
OUTDOORS
HOME
CHILDREN
PETS
TRANSPORT
RESOURCES

A&E DEPARTMENTS

Accident and Emergency departments
cover the whole of the capital; to find your
nearest call the **NHS Direct** (*see p107*).

EMERGENCY EYE CLINICS

London has two 24-hour emergency
departments dealing specifically with
eye injuries, although if your injuries
are more extensive you should go to a
regular A&E department.

Moorfields Eye Hospital
*162 City Road, EC1V 2PD (7253 3411,
www.moorfields.nhs.uk). Old Street tube/rail.*
Moorfields also has a nurse-led telephone
helpline on 7566 2345, open 9am-4.30pm
Monday to Friday.

Western Eye Hospital
*171 Marylebone Road, NW1 5QH (3312
6666, www.imperial.nhs.uk/westerneye).
Marylebone tube/rail.*
Western Eye Hospital is open 24 hours a day
for ambulance and walk-in cases.

DENTISTS

Find your nearest dentist via the **British
Dental Association** website at www.
bda.org. The search facility allows you to
specify a range of different criteria,
including NHS dentists and those with
disabled access. NHS dentists who are
taking on new patients are also listed at
www.nhs.uk.

   If you need an emergency dentist,
your first call should be to your own
dentist. Even out of hours, they should
have emergency information on their
answerphone. If you don't have a dentist,
call the **NHS Direct** or ring **Guy's
Hospital's Dental Emergency Care
Service** on 7188 0512. Guy's also provides
free walk-in emergency treatment (Guy's
Hospital, St Thomas Street, SE1 9RT, 7188
0511); it's open 9am-3.30pm Monday to
Friday, but queues start forming at 8am.
Arrive by 10am if you're to be seen at all.

WALK-IN CENTRES

NHS Walk-in Centres offer confidential
advice and treatment for minor injuries
and illnesses. Staffed by experienced
nurses, they're often open seven days a
week (hours vary) and you don't need an
appointment. Find your nearest through
the **NHS Direct** (*see p107*).

Canary Wharf NHS Walk-In Centre
*30 Marsh Wall, E14 9TP (7517 3300).
Canary Wharf tube/DLR or South Quays
DLR. Open 7am-7pm Mon-Fri and
bank holidays.*

**City & Hackney Teaching PCT Walk
In Centre** *Tollgate Primary Care Centre,
57 Stamford Hill, N16 5SR (7689 3140).
Seven Sisters tube. Open 8am-8pm Mon-Fri;
10am-6pm Sat, Sun and bank holidays.*

Charing Cross NHS Walk-In Centre
*Charing Cross Hospital, Fulham Palace
Road, W6 8RF (8383 0904). Hammersmith
Broadway tube. Open 8am-10pm daily.*

Hackney NHS Walk-In Centre
*Homerton University Hospital, Homerton
Row, E9 6SR (8510 5342). Homerton
rail. Open 8am-10pm Mon-Fri; 9am-
10pm Sat, Sun and bank holidays.*

Liverpool Street Walk-In Centre
*Exchange Arcade, EC2M 3WA (0845 880
1242). Liverpool Street tube/rail. Open 7am-
7pm Mon-Fri.*

Newham Walk-In Centre
*Glen Road, E13 8SH (7363 9200). Upton
Park tube, then 376 bus. Open 7am-11pm
Mon-Fri; 9am-11pm Sat, Sun and bank
holidays.*

Parsons Green NHS Walk-In Centre
*5-7 Parsons Green, SW6 4UL (8846 6758).
Parsons Green tube. Open 8am-8pm Mon-
Fri; 9am-1.30pm Sat, Sun.*

Soho NHS Walk-In Centre *1 Frith
Street, W1D 3HZ (7534 6500). Tottenham*

FREE EVENTS

Instead of shelling out to join a gym, sign up for some of London's free sporting events. One of the most high-profile is the **Critical Mass Monthly Cycle** (www.criticalmasslondon.org.uk) on the last Friday of every month. These monthly mass outings welcome all manner of wheels, including cyclists, skateboarders and wheelchair users. Meet by the BFI Southbank under Waterloo Bridge at 6pm.

Friday Night Skates (www.thefns. com) are equally adrenaline-charged, as hundreds of skaters take to the city streets on weekly changing routes, accompanied by a pounding sound system. Be warned: the ten- to 12-mile route is fast and furious, so you'll need to be able to keep up. Skaters assemble at 7.30pm at the Duke of Wellington Arch, at Hyde Park Corner.

For a more calming ride, join a Saturday or Sunday outing with the **Pollards Hill Cyclists** (www.pollardshillcyclists. org.uk). The group takes its cycling seriously, but with plenty of stops for lunch, tea and a quick half. Routes often venture beyond south London into the Surrey countryside.

If jogging, yoga, boxercise or circuit training are more your thing, clothing brand **Sweaty Betty** organises free group fitness events across London; see www.sweatybetty.com/sweatyclub for details of upcoming gatherings.

The **Richmond Park Time Trial** (Richmond Gate, TW10, www.parkrun. com/richmond), held every Saturday at 9am, is another sociable event. The free 5km runs are open to all; simply register online by Friday noon.

Another energetic option is the one-of-a-kind **London Bike Polo**, various locations (listed on website), held on Sunday afternoons at the corner of Shacklewell Street and Brick Lane (www.londonbikepolo.wordpress.com). Mallets and balls are provided and anyone's welcome.

Finally, you can get to grips with tai chi for free every Wednesday, thanks to the **London Spirituality Network** (Rosslyn Hill Unitarian Chapel, Pilgrim's Place, NW3 1NG, 7433 3267,www.rosslynhillchapel.com). The class begins at 5.45pm and is suitable for all ages and levels.

Court Road tube. Open 8am-8pm Mon-Fri; 10am-8pm Sat, Sun and bank holidays.

Tooting NHS Walk-In Centre
Clare House, St Georges Hospital, Blackshaw Road, SW17 0QT (8700 0505). Tooting Broadway tube, then G1 bus. Open 7am-10pm daily.

Victoria NHS Walk-In Centre
63 Buckingham Gate, SW1E 6AS (7340 1190). Victoria or St James Park tube. Open 7am-7pm Mon-Fri and bank holidays.

Whitechapel NHS Walk-In Centre
Whitechapel Hospital, 174 Whitechapel Road, E1 1BZ (7943 1333). Whitechapel

tube. Open 7am-10pm Mon-Fri; 9am-10pm Sat, Sun and bank holidays.

Wembley NHS Walk-In Centre
116 Chaplin Road, Middlesex, HA0 4UZ (8795 6000). Wembley Central tube. Open 10am-7pm Mon-Fri.

LATE-NIGHT CHEMISTS

Below are details for late-night, central London branches of Boots, along with a couple of independent chemists that stay open late.

Boots Queensway *114 Queensway, W2 4QS (7229 1183). Bayswater or Queensway*

GOING OUT
BEAUTY
FASHION
PARTIES
FOOD
HEALTH
ECO
OUTDOORS
HOME
CHILDREN
PETS
TRANSPORT
RESOURCES

GOING OUT

BEAUTY

FASHION

PARTIES

FOOD

HEALTH

ECO

OUTDOORS

HOME

CHILDREN

PETS

TRANSPORT

RESOURCES

tube. Open 9am-midnight Mon-Sat; noon-6pm Sun.

Boots Piccadilly *44-46 Regent Street, W1B 5RA (7734 6126). Piccadilly Circus tube. Open 8am-midnight Mon-Fri; 9am-midnight Sat; noon-6pm Sun.*

Boots Victoria Station *Victoria Station, SW1V 1JT (7834 0676). Victoria tube/rail. Open 7am-midnight Mon-Fri; 8am-midnight Sat; 9am-9pm Sun.*

Bliss Chemists *5-6 Marble Arch, W1H 7EL (7723 6116). Marble Arch tube. Open 9am-midnight daily.*

Zafash *233-235 Old Brompton Road, SW5 0EA (7373 2798). Earl's Court tube. Open 24hrs daily.*

SEXUAL HEALTH

In addition to the services of **NHS Direct** (*see p107*), the 24-hour service **Sexual Healthline** (0800 567123) is free and confidential. Either service will locate your nearest **NHS Genito-Urinary Clinic**. These provide free, confidential treatment of STDs and other problems such as thrush and cystitis; they also offer counselling and advice on HIV and other STDs and can carry out blood tests.

Worth Talking About (0800 282930, www.nhs.uk/worthtalkingabout) is an advice centre aimed at young people aged 19 and under that can provide free, confidential advice about sex and contraception, as well as on relationships in general.

The **British Pregnancy Advice Service** (0845 730 4030, www.bpas.org) offers callers advice, contraceptives, the morning-after pill, pregnancy tests and referrals to BPAS nursing homes for private abortions, and has outposts across the city. For under-25s, **Brook** (0808 802 1234, www.brook.org.uk) runs eight London clinics. For over 25s there's also **Sexual Health Direct**,

run by the Family Planning Association: 0845 122 8690, www.fpa.org.uk.

The **Terrence Higgins Trust** (0845 122 1200, www.tht.org.uk) is an excellent source of information and advice on sexual health and particularly HIV, with an advice and support line, plus friendly drop-in centres in Waterloo, Peckham and Notting Hill. There is also a counselling service.

Yoga

For children's yoga classes, try **Yoga Bugs** (www.yogabugs.com), which caters for three- to seven-year-olds. **Triyoga** (*see below*) also runs excellent classes for children of all ages.

Iyengar Yoga Institute

223A Randolph Avenue, W9 1NL (7624 3080, www.iyi.org.uk). Maida Vale tube. Open call for details. Classes £9-£11.
Housed in two airy, light studios in a leafy Maida Vale street, the Iyengar Institute runs some 50 classes, with a maximum of 35 people per class. Novices can try a free class; the six-week beginners' course costs £60.

Jeff Phenix Yoga

07870 569466, www.yogajeff.co.uk Classes £8-£12.
British Wheel of Yoga-accredited Jeff Phenix runs classes at several top centres, including Triyoga at Covent Garden and Primrose Hill and the Life Centre in Notting Hill, with an emphasis on meditation; see the website for details.

Jivamukti Yoga

300 Kensal Road, W10 5BE (8960 3999, www.jivamuktiyoga.co.uk). Ladbroke Grove or Westbourne Park tube. Open 7.30am-8pm Mon-Fri; 9am-5pm Sat, Sun. Classes £13-£15.
Jivamukti offers ashtanga-based yoga in a range of vigorous classes, with an emphasis on spiritual elements such as chanting and meditation. This is the London offshoot of the successful New York studio.

The Life Centre

15 Edge Street, W8 7PN (7221 4602, www. thelifecentre.com). Notting Hill Gate tube. Open 6am-9.30pm Mon-Fri; 8.15am-7.30pm Sat, Sun. Classes £7-£15.

The Life Centre was of London's first yoga studios, and still one of its prettiest. The space is small enough to feel intimate, but there's still a great selection of classes on offer – more than 80 a week – and the teaching quality is superb.

The Studio

89A Rivington Street, EC2A 3AY (7729 0111, www.bodystudio.co.uk). Old Street tube/rail. Open times vary; call for details. Classes £10.

This studio hosts a whole range of yoga and Pilates classes, as well as various martial arts classes. Of particular note are the weekday morning (7am-9am) Mysore-style ashtanga vinyasa classes.

Triyoga ★

6 Erskine Road, NW3 3AJ (7483 3344, www.triyoga.co.uk). Chalk Farm tube. Open 6am-9.30pm Mon-Fri; 8am-7.45pm Sat; 9am-9pm Sun. Classes £12-£14.

The original Triyoga studio, and still the best. Most of London's top teachers lead classes here. Beloved by serious enthusiasts as well as a great starting ground for beginners.
Other locations *Triyoga Covent Garden, 2 Dryden Street, WC2E 9NA (7483 3344); Triyoga Soho, 2nd Floor, Kingly Court, W1B 5PW (7483 3344).*

Yoga Biomedical Trust

For listings see p107. Classes £12-£15.

The YBTt's centre is dedicated to the development of yoga therapy as an integral part of complementary and alternative medicine. The pregnancy yoga classes with Francoise Barbira-Freedman are highly recommended, while other specialisms include yoga for menopause, depression and anxiety, and sessions for children with asthma.

Yogahome

11 Allen Road, N16 8SB (7249 2425, www.yogahome.com). Highbury & Islington

tube/rail or Angel tube, then 73 bus or Dalston Kingsland rail. Open 10am-10pm Mon-Thur; 10am-2pm Fri-Sun. Classes from £7.50.

Set up by Maria Gandy and Billie Chan in 1998, Yogahome has won a loyal fan base. An extensive range of classes (including pregnancy yoga led by Billie and hatha fusion yoga by Maria) are taught in the warm, friendly studio.

Yoga Junction

93a Weston Park, N8 9PR (8347 0000, www.yogajunction.co.uk). Crouch Hill tube or Hornsey rail. Open times vary; check online for details. Classes £9-£10.

A nicely chilled space with a good mix of classes and styles, including ashtanga self-practice, vinyasa flow and hatha. Therapeutic sessions for sufferers of Parkinson's Disease and ME, as well as children's classes, are held in the bright and peaceful studio.

Yoga Place ★

1st Floor, 449-453 Bethnal Green Road, E2 9QH (7739 5195, www.yogaplace.co.uk). Bethnal Green tube/rail. Open times vary; check online for details. Classes £10-£12.

Some 30 classes are held each week, from shadow yoga and deep relaxation sessions to post-natal classes. The calm, warm space feels a long way from the grit and grime of Bethnal Green Road outside. Other therapies such as massage, are also available.

GOING OUT

BEAUTY

FASHION

PARTIES

FOOD

HEALTH

ECO

OUTDOORS

HOME

CHILDREN

PETS

TRANSPORT

RESOURCES

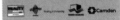

Sport & fitness

Fitness venues from skateparks to lidos. For yoga centres, *see p111*.

Climbing centres

Along with dedicated climbing centres, six of London's sports centres with climbing walls have clubbed together to form **Climb London** (0845 363 1144, www.climblondon.co.uk). Taster sessions, workshops and weekends are all offered.

Castle
Green Lanes, N4 2HA (8211 7000, www.castle-climbing.co.uk). Open 2-10pm Mon-Fri; 10am-7pm Sat, Sun. Admission £7-£12.
Spectacularly set in a converted Victorian water-pumping station, the Castle offers over 400 routes (changed every four months). It can get very crowded, though.

Mile End Climbing Wall ★
Haverfield Road, E3 5BE (8980 0289, www.mileendwall.org.uk). Mile End tube. Open noon-9.30pm Mon-Thur; noon-9pm Fri; 10am-6pm Sat, Sun. Admission £7-£12.
Housed in an old pipe-engineering works, the huge climbing wall caters to all levels and provides a range of surfaces. A first climb deal, including shoe hire, is just £12.

Vertical Chill at Ellis Brigham
Tower House, 3-11 Southampton Street, WC2E 7HA (7395 1010, www.vertical-chill.com). Covent Garden tube. Open 12.30-5.30pm Tue; 10.30am-3.30pm Wed, Fri; 10.30am-6.30pm Thur; 10am-5pm Sat; noon-4pm Sun. Admission £25-£50.
This eight-metre indoor ice wall offers a unique climbing adventure: a lesson with a qualified guide costs £50.

Westway Climbing Complex
Westway Sports Centre, 1 Crowthorne Road, Ladbroke Grove, W10 6RP (8969 0992, www.westwaysportscentre.org.uk). Ladbroke Grove or Latimer Road tube. Open 10am-10pm Mon-Wed, Fri; 8am-10pm Thur; 10am-8pm Sat, Sun. Admission £7-£8.50.
Over 300 top rope and lead rope climbing routes and caters to all climbing levels.

Dance

The **London Dance Network** (www.londondance.com) has a full directory of classes and workshops in everything from tango to wedding dance tuition.

Cecil Sharp House
2 Regent's Park Road, NW1 7AY (7485 2206, www.efdss.org). Camden Town tube. Open times vary; call for details. Classes £3-£10. No credit cards.
If salsa's too saucy and rumba too raunchy, this might be the place for you: the home of the English Folk Dance and Song Society. There are lessons in everything from cajun to clog dancing, and a whole range of ceilidhs.

Chisenhale Dance Space
64-84 Chisenhale Road, E3 5QZ (8981 6617, www.chisenhaledancespace.co.uk). Mile End tube. Open 10am-9pm daily. Classes £5.50-£6; £3.50 reductions.
Chisenhale runs children's and adults' African and creative dance classes, and also offers cheap studio space.

Danceworks
16 Balderton Street, W1K 6TN (7629 6183, www.danceworks.net). Bond Street tube. Open 8.30am-10pm Mon-Fri; 9am-6.30pm Sat, Sun. Membership call for details. Classes £4-£8, plus £5 charge for non-members.

GOING OUT
BEAUTY
FASHION
PARTIES
FOOD
HEALTH
ECO
OUTDOORS
HOME
CHILDREN
PETS
TRANSPORT
RESOURCES

An enormously diverse spread of classes, held in six well-appointed studios, ranges from bhangra and ballet to flamenco and jazz.

The Factory Gym & Dance
407 Hornsey Road, N19 4DX (7272 1122, www.factorylondon.com). Archway tube/ Finsbury Park tube/rail. Open 8am-10pm Mon, Thur; 9.30am-10pm Tue, Wed; 9.30am-9pm Fri; 9.30am-7pm Sat; 9.30am-6pm Sun. Membership from £35. Classes £7.
The Factory's individual and group lessons include pole-dancing and Argentinian tango, as well as wedding first dance lessons.

Greenwich Dance
Borough Hall, Royal Hill, SE10 8RE (8293 9741, www.greenwichdance.org.uk). Greenwich rail. Open 9am-9pm Mon-Thur; 9am-5.30pm Fri; 9am-3pm Sat. Classes £3.50-£6.
Greenwich Dance runs an appealing range of drop-in classes and courses.

Laban
Creekside, SE8 3DZ (8691 8600, www.laban. org). Deptford rail. Open 8.30am-8pm Mon-Fri; 9am-3.30pm Sat, Sun. Classes £88-£121/term.
Laban offers year-long evening courses for keen amateurs, including classical ballet, Africanist Movement and jazz.

Pineapple
7 Langley Street, WC2H 9JA (7836 4004, www.pineapple.uk.com). Covent Garden tube. Open 9am-10pm Mon-Fri; 9am-7pm Sat; 10am-6pm Sun. Classes £5-£8 plus £2-£4 membership fee.
Founded in 1979, Pineapple hosts more than 30 dance classes every day. Prices are affordable, and beginners warmly welcomed.

The Place
17 Duke Road, WC1H 9PY (7121 1101, www.theplace.org.uk). Euston Square tube or Euston tube/rail. Open noon-7pm Mon-Sat. Classes £4-£10.
Known for its excellent professional training, the Place also offers ballet and contemporary classes and courses for amateurs, whether adults or children.

Ice skating

The first stop for anyone looking to glide their way to fitness should be the **London Skaters** website (www. londonskaters.com), which lists all of the capital's indoor rinks.

INDOOR RINKS

Lee Valley Ice Centre
Lea Bridge Road, E10 7QL (8533 3154, www.leevalleypark.org.uk). Clapton rail. Open see website for details. Admission £6.90; £2.70-£5.90 reductions (plus £1.60 skate hire).
Lee Valley's modern, well-maintained rink attracts both nervous novices and confident figure skaters, but rarely feels crowded.

Queens Ice Bowl ★
17 Queensway, W2 4QP (7229 0172, www.queensiceandbowl.co.uk). Bayswater or Queensway tube. Open 10am-11pm Mon-Sat; 10am-10.30pm Sun. Admission £10.50 (plus £2 skate hire).
Our favourite indoor rink organises disco nights on Friday and Saturday nights, and also runs very friendly drop-in classes for beginners – so get your skates on.

Streatham Ice Arena
386 Streatham High Road, SW16 6HT (8769 7771, www.streathamicearena.co.uk). Streatham rail. Open see website for details. Admission £8 (inc skate hire).
Beloved by locals, Streatham's rink offers six-week courses for all ages – including special sessions for toddlers.

OUTDOOR RINKS

Check online for dates and opening times.

Broadgate Ice Arena
Broadgate Circle, EC2M 2QS (7505 4000, www.broadgateinfo.net). Liverpool Street tube/rail.
A small, resolutely urban spot that's often less crowded than other outdoor rinks.

Natural History Museum

Cromwell Road, SW7 5BD (7942 5011, www. nhmskating.com). South Kensington tube.
A fairytale winter ice rink and Christmas fair.

Somerset House ★

Strand, WC2R 1LA (7845 4600, www. somersethouse.org.uk). Covent Garden or Temple tube/Charing Cross tube/rail.
Somerset House's magnificent courtyard is the most attractive rink in London.

Tower of London

Tower Hill, EC3N 4AB (tickets 0844 412 4636, www.toweroflondonicerink.com). Tower Hill tube/Tower Gateway DLR/Fenchurch Street rail.
This rink is set right in the Tower's moat.

Lidos

For **Hampstead Heath Ponds**, *see p137.*

Brockwell Lido *Brockwell Park, Dulwich Road, SE24 0PA (7274 3088, www.brock welllido.com). Herne Hill rail. Open May-Sept 6.30am-8pm Mon-Fri; 10am-6pm Sat, Sun. Admission £5.20; free-£3.60 reductions.*

Hampton Pool *High Street, Hampton, Middlesex TW12 2ST (8255 1116, www. hamptonpool.co.uk). Hampton rail. Open 6am-9pm Mon-Fri, 8am-8pm Sat, Sun. Admission £4.60-£6.50; £2.90-£3.70 reductions.*

London Fields Lido *London Fields Westside, E8 3EU (7254 9038, www.gll.org). Liverpool Street tube/rail then 48, 55 bus. Open Apr-May 7am-7pm Mon-Fri; 8am-5pm Sat, Sun. June-Sept 6.30am-8pm Mon-Fri; 8am-7pm Sat, Sun. Oct-Mar reduced hours; check website for details. Admission £4.15; free-£2.50 reductions.*

Parliament Hill Lido *Parliament Hill Fields, Gordon House Road, NW5 2LT (7485 3873, www.camden.gov.uk). Gospel Oak rail. Open May-Sept 7-9am, 10am-6pm Tue, Wed, Fri-Sun; 7-9am, 10am-6pm, 6.45-8pm Mon, Thur. Oct-Apr 7am-noon daily. Admission £2-£4.50; £1-£2.90 reductions.*

Richmond Lido *Twickenham Road, Richmond, Surrey TW9 2SF (8940 0561, www.poolsonthepark.com). Richmond rail. Open Apr-Sept 6.30am-8pm Mon-Fri; 8am-5.45pm Sat; 7am-5.45pm Sun. Admission £4.20; £1.70-£3.30 reductions.*

Serpentine Lido *Hyde Park, W2 2UH (7706 3422, www.serpentinelido.com). Knightsbridge or South Kensington tube. Open May-mid June 10am-6pm Sat, Sun. Mid June-mid Sept 10am-6pm daily. Admission £3.50-£4; 80p-£3 reductions.*

Tooting Bec Lido *Tooting Bec Road, SW16 1RU (8871 7198, www.dcleisurecentres.co.uk). Streatham rail. Open late May-Aug 6am-7.30pm daily. Oct-May members only. Admission £5; £3.20 reductions.*

Riding stables

For a full list of **British Horse Society**-approved riding stables in the capital, visit www.bhs.org.uk. Lessons must be booked in advance, and you should discuss equipment needs with the venue. If you're just after a simple pony ride, a number of city farms offer children's riding sessions, among them **Kentish Town**, **Vauxhall**, and **Mudchute** (*see pp168-170*).

Ealing Riding School

17-19 Gunnersbury Avenue, W5 3XD (8992 3808, www.ealingridingschool.biz). Ealing Common tube. Lessons Group £28/hr; £27/hr reductions. Individual £39/hr; £36/hr reductions.
Lessons for beginners through to advanced; pony days (£60) include stable management.

Hyde Park & Kensington Stables

63 Bathurst Mews, W2 2SB (7723 2813, www.hydeparkstables.com). Lancaster Gate tube. Lessons Group £55-£59/hr. Individual £89-£99/hr.
Ride down Rotten Row and explore Hyde Park's five miles of charming bridle paths; unsurprisingly, steep prices reflect the centre's glamorous setting.

Lee Valley Riding Centre
Lea Bridge Road, E10 7QL (8556 2629, www.leevalleypark.org.uk). Clapton rail or 48, 55, 56 bus. Lessons Group £25/hr; £18.20/hr reductions. Individual £35-£40/30mins.
The centre's 35 horses and ponies enjoy the open spaces of Walthamstow Marshes and delight a devoted band of regulars. More experienced riders can try the jumping facilities and cross-country course.

London Equestrian Centre
Lullington Garth, N12 7BP (8349 1345, www.londonridingschool.com). Mill Hill East tube. Lessons Group £30/hr; £28/hr reductions. Individual £26-£38/30mins.
Set in 34 rolling acres, riding here feels like being in the heart of the country, rather than a mere eight miles away from Oxford Street.

Trent Park Equestrian Centre
East Pole Farmhouse, Bramley Road, N14 4UW (8363 9005, www.trentpark.com). Oakwood tube. Lessons Group £30-£37/hr; £23-£30/hr reductions. Individual £42-£48/hr; £38-£42/hr reductions.
The leafy acres of Trent Park make this a popular place to ride, and there are twice-weekly women-only riding sessions (£25) – the Blazing Saddles Ladies' Riding Club.

Willowtree Riding Establishment
The Stables, Ronver Road, SE12 0NL (8857 6438, www.willowtreeridinglondon.co.uk). Grove Park or Lee rail. Lessons Group from £10/30mins. Individual from £20/30mins.
This friendly local offers some of the cheapest prices around and is home to over 40 ponies and horses, including some pure-bred Arab.

Wimbledon Village Stables
24 High Street, SW19 5DX (8946 8579, www.wvstables.com). Wimbledon tube/rail. Open 9am-5pm Tue-Sun. Lessons Individual £50-£55/hr, £28/30mins.
This bucolic London riding school has been providing quality horse riding for over 100 years. A wide range of lessons, courses and pony riding sessions are available on quiet, safe ponies.

Skateparks

Skaters often prefer unofficial street spots such as the **South Bank** under the Royal Festival Hall or the northside approach to the Millennium Bridge, but the capital has some decent dedicated skate parks too. **Stockwell Skatepark** (www.stockwellskatepark.com), also known as Brixton Beach, has re-opened after a major refurbishment and resurfacing project.

Baysixty6 Skate Park ★
Bay 65-66, Acklam Road, W10 5YU (8969 4669, www.baysixty6.com). Ladbroke Grove tube. Open 11am-4pm and 5-9pm Mon, Thur, Fri; 11am-4pm and 5-10pm Tue, Wed; 10am-4pm and 5-9pm Sat, Sun. Admission £6.
This famed skatepark's features include four halfpipes, a mini-ramp and loads of funboxes, grind boxes, ledges and rails.

Cantelowes Skatepark
Cantelowes Gardens, Camden Road, NW1 (www.cantelowesskatepark.co.uk). Camden Town tube. Open daily 11am-9pm.
Opened in April 2007 as part of the park's £1.5m redevelopment, this free skatepark is phenomenally popular. The local BMX and skateboarders' group, the Cantelocals, helped with the park's design.

Meanwhile
Meanwhile Gardens, off Great Western Road, W10 5BN (8960 4600, www.mgca. f2s.com). Westbourne Park tube.
This community garden's skatepark offers three concrete bowls of varying steepness but no flatland, so it's not for beginners.

Mile End Skatepark
Mile End Park, Mile End Road, E3 5BH (www.mileendskatepark.co.uk). Mile End tube. Open daily 8am-8pm.
This council-run park is free and popular with skaters. LCB Skate Store offer free lessons at the site as well as a range of skate hardwear and drinks from 11am daily.

Tennis

Plenty of parks around the city have affordable council-run courts, while **London Tennis** (www.londontennis.co.uk) will match you up with an opponent if you need one. The site also has a very good tennis courts database.

For grass courts, consult the **Lawn Tennis Association** (8487 7000, www.lta.org.uk), and for a useful list of London's free courts by borough, see **Tennis for Free** (www.tennisforfree.com).

If your racket needs restringing, take it in to **Wigmore Sports** (39 Wigmore Street, W1U 1PD, 7486 7761, www.wigmoresports.co.uk). The service takes 24 to 48 hours and costs between £16-£70. The shop also lend outs certain racquets for a week's trial for £20 (plus £100 deposit), redeemable against purchase.

COURTS FOR HIRE

Battersea Park
Battersea Park Millennium Arena, Battersea Park Road, SW11 4NJ (8871 7542, www.wandsworth.gov.uk). Battersea Park rail. Open 8am-10pm Mon-Fri; 8am-7pm Sat, Sun. Court hire £6.40-£8.70/hr. Membership £28-£40/yr.
Battersea Park's 19 floodlit courts are bookable seven days in advance.

Highbury Fields
Baalbec Road, N5 1QN (7226 2334). Highbury & Islington tube/rail. Open 8am-9pm daily. Court hire £7/hr; £6/hr reductions.
The 11 very popular pay and play courts (seven are floodlit) are set in a pretty location on the edge of the park.

Islington Tennis Centre
Market Road, Islington, N7 9PL (7700 1370, www.aquaterra.org). Caledonian Road tube/Caledonian Road & Barnsbury rail. Open 7am-11pm Mon-Thur; 7am-10pm Fri; 8am-10pm Sat, Sun. Court hire Indoor £20/hr; £9/hr reductions. Outdoor £9.50/hr; £7.10/hr reductions.

The centre offers subsidised coaching and tennis courses; non-members are welcome.

Parliament Hill Fields Tennis Courts
Highgate Road NW5 1QR (7332 3773, www.cityoflondon.gov.uk). Kentish Town tube/rail. Open 8am-sunset daily. Court hire £5.10; £2.80 reductions. Membership £11/yr.
Ten hard courts are bookable in advance, or you can try your luck on the day. Group coaching sessions with qualified LTA coaches are held throughout the summer.

Paddington Recreation Grounds
Randolph Avenue, W9 1PD (7641 3642, www.westminster.gov.uk). Maida Vale or Kilburn Park tube. Open Summer 8am-9pm daily. Winter 8am-dusk Sat, Sun. Court hire £7.60-£11.60/hr.
There are 12 pay and play courts – four open tarmac, two enclosed tarmac and six synthetic. Members can book in advance.

Redbridge Sports & Leisure Centre
Forest Road, Barkingside, Essex IG6 3HD (8498 1000, www.rslonline.co.uk). Fairlop tube. Open 9am-11pm Mon-Fri; 9am-9pm Sat; 9am-10pm Sun. Court hire varies; call for details.
This outstanding multi-sports centre has eight indoor and six outdoor courts.

Regent's Park Tennis Centre
York Bridge Road, Inner Circle, Regent's Park, NW1 4NU (7486 4216, www.tennisintheparks.co.uk). Regent's Park tube. Open call for details.
Along with four pay and play floodlit courts, this popular centre offers drop-in coaching, tournaments and a dedicated children's zone.

Westway Tennis Centre
1 Crowthorne Road, W10 6RP (8969 0992, www.westwaysportscentre.org.uk/tennis). Latimer Road tube. Open 8am-10pm Mon-Fri; 8am-8pm Sat; 10am-10pm Sun. Court hire Indoor £16-£22.50/hr; £13-£16/hr reductions. Outdoor £8-£9/hr; £5-£7/hr reductions.
Eight indoor and four outdoor clay courts – the only ones in London open to the public.

GOING OUT

BEAUTY

FASHION

PARTIES

FOOD

HEALTH

ECO

OUTDOORS

HOME

CHILDREN

PETS

TRANSPORT

RESOURCES

GOING OUT
BEAUTY
FASHION
PARTIES
FOOD
HEALTH
ECO
OUTDOORS
HOME
CHILDREN
PETS
TRANSPORT
RESOURCES

Address Book Secrets
Bruce Butler
Personal trainer & sports injury specialist

Big corporate fitness farms are just too crowded in my opinion. You spend half your time queuing for machines instead of achieving results. There's a definite trend towards more bespoke training now – people are prepared to pay more to get a better one-to-one service in a pleasant environment. I really recommend **Ultimate Performance** (44 Paul Street, EC2A 4LB, 7033 1942, www.upfitness. co.uk), particularly for anyone with aesthetic objectives – it's great for weight training. Another great personal training studio I work with is **NKD Ambition** (91 New Cavendish Street, W1W 6XE, 7631 1226, www.nkd ambition.com). It's central, relatively new, very well kitted out and offers a slick, professional bespoke service.

Fitness trends like PowerPlate (www.powerplate.com) and Kranking (www.krankcycle.com) aren't really my scene. I prefer more basic, gimmick-free training methods. That said, a lot of my clients have really benefited from taking up **Bikram Yoga** (Bikram Yoga West, 260 Kilburn Lane, W10 4BA 3368 6966, www.bikramyoga.co.uk).

There's nothing quite like getting outside to exercise. I often take clients to **London Fields Lido** (London Fields Westside, E8 3EU, 7254 9038, www.gll.org) – it's heated so it can be used all year round.

I also like Victoria Park for its nice, big open spaces. I'm a member of the **Victoria Park Harriers** (www.vphthac. org.uk) and train both there and at

Mile End Park. **Mile End Stadium** (Rhodeswell Road, E14 7TW, 8980 1885) has a great track surface and anyone can use it. The track at **Parliament Hill Fields** (Highgate Road, NW5 1QR, 7433 1917) is good for its Hampstead Heath backdrop too.

Runners Need (34 Parkway, NW1 7AH, 7267 7525, www.runnersneed. co.uk) is a good resource for running shoes. For cycling equipment and clothing, I like **Condor Cycles** (51 Gray's Inn Road, WC1X 8PP, 7269 6820, www.condorcycles.com). Another bike shop I love is **14 Bike Co** (13 Elys Yard, E1 6QL, http:// 14bikeco.wordpress.com). They build totally bespoke, custom cycles so each customer gets exactly what they want – it's a bit of an art gallery for the fixed-wheel community!

Lumen Café (88 Tavistock Place, WC1H 9RF, 7278 2203, www.lumen cafe.com) is a bit of an oasis on the cycle route from the West to East End – it never seems to get too busy. I really like the **Pavilion Café** (corner Old Ford Road & Grove Road, E2 7DE, 8980 0030, www.the-pavilion-cafe.com) in Victoria Park too. It's great for refueling after park-based training or team sports.

At weekends, I head to **Broadway Market** (E8 4PH, www.broadway market.co.uk) for organic meat and fresh stuff. I like the **Cat & Mutton** (76 Broadway Market, E8 4QJ, 7254 5599, www.catandmutton.co.uk) for a bit of Saturday afternoon relaxation too.

Food

Live the *Good Life*.

Allotments

Got a vision of yourself pottering around a neat, prosperous plot, pulling muddy spuds from the earth and picking plump home-grown tomatoes for that night's dinner? That'll be you and several thousand other Londoners, then. Indeed, current trends for organic food and self-sufficiency mean that getting your hands on an allotment requires luck, perseverance and a lengthy stint on a waiting list. In fact, prospective gardeners in some boroughs have given up hope of securing a plot for themselves but have put their children down on the list in the hope that by the time they fancy a spot of leek propagation their name will have come up. If you are lucky enough to succeed, expect to pay around £30-£40 per year for the plot.

In some boroughs waiting lists are closed: at the time of writing, this was the case in **Lambeth** (7926 9000, www.lambeth.gov.uk), **Camden** (7974 8819, www.camden.gov.uk), **Islington** (7527 4953, www.islington.gov.uk), **Richmond** (8831 6110, www.richmond.gov.uk) and for the **Hackney Allotments Society** (www.hackneyallotments.org.uk).

We've listed London boroughs with available plots or open waiting lists below; details were correct at the time of going to press. Note there are no allotments in **Westminster, Kensington & Chelsea** or the **City of London.**

PLOTS AVAILABLE

Bromley
8313 4471, www.bromley.gov.uk.

One or two of Bromley's 52 sites currently have free plots; elsewhere, waiting lists apply. Applicants don't have to live in the borough.

Ealing
8825 5938, www.ealing.gov.uk.
With 45 council-managed sites, Ealing has limited plots available (for local residents only) in Greenford, Northolt and Southall.

Enfield
8379 3722, www.enfield.gov.uk.
There are free plots at several of Enfield's 40 sites. The yearly rate is £30 for locals, slightly more for non-borough residents.

Harrow
8424 1756, www.harrow.gov.uk/allotments. See also www.harrowinleaf.org.uk.
Limited plots are available at some of Harrow's 32 sites; others have lengthy waits.

Hillingdon
01895 250635, www.hillingdon.gov.uk.
Half of Hillingdon's 35 sites have vacant plots, while the longest waiting list is around a year. You don't have to live in the borough.

City Secret

While you're waiting for that elusive allotment space to come up, check out **Landshare** (www.landshare.net). Created by Hugh Fearnley-Whittingstall, it's a national organisation that connects people who want to grow veg but don't have anywhere to do so, with people who have space they're prepared to share. It's proving a useful resource for green-fingered Londoners.

WAITING LISTS

Barking & Dagenham
8227 3381, www.barking-dagenham.gov.uk.
All 13 sites currently have waiting lists.

Barnet
8359 7829, www.barnet.gov.uk.
See also www.bfahs.org.
The waiting list for sites in Barnet currently runs to between two months and ten years, depending on location. If you do secure a plot, the cost is £73 per year for residents, more if you live outside the borough.

Bexley
8294 6494, www.bexley.gov.uk.
See also www.bfalg.co.uk.
Bexley currently has waiting lists of between six months and two years for allotments.

Brent
8937 5619, www.brent.gov.uk.
Waiting lists vary from six months to nine years at Brent's 23 sites.

Croydon
8726 6900, www.croydon.gov.uk. See also www.spahill.org.uk.
The shortest wait at any of Croydon's 16 sites is currently four years, and lists may close in the near future.

Greenwich
8856 2232, www.greenwich.gov.uk.
Waiting lists range up to nine years at Greenwich's 18 sites.

Hammersmith & Fulham
8748 3020, www.lbhf.gov.uk.
There are only two sites, and waiting lists of up to two years.

Haringey
8489 0000, www.haringey.gov.uk.
The average wait for a plot is four years, though 11 waiting lists remain open.

Havering
01708 434343, www.havering.gov.uk. See also www.romfordsmallholderssociety.org.uk.
Call for vacancies at the 25 allotment sites or fill in an application online. You'll need to be a member (membership costs £1 per year).

Hounslow
0845 456 2796, www.hounslow.gov.uk.
Those looking for an allotment in Hounslow are currently looking at a wait of between two and 10 years.

Kingston upon Thames
8546 9842, www.kingston.gov.uk.
Waiting lists (ranging from a couple of months to five years) remain open at all sites.

Lewisham
8314 2277, www.lewisham.gov.uk.
The average wait in Lewisham is a year and a half, with a healthy 39 sites; borough residents get priority.

Merton
8545 3665, www.merton.gov.uk.
Of Merton's 18 sites, all currently have waiting lists (between a year and 10 years).

Newham
8430 2000, www.newham.gov.uk.
Waiting times at the seven allotments vary; four years is currently the longest wait.

Redbridge
8708 3091, www.redbridge.gov.uk.
Sites in Redbridge currently have waiting lists of between one and 20 years.

Southwark
7525 1050, www.southwark.gov.uk.
Nine allotment sites, all with waiting lists.

Sutton
8770 5070, www.sutton.gov.uk.
The waiting list here is between one and six years long.

Tower Hamlets
7364 5020, www.towerhamlets.gov.uk.
The seven sites are not run by the council but information is available on the council website. Two have closed lists, the others all have waits.

GOING OUT

BEAUTY

FASHION

PARTIES

FOOD

HEALTH

ECO

OUTDOORS

HOME

CHILDREN

PETS

TRANSPORT

RESOURCES

Waltham Forest
8496 3000, www.walthamforest.gov.uk.
You'll wait around a year for a plot at one of Waltham's 38 sites.

Wandsworth
8871 6441, www.wandsworth.gov.uk. See also www.roehamptonallotments.co.uk.
Wandsworth's nine sites have an average wait of five to six years.

Groceries

See also **Daylesford Organic** (*p132*).

Bumblebee
30, 32 & 33 Brecknock Road, N7 0DD (7607 1936, www.bumblebeenatural foods.co.uk). Kentish Town tube/rail. Open 9am-6.30pm Mon-Sat.
This friendly, old-school health food store sells quality organic groceries and delicious home-made goodies: bread, cakes and a small but excellent selection of takeaway dishes.

Farm W5
19 The Green, W5 5DA (8566 1965). Ealing Broadway tube/rail. Open 8am-7.30pm Mon-Fri; 9am-7.30pm Sat; 10am-6pm Sun.

City Secret

The latest brainchild of Arthur Poots Dawson (of eco-restaurant Acorn House fame) is the **People's Supermarket** (www.peoples supermarket.org) – a supermarket run by the people for the people that aims to sell good food at reasonable prices. Anyone can join the revolution in exchange for a few hours of their time on the shop floor each month and a small membership fee (£25). Members decide everything from how the shop is run to what it sells. The shop is also open to passing trade.

This organic and Slow Food market supports small British producers – so fish comes fresh from Cornwall, chutney from the New Forest and honey from down the road in Ealing.

Natural Kitchen
77-78 Marylebone High Street, W1U 5JX (7486 8065, www.thenaturalkitchen.com). Baker Street tube. Open 8am-8pm Mon-Fri; 9am-7pm Sat; 11am-6pm Sun.
The ethical ethos here centres on seasonality, sustainability, traceability and good animal welfare.
Other locations *15-17 New Street Square, EC4A 3AP (3012 2123).*

Unpackaged ★
42 Amwell Street, EC1R 1XT (7713 8368, www.beunpackaged.com). Angel tube. Open 10am-7pm Mon-Fri; 9am-6pm Sat.
Bring your own pots and bags to this lovely little grocery store, and get a discount on washing powder, grains, spices, coffee and pulses, ladled from handsome glass jars.

Whole Foods Market
The Barkers Building, 63-97 Kensington High Street, W8 5SE (7368 4500, www. wholefoodsmarket.com). High Street Kensington tube. Open 8am-10pm Mon-Sat; noon-6pm Sun.
This vast supermarket-style space groans with a huge range of organic and natural produce, cosmetics and homeware.
Other locations *throughout the city.*

Organic box schemes

For details of London's **farmers' markets**, *see p99*.

Abel & Cole
0845 262 6262, www.abel-cole.co.uk. Boxes £10.95-£22.95.
The king of delivery boxes in London, Abel & Cole offers organic meats, sustainably caught fish, dairy and freshly baked bread as well as seasonal fruit and veg from over 50 British producers. A small mixed box of fruit and vegetables, at £10.95, contains four

vegetables and three fruits, plus potatoes. The box always includes a couple of tasty recipes to make use of one of two of your fruits or vegetables.

Capricorn Organics

8306 2786, www.capricornorganics.co.uk.
Boxes prices vary; call for details.

This south-east London company specialises in individual orders (though mixed boxes are available too), which you make up from a list on the website – so if you want just two tomatoes in your veg selection (minimum of £10), then that's what you'll get. Deliveries to south-east London cost around 50p to £1.

Farmaround

7627 8066, www.farmaround.co.uk.
Boxes £8.90-£19.50.

Farmaround delivers organic fruit and veg boxes all over London. Produce is seasonal and as local as possible, and the site is updated regularly with recipes to use up your supplies – plus customers receive occasional gifts of chutney and honey. A vegetable bag for one person is £9.20, though the minimum spend is £11.50.

Growing Communities ★

7502 7588, www.growingcommunities.org.
Boxes £6-£11.50.

This social enterprise claims to have been the first organic box provider in the country. Produce is Hackney grown, and to cut down on fuel use local customers are encouraged to pick up their own boxes from points across the borough. Local growers are encouraged to bring along their own produce too. Prices start at £26 a month for a small weekly vegetable bag, filled with six varieties of seasonal produce.

Natoora

7627 1600, www.natoora.co.uk.
Boxes £12.45-£32.

Natoora's range of fruit and veg boxes starts with the 2kg vegetable box (£19.85), which might include peas, asparagus, cherry tomatoes, courgettes, fresh herbs and onions. It also stocks some 3,500 products

sourced directly from farmers and producers in the UK, France and Italy, from artichoke tortellini and a wide range of cheeses to Cornish fish and veal from Auvergne.

Organic Delivery Company

7739 8181, www.organicdelivery.co.uk.
Boxes £11.95-£25.

Along with an impressive fruit and veg box selection (including a small seasonal salad box), there's also chocolate, cleaning products, booze, a range of organic pet food and more, all sourced with vigilant attention to food miles and origin.

Riverford

0845 600 2311, www.riverford.co.uk.
Boxes £8.95-£17.15.

One of the larger box scheme operators, Devon-based Riverford offer a variety of different sized boxes filled with vegetables, salad, fruit or a mixture of all three. There's also a great range of meat boxes (starting at £40 for a small box).

Specialist delivery companies

A Lot of Coffee

0845 094 6498, www.alotofcoffee.co.uk.

This company roasts its coffee freshly every week and delivers beans and grounds all over London. There's a wide variety of beans, from Mexico, Columbia, Papua New Guinea, Sumatra and Ethiopia; all are organic and fairly traded, with the website providing full details of suppliers you're buying from.

Jefferson's Seafoods

01503 269076.

Certificated by the Organic Food Federation and the RSPCA Freedom Foods, this Cornwall-based company supplies the likes of Locanda Locatelli and the Ritz with fillets of fresh, sustainable fish. Sign up for the flourishing home delivery service and choose from a wonderful array of fresh seafood and chunky, own-made fish cakes; for kids, there's monkfish and lemon zest nuggets.

GOING OUT

BEAUTY

FASHION

PARTIES

FOOD

HEALTH

ECO

OUTDOORS

HOME

CHILDREN

PETS

TRANSPORT

RESOURCES

Recycling

You might be chucking it out, but someone, somewhere can probably get some use out of it.

General recycling

Many boroughs now run segregated box systems for garden waste, food leftovers and miscellaneous waste. For services and collection days in your borough, use the postcode finder at **Recycle for London** (www.recycleforlondon.com).

Another useful resource is **Direct Gov** (www.direct.gov.uk), which has details of local recycling and waste services, and a link that lets you apply for a bulky items collection. The **London Community Recycling Network** (www.lcrn.org.uk) is also a useful resource. For eco-friendly junk collection services, see p162.

Charity shops always welcome donations. If you don't know where to find your nearest shop, check with the **Association of Charity Shops** (www.charityshops.org.uk). Alternatively, post an ad on **Freecycle** (www.freecycle.org), **Preloved** (www.preloved.co.uk) or the smaller **Reuze** (www.reuze.co.uk) and give your goods away.

It's also worth noting that most branches of **Boots** (www.boots.com) provide recycling for household batteries.

Specialist services

COMPUTERS & PRINTER CARTRIDGES

Computer Aid International
10 Brunswick Industrial Park, Brunswick Way, N11 1JL (8361 5540, www.computer aid.org).
Donate your old or unwanted computers to developing countries by dropping off your PC at the workshop, where it will be data-wiped and refurbished, then shipped off to a school or community project.

GREEN VOLUNTEERING

For more general volunteering, try **Do-It** (www.do-it.org.uk) or **Timebank London** (http://london.timebank.org.uk). Or consider **Guerilla Gardening** (www.guerrillagardening.org), whose laudable aim is illicitly cultivating unloved and unlovely public spaces.

Green Gym
7278 4294, www.btcv.org.uk.
Shape up without hitting the gym by volunteering to help maintain London's green spaces. Involving hands-on gardening and conservation work, the sessions kick off with a group warm-up and generally last two to three hours.

Heath Hands
8458 9102, www.heath-hands.org.uk.
Help keep Hampstead Heath green and litter-free. Work sessions, open to anyone over 16, run five days a week.

Thames 21
7248 7171, www.thames21.org.uk.
Thames 21 runs regular clear-ups and of London's waterways and canals.

Each One Counts
0800 435576, www.eachonecounts.co.uk.
Inkjet cartridges, laser toners and mobiles can all be recycled here. Register and order freepost bags online, then send the item off; the proceeds go to various charities.

Eco-chip
0845 257 7249, www.ecochip.co.uk.
If your computer and peripherals are less than eight years old, Eco-chip will collect, datawipe and refurbish them for free before donating them to charity.

FURNITURE

The **Furniture Re-use Network** (www.frn.org.uk) lists local projects in need of furniture and electrical items.

Furniture Aid South Thames
7793 7787, www.furniture-aid.co.uk.
This south London company will collect large donations of furniture and working white goods from central and south London free of charge (minus congestion charges).

ReStore Community Projects
8493 0900, www.restorecommunity projects.org.
Restore will collect most bulky household goods (though not single items) for £10, in two daily time slots. Items must be in good condition as they're given to families in need.

IPODS

Apple Recycling Programme
www.apple.com/environment.
Buy an Apple product and you can return its equivalent piece of kit to any Apple Retail Store. If you return an iPod for recycling, you'll get a 10% discount on a new one.

MOBILE PHONES

Most big charities accept mobile phones for recycling, including **Age UK** (7278 1869, www.ageuk.org.uk), **Oxfam** (0300 200 1300, www.oxfam.org.uk) and **WaterAid** (0845 600 0433, www.wateraid.org/uk).

City Secret

The Glastonbury of the insect world (celebrating insects and art), **Pestival** (pestival.org) attracted some 200,000 visitors to its 2009 festival at the Southbank Centre. The festival attracted global interest with its unique combination of science, research, music, comedy, art and, of course, insect enthusiasts. The next Pestival will be held at London Zoo in May 2012, following a three-year Zoo Art Fellowship at the zoo.

Fonebak
01708 683432, www.fonebak.com.
Fonebak makes a donation to Children in Need and pays you around 60% of what they can sell the handset on for. They also recycle phones that are not reusable.

Refuge
0808 200 0247, www.refuge.org.uk.
For each phone donated to Refuge, the charity gets £3.50 from a partner group, which will reformat your phone for use in the developing world. Just post the phone in, free of charge, following online instructions.

PAINT

Community RePaint
0113 2003959,
www.communityrepaint.org.uk.
This scheme will accept old household paints which will then be used for community projects or given to charities. The project doesn't pick up, but has lots of local collection points.

SPECTACLES

Vision Aid Overseas
01293 535016, www.vao.org.uk.
Opticians working with the charity (including the Vision Express chain) will accept old frames, then pass them on for distribution in developing countries.

GOING OUT
BEAUTY
FASHION
PARTIES
FOOD
HEALTH
ECO
OUTDOORS
HOME
CHILDREN
PETS
TRANSPORT
RESOURCES

GOING OUT

BEAUTY

FASHION

PARTIES

FOOD

HEALTH

ECO

OUTDOORS

HOME

CHILDREN

PETS

TRANSPORT

RESOURCES

Shopping & services

Live greener everyday.

Banking

The excellent **Ethical Consumer** site (www.ethicalconsumer.org) suggests building societies that have some level of ethical credibility, such as Norwich & Peterborough. In terms of banks, the choice is more limited.

Co-operative Bank
08457 212212, www.thecooperative bank.co.uk.
One of the first banks to adopt an ethical policy, the Co-Op encourages its customers to raise issues of concern and will not invest in areas customers vote against. A range of other ethical policies, detailed on the website, puts it way ahead of other high street banks.

Ecology Building Society
0845 674 5566, www.ecology.co.uk.
This Yorkshire-based building society offers savings accounts, along with mortgages for renovations or new builds with 'an environmental benefit'. Interest rates on savings can be on the low side.

Smile
0870 843 2265, www.smile.co.uk.
The online offshoot of the Co-operative Bank sources 98% of electricity from renewable sources and refuses to invest in companies involved in the arms trade or whose core activity adds to climate change.

Triodos
0117 973 9339, www.triodos.co.uk.
Triodos only finances companies and projects that benefit people and the environment. No high street presence (and an unwieldy website) can mean more effort to manage your money, though.

Beauty

CONTENT beauty
14 Bulstrode Street, W1U 2JG (3075 1006, www.beingcontent.com). Bond Street or Baker Street tube/Marylebone tube/rail. Open 10.30am-6pm Tue, Wed, Fri, Sat; 10.30am-7pm Thur.
This gorgeous little boutique, opened in 2008, houses organic beauty brands such as Laid Bare, Stemp Organics and Suki Colour, plus perfume, vegan beauty buys, men's grooming products and baby ranges.

Organic Pharmacy ★
396 King's Road, SW10 0LN (7351 2232, www.theorganicpharmacy.com). Fulham Broadway or Sloane Square tube. Open 9.30am-6pm Mon-Sat; noon-6pm Sun.
This slick mini-chain stocks its own-brand of organic skin care products, a host of natural remedies, supplements to suit men, women, children and mothers-to-be, sun protection, hair products and baby essentials.
Other locations *throughout the city.*

Energy-saving

A number of services offer eco advice, including **Green Electricity** (www.greenelectricity.org), which locates your nearest green energy providers, and **Energy Saving Trust** (0800 512012, www.energysavingtrust.org.uk), where a home energy check questionnaire results in advice on improving energy efficiency.

If you want another do-it-yourself eco audit you can check out the **Carbon Calculator** website at www.carbon calculator.com.

DIY Kyoto

7729 7500, www.diykyoto.com.
This company sells a nifty wireless gadget, the Wattson, which monitors your home's energy usage and changes colour accordingly. At £99.95 it's not cheap, but DIY Kyoto thinks you can save five to 20% on annual electricity bills.

3 Acorns

7703 8748, www.3acorns.co.uk.
Donnachadh McCarthy audits your carbon footprint, taking in energy and transport use as well as waste and shopping habits. He then suggests ways to reduce your carbon footprint. The price is around £250.

Homeware

The annual **Eco Design Fair** (www.ecodesignfair.co.uk) in Islington gathers together the best emerging talent in eco design, including suppliers who don't normally sell direct to the public.

Eco Age ★

213 Chiswick High Road, W4 2DW (8995 7611, www.eco-age.com). Turnham Green tube. Open 10am-6pm Tue-Sat.
Eco is the (sunlit, solar-powered and -heated) joint project of actor Colin Firth and his wife. Stock ranges from energy-saving lightbulbs to bigger investments such as solar panels and wind turbines. The stylish furniture is worth a look even if you're not eco-minded.

Karavan Eco Shop

167 Lordship Lane, SE22 8HX (8299 2524, www.karavan.co.uk). East Dulwich rail. Open 10.30am-5.30pm Mon-Fri; 10am-6pm Sat; noon-4pm Sun.
Karavan is packed to the brim with a great mix of beautiful and useful products for the home, all manufactured using sustainable materials and methods, or geared to making your life more environmentally friendly.

Siecle

53 Grove Vale, SE22 8EQ (7207 1120, www.sieclecolours.com). East Dulwich rail.
Open 10am-7pm Tue-Thur; 10am-6pm Fri, Sat; 11am-4pm Sun.
Siecle manufactures more than 200 bright, lead-free Latex-based colours, including wall paint (£30/2.5 litres), and water-soluble semi-gloss emulsion for wood, metal and plastic at £19 a litre.

Junk mail prevention

Mailing Preference Service

www.mpsonline.org.uk.
Registering with the MPS will deter companies who may have bought your details from databases.

Stop Junk Mail

www.stopjunkmail.org.uk.
This useful site offers loads of handy tips for reducing the amount of junk mail you receive, including a suggestion to opt out of the Royal Mail's door-to-door junk mail deliveries by emailing them at optout@royalmail.com.

Stop Junk Mail

www.stopjunkmail.org.
Get a 'no junk mail' sticker from this site; it's a simple but effective strategy, particularly against local taxi firms and takeaways.

Motoring

Environmental Transport Association

0800 212 810, www.eta.co.uk.
This carbon-neutral motoring organisation offers an award-winning international rescue service, and can also help you offset the carbon emissions of your car, flights and home energy consumption.

Liftshare

www.liftshare.com
Liftshare helps people to travel sustainably by sharing their journey. An online network matches people who want to make similar journeys so they can cut their carbon footprint and save cash.

GOING OUT
BEAUTY
FASHION
PARTIES
FOOD
HEALTH
ECO
OUTDOORS
HOME
CHILDREN
PETS
TRANSPORT
RESOURCES

GOING OUT
BEAUTY
FASHION
PARTIES
FOOD
HEALTH
ECO
OUTDOORS
HOME
CHILDREN
PETS
TRANSPORT
RESOURCES

Address Book Secrets
Rachel de Thample
Resident foodie at Abel & Cole

To get a taste of classic British cuisine, I go my local pub, **The Mansion** (255 Gipsy Road, SE27 9QY, 8761 9016, www.themansiondulwich. co.uk). They work so closely with their British suppliers that they can even tell you the name of the pig they made their homemade pork pies with. The pub landlord's wife makes a cake every day, which is housed in a domed cake plate perched on the bar. They also sell mouth-watering little pots of pork crackling with apple sauce.

Hayne's Lane Market (www.haynes lanemarket.com) is an amazing treasure trove of old things – I've picked up some vintage china gems from there for Abel & Cole recipe shoots. My favourite purchase is a hand-painted Victorian serving dish with a gold rim. All the people selling at Hayne's Lane Market, which also sells vintage records, clothes, second-hand books and a few locally-made crafty things, are true characters.

I get all my shoes and my son's shoes from **Merlin Shoes** (44 Westow Street, SE19 3AH, 8771 5194). They look fairly stylish and, as a bonus, they're produced with an eco conscience. They're slightly more expensive than shoes you'd buy at a high street chain but they last much longer and they're so much nicer to your feet. Merlin also recycles used shoes.

My son and I go to **Luca's Bakery** (145 Lordship Lane, SE22 8HX, 8613 6161, lucasbakery.com) for breakfast. Their lattés are made with organic milk

from Somerset and fair-trade organic coffee. My son has a small glass of organic English apple juice and we share one of their delicious cinnamon rolls made with stone-ground flour from Stoats in Dorset. I like to know where all the ingredients in my food have come from.

Living Water Satisfies Community Café (46-48 Westow Street, SE19 3AF, 8653 4011, www.livingwate satisfies.org.uk) is a lovely place. All of the proceeds earned go to a charity that looks after women affected by domestic violence or mental health issues. They also serve delicious food. My favourite is scrambled free-range eggs on toast – the bread is sourced from Dulwich Bakery, with feta and spring onions.

I like to go to **Postcard Teas** (9 Dering Street, W1S 1AG, 7629 3654, www. postcardteas.com) – a wonderful shop near Bond Street. It's got the best tea I've ever had, and I think it's the best place in the country to buy tea. They sell a whole range of different flavours so there is plenty to choose from.

To get the best plant feed I head down to my local garden centre, **The Secret Garden** (70 Westow Street, SE19 3AF, 8771 8200, www.thesecretgarden centre.com). They sell a stunning selection of English apples in the autumn, as well as organic seeds and compost. They also have a little Apple Day festival when the season starts. I'm currently growing tomatoes and herbs in my windowsill.

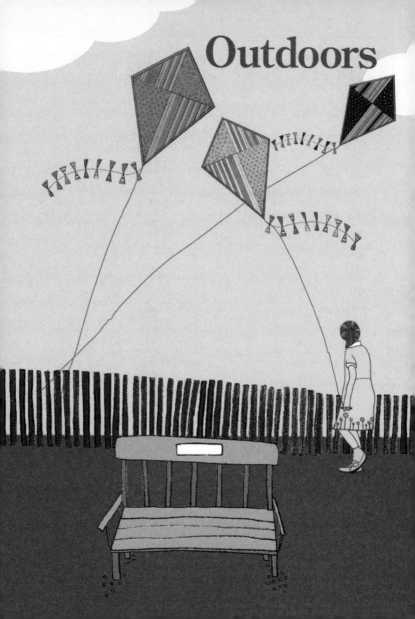

Outdoors

Alfresco eating

Bookmark this page for the first sign of sun: below you'll find some of our favourite park cafés and ready-assembled picnic suppliers.

Park cafés

CENTRAL

Garden Café at Russell Square
Russell Square Gardens, WC1B 5EH (7637 5093). Russell Square tube. Open 7am-6pm Mon-Fri; 8am-5pm Sat, Sun (closed Sun Nov-Mar). No credit cards. Takeaway service. £.
Overlooking a lovely, leafy garden square, the sprawling patio at this Italian family-run café is a wonderfully relaxing spot. Tuck into a top-notch English breakfast, or tea and cakes.

Inn The Park
St James's Park, SW1A 2BJ (7451 9999, www.innthepark.com). St James's Park or Westminster tube. Open Summer 8am-11pm Mon-Fri; 9am-11pm Sat; 9am-6pm Sun. Winter times vary; phone for details. Takeaway service. ££.
Part Modern British restaurant, part café, this stylish joint is perfect for laid-back breakfasts and lunches or romantic suppers. There are splendid ice-creams, cakes and afternoon teas; if you'd rather picnic, takeaways are available.

NORTH

Brew House
Kenwood, Hampstead Lane, NW3 7JR (8341 5384). Bus 210. Open Oct-Mar 9am-dusk daily. Apr-Sept 9am-6pm daily. Takeaway service. £.
In warm weather, the terrace is always buzzing at this lovely café, which occupies part of neoclassical Kenwood House. The homely (often organic and free-range) grub and own-made cakes are equally enticing.

Finsbury Park Café
Hornsey Gate, Endymion Road, N4 2NQ (8880 2681, www.finsburyparkcafe.co.uk). Finsbury Park or Manor House tube. Open 9am-6pm daily. £
This pleasant park café is set in Finsbury Park's 115 acres meaning easy access to the popular boating lake, children's play area, splash fountain and sandpit. Café basics are decent quality and include breakfasts, sandwiches, baked potatoes, omelettes, soups and salads, as well as cakes and pastries. There's a dedicated menu of child-pleasers ranging from egg on toast to penne with tomato and basil.

Garden Café
Inner Circle, Regent's Park, NW1 4NU (7935 5729, www.companyofcooks.com). Baker Street or Regent's Park tube. Open June-Sept 9am-8pm daily; Oct-May 9am-6pm daily. £-££.
The interior of this revamped 1960s café is surprisingly chic; the terrace, surrounded by rose beds, is glorious. Superior-quality lunches (Sussex Slipcote salad or goats'

City Secret

For hassle-free alfresco eating, drop by **UP Box** (Café Fraiche, 5 New Bridge Street, EC4V 6AB, 8968 7514, www.up-box.co.uk). From Café Fraiche in the City and a small kiosk by Clapham Junction station (they can also deliver), UP offers five ready-packed lunchboxes a day (the initials stand for 'urban picnic'), each with a different global influence and complete with mini-dessert.

cheese and courgette tart, perhaps), seasonal mains and super puddings are on offer.

Pavilion Café ★
Highgate Woods, Muswell Hill Road, N10 3JN (8444 4777). Highgate tube. Open Summer 9am-7pm daily. Winter 9am-4pm daily. Takeaway service. £.
This little treasure is deservedly popular, thanks to its tasty, well-presented global food and alcohol licence. If in doubt, plump for one of the amazing free-range burgers.

EAST

Spark Café
White Mansion Lodge, Springfield Park, E5 9EF (8806 0444, www.sparkcafe.co.uk). Stamford Hill or Stoke Newington rail. Open Apr-Oct 10am-6pm daily. Nov-Mar 10am-4pm daily. No credit cards. £.
Set in the beautiful White Lodge Mansion, Spark offers a fabulous menu: Springfield Special sandwiches, own-made soups, tasty cakes, shakes and organic juices.

Pavilion Café Victoria Park ★
Victoria Park, by Old Ford Road & Grove Road, E9 5DU (8980 0030, www.the-pavilion-cafe.com). Bethnal Green tube/rail, then D6 or 8 bus. Open 8am-4.30pm Mon-Fri; 8am-5.30pm Sat, Sun. £.
The lakeside location is an absolute treat – as is the food. Huge breakfasts (with meat and veggie options) feature biodynamic eggs and

sensational sausages from nearby Victoria Park's Ginger Pig (*see p133*). The menu changes regularly and wonderfully tasty and healthy lunches are also on offer. Look out for the fabulous victoria sponge cake too.

SOUTH

Common Ground
Wandsworth Common, off Dorlcote Road, SW18 3RT (8874 9386). Wandsworth Common rail. Open 9am-5.30pm daily. Takeaway service. £.
The cosy back room of this child-friendly cafe is a heavenly retreat on a winter's day. The food is own-made, including cakes, sandwiches and children's mini meals.

Pavilion Café
Dulwich Park, off College Road, SE21 7BQ (8299 1383, www.pavilioncafedulwich.co. uk). North Dulwich or West Dulwich rail. Open Summer 8.30am-6pm Mon-Fri; 9am-6pm Sat, Sun. Winter 8.30am-4pm Mon-Fri; 9am-4pm Sat, Sun. Takeaway service. £.
The glass-fronted, licensed café is a lovely place to while away an hour or two at any time of day. There are freshly made sandwiches, soups, own-made burgers and quiches. Much of the produce is freerange and locally sourced.

Pavilion Tea House
Greenwich Park, Blackheath Gate, SE10 8QY (8858 9695). Blackheath rail or Greenwich rail/DLR. Open Summer 9am-5.30pm Mon-Fri; 9am-6pm Sat, Sun. Winter 9am-4pm mon-Fri; 9am-4.30pm Sat, Sun. £.
Tuck into hearty soups, welsh rarebit, scrambled eggs or smoked salmon on toast in this licensed hexagonal café, while the kids eat ice-cream in a garden hedged off from the central thoroughfare.

WEST

Holland Park Café
Holland Park, Ilchester Place, W8 6LU (7602 6156). Holland Park or High Street Kensington tube. Open Summer 9.30am-

GOING OUT

BEAUTY

FASHION

PARTIES

FOOD

HEALTH

ECO

OUTDOORS

HOME

CHILDREN

PETS

TRANSPORT

RESOURCES

HAMPERS

With branches across the city, **Carluccio's** (www.carluccios.com) can also rustle up splendid picnics for two, with prices from £45; order 24 hours in advance.

Betty Blythe

73 Blythe Road, W14 0HP (7602 1177, www.bettyblythe.co.uk). Shepherd's Bush tube. Open 8am-7pm Mon-Sat.

This small but utterly charming café and fine food store prepares delicious picnic hampers (which, if preordered, can be hand-delivered to nearby parks, along with rugs and vintage crockery) tailored to customers' tastes. Choose from cakes, scones, finger sandwiches, grilled meats, cheeses, salads, relishes and biscuits to create the perfect hamper for you.

Paul

47 Thurloe Street, SW7 2LQ (7581 6034, www.paul-uk.com). South Kensington tube. Open 7am-9pm Mon-Sat; 8am-8pm Sun.

In summer, when you spend over £20 at selected branches of Paul, you're given a sweet little *pique nique* box in which to carry your spoils to the park. Choose from delightful quiches, salads, sarnies and speciality breads.

Selfridges

400 Oxford Street, W1A 1AB (7318 3900, www.selfridges.com). Bond Street or Marble Arch tube. Open 9.30am-9am Mon-Sat; 12am-6pm Sun.

With 24 hours' notice, the fabulous food hall here will put together a picnic box for you for a flat fee of £10 plus the price of whatever comestibles your heart desires.

9.30pm daily. Winter 9.30am-4.30pm daily. Takeaway service. £.

Hot and cold homemade food (from soups and sarnies to jacket potatoes and cod goujons), in one of the nicest – and possibly cheapest – places to eat in Kensington, set in an historic Dutch garden.

Fait Maison in Ravenscourt Park

Ravenscourt Park, Paddenswick Road, W6 0UL (8563 9291, www.fait-maison.co.uk). Ravenscourt Park tube. Open 9am-7pm daily. No credit cards. £.

This pleasant park stop offers cakes, salads, sandwiches and panini – all freshly made that morning.

Picnics

If you're heading to the following parks, here are some handy spots to pick up a sumptuous picnic.

BATTERSEA PARK

Daylesford Organic

44B Pimlico Road, SW1W 8LP (7881 8060, www.daylesfordorganic.com). Sloane Square tube. Open 8am-7pm Sat; 10am-4pm Sun.

If you're coming from the Chelsea side of the river, this is the place to pick up some wholesome treats on your way. Handsome, free-range meat pies, award-winning breads and pastries and artisan cheeses from Daylesford's own herd of happy Friesians are all perfect picnic fare.

CLAPHAM COMMON

Esca

160 Clapham High Street, SW4 7UG (7622 2288). Clapham Common tube. Open 8am-9pm Mon-Fri; 9am-9pm Sat, Sun.

Handily situated at the Clapham Common end of the high street, Esca has a dazzling selection of too-good-to-be-true cakes in the window, complemented by huge salads and hot specials inside, which can be packed up for your convenience in a little brown box.

GOING OUT

BEAUTY

FASHION

PARTIES

FOOD

HEALTH

ECO

OUTDOORS

HOME

CHILDREN

PETS

TRANSPORT

RESOURCES

GREEN PARK

Fortnum & Mason

181 Piccadilly, W1A 1ER (7734 8040, www.fortnumandmason.com). Green Park or Piccadilly Circus tube. Open 10am-8pm Mon-Sat; noon-6pm Sun.

If it's a superior spread you're after, pitch your blanket near Fortnum's. The mega-extravagant pre-packaged picnics start at £85 for a wicker hamper packed with olives, Wiltshire ham, pork rillettes, crusty bread, poached salmon, moroccan chicken pie, crudités, strawberries, cupcakes, wine, water and all the cutlery and crockery you need to dine in style. Alternatively, assemble your own choice of comestibles from the food hall. Here, a dazzling profusion of cheese, charcuterie, pâtés and pies awaits.

HOLLAND PARK

Ottolenghi

1 Holland Street, W8 4NA (7937 0003, www. ottolenghi.co.uk). High Street Kensington tube. Open 8am-8pm Mon-Fri; 8am-7pm Sat; 9am-6pm Sun.

Blending Mediterranean and Middle Eastern influences, this chic deli and bakery provides wonderful alfresco fare. Pick up a takeaway box and fill it with immaculately fresh, inventive salads, tarts and sandwiches – not forgetting the amazing chocolate meringues.

HYDE PARK

Mount Street Deli

100 Mount Street, W1K 2TG (7499 6843, www.themountstreetdeli.co.uk). Bond Street or Marble Arch tube. Open 8am-7pm Mon-Fri; 8am-9pm Sat.

You could just pick up a sandwich or two at this lovely deli, but if you're feeling flash why not go the whole hog with a luxury hamper? They start at £40 per person and include such delights as quails' eggs, charcuterie (mortadella, prosciutto, venison salami), quiche lorraine, parmesan nuggets, roast beef sandwiches, piccalilli, lemon tarts, cookies and water. Swankier still options include champagne, caviar and smoked salmon.

PRIMROSE HILL

Melrose & Morgan

42 Gloucester Avenue, NW1 8JD (7722 0011, www.melroseandmorgan.com). Chalk Farm tube. Open 8am-7pm Mon-Fri; 8am-6pm Sat; 9am-5pm Sun.

This famed deli offers ready-assembled picnics such as a simple ploughman's picnic (£30 for two), or a more opulent spread (£65) starring mackerel pâté, bread, free range roast chicken with white bean and tomato relish, salad, eton mess, cheese and oatcakes, and a bottle of rosé. Order 24-48 hours ahead.

REGENT'S PARK

Villandry

170 Great Portland Street, W1W 5QB (7631 3131, www.villandry.com). Great Portland Street tube. Open 8am-7pm Mon-Sat; 9am-4pm Sun.

This superb foodstore, bakery, restaurant and bar offers fantastic food to takeaway. The dedicated hamper service is good value: £50 gets you a sizeable picnic for two, including own-made sausage rolls, fresh bread rolls, poached salmon salad, green bean, tomato and onion salad, ham and gruyere tartlets, olives, crisps, lemon tart, own-made cake, a bottle of wine, Hildon water, disposable glasses and a navy Villandry cool bag.

VICTORIA PARK

Ginger Pig ★

99 Lauriston Road, E9 7HJ (8986 6911, www.thegingerpig.co.uk). Mile End tube then 277 bus. Open 9am-5.30pm Tue; 9am-6.30pm Wed-Fri; 9am-6pm Sat; 9am-3pm Sun.

Bypass the tremendous butcher's upstairs (wonderful as it is) and head to the downstairs deli to stock up on sausage rolls, handmade pies, cooked meats, Neal's Yard cheeses, olives, bread, quiches, chutneys, wine and beer. Perfect picnic fodder for an afternoon's lounging in Victoria Park.
Other locations *Borough Market, SE1 1TL (7403 4721); 8-10 Moxon Street, W1U 4EW (7935 7788); 27 Lower Marsh, SE1 7RG (7921 2975).*

Green spaces

Escape from the city without leaving town.

Boating lakes

Alexandra Park

Alexandra Palace Way, N22 7AY (7262 1330, www.alexandrapalace.com). Wood Green tube, then W3 bus. Boat hire Easter-July, Sept 10am-6pm Sat, Sun & school hols. Late July, Aug 10am-6pm daily. Rates £4/30mins; £2/30mins reductions. No credit cards.

This small, man-made lake went through a bit of a gunky phase a few years ago, but has since been cleaned up and is now home to a large number of coots, mallards, Canada geese and ducks. Pedalos and rowing boats are available for hire; under-12s must wear a life jacket.

Battersea Park

Albert Bridge Road, SW11 4NJ (7262 1330, www.batterseapark.org). Battersea Park rail. Boat hire Easter-late July, Sept 10am-6pm Sat, Sun & school hols. Late July-Aug 10am-6pm daily. Rates £4/30mins; £2/30mins reductions. No credit cards.

Built in the 1850s as part of the park's mission to encourage morally desirable leisure activities, the boating lake is surrounded by ancient trees. Two islands, forbidden to human feet, shelter herons, cormorants and grebes, while a restaurant hosts live music in summer. Under-eights must be accompanied.

Finsbury Park

Seven Sisters Road, N4 1EE (07905 924282, www.finsburyparkboats. co.uk). Manor House tube or Finsbury Park tube/rail. Boat hire noon-6pm Mon-Fri; noon-7.30pm Sat, Sun. Rates £6/30mins. No credit cards.

Restored to its former glory following a hefty Lottery grant, the park and its once-neglected boating lake are now looking their best. Rowing boats carry up to four people each, with life jackets available for children.

Greenwich Park

Romney Road, SE10 9NF (7262 1330, www.royalparks.org.uk). Cutty Sark DLR, or Maze Hill or Greenwich rail. Boat hire Easter-mid July, Sept 10.30am-5pm Sat, Sun & school hols. Mid July-Aug 11am-5pm daily. Rates £3/20mins; £2/20mins reductions. No credit cards.

This 2ft deep concrete pond may not be as beautiful as some of its greener rivals, but remains popular. Situated near the St Mary's Gate entrance, it has pedalos and rowing boats – and often stays open late on sunny days. Under-eights must be accompanied.

Hyde Park

Serpentine Road, W2 2UH (7262 1330, www. royalparks. org.uk). Hyde Park Corner, Marble Arch or

Knightsbridge tube. Boat hire Easter-Sept 10am-7pm daily. Rates £7/30mins, £9/hr; £3/30mins, £4/hr reductions; £17/30 mins, £22/hr family.

London's biggest boating lake covers 64 acres of water and has over 130 pedal and row boats for hire. It's also home to the Serpentine Solar Shuttle, the UK's first solar powered passenger craft, which ferries up to 40 eco-voyagers around the lake, starting at the boat house (£3, £2 reductions; noon-6pm).

Regent's Park
Outer Circle, NW1 4NR (7724 4069, www.royalparks.org.uk). Baker Street or Regent's Park tube. Boat hire times vary; phone for details. Rates £4.85/30mins, £6.50/hr; £3.35/30mins, £4.40/hr reductions; £20/hr family. No credit cards.

The boating lake near Hanover Gate is home to more than 650 waterfowl, including 260 pairs of ducks. Thirty pedalos and 20 rowing boats are available for hire, with a £5 deposit required.

Community gardens

Discover the true meaning of a grassroots movement by visiting one of the capital's community gardens: there are now over 100. Download a map with information on each project at www.farmgarden.org.uk/london. Every June, **Open Squares Weekend** (www.opensquares.org) gives you the keys to even more secret gardens in London, as 175 private green spaces briefly go public.

Calthorpe Community Garden
258-274 Grays Inn Road, WC1X 8LH (7837 8019, www.calthorpeproject.org.uk). Russell Square tube or King's Cross tube/rail. Open Winter 9am-5pm Mon-Fri; 11am-5pm Sat, Sun. Summer 10am-6pm Mon-Fri; 10am-6pm Sat, Sun.

A former dumping ground rescued from developers in 1984 by local residents, this 1.2-acre haven now features a waterfall, children's gardens, wildlife areas and a café.

Culpeper Community Garden
1 Cloudesley Road, N1 0EG (7833 3951, www.culpeper.org.uk). Angel tube. Open 8am-dusk daily.

Started up in 1982 in order to teach the local schoolchildren how to grow vegetables, the Culpeper continues to support various community groups. Its verdant lawns, ponds, rose pergolas, ornamental beds, vegetable plots and wildlife area also soothe frazzled shoppers. Keep an eye on the website for seasonal events too.

The Gardens Community Garden
Doncaster Gardens, N4 1HX (8374 7721, www.gardensresidents.blogspot.com). Manor House tube or Harringay Green Lanes rail. Open 9am-dusk daily.

As much a social centre as a horticultural one, the Gardens hosts Easter egg hunts, a summer fair, a Halloween party and Christmas carols. Winner of the London in Bloom Best Community Garden award in 2007, it's an enchanting spot: features include beautifully kept beds of flowers and ferns, a community mosaic and willow sculptures.

Harleyford Road Community Garden
Entrances on Harleyford Road or by 37 Bonnington Square, SE11 5AX (7485 5001). Oval tube or Vauxhall tube/rail. Open 9am-dusk daily.

This former wasteland in the middle of traffic-choked Vauxhall now comprises a secret garden with mosaic pathways winding between trees and flower beds, a pond, picnic tables and a children's play area. Wilder areas of long grass encourage butterflies to visit.

Phoenix Garden
21 Stacey Street (entrance on St Giles Passage), WC2H 8DG (7379 3187, www. phoenixgarden.org). Tottenham Court Road tube. Open dawn-dusk daily.

In the heart of the West End, this award-winning oasis was planted by the local community on the site of a former car park. Office workers in the know sun themselves here as they eat their sandwiches, in the company of frogs, beetles and woodpeckers.

GOING OUT
BEAUTY
FASHION
PARTIES
FOOD
HEALTH
ECO
OUTDOORS
HOME
CHILDREN
PETS
TRANSPORT
RESOURCES

Roots and Shoots

Walnut Tree Walk, SE11 6DN (7587 1131, www.rootsandshoots.org.uk). Lambeth North tube or Elephant & Castle tube/rail. Open 10am-5pm Mon-Fri.

Set up in 1982, Roots and Shoots has transformed a derelict civil defence site into an inspiring half-acre garden featuring a summer meadow, hazel coppice, beehives and two ponds. It's beautiful and slightly wild – just how the butterflies, dragonflies and grasshoppers like it. In autumn, there's fresh apple juice, pressed in the barn.

Graveyards

The city has an abundance of wonderfully atmospheric Victorian graveyards to explore, where ivy-covered headstones lean at unlikely angles and stone angels overlook the tangled pathways. Unless otherwise stated, admission is free.

Abney Park Cemetery

Stoke Newington High Street, N16 0LN (7275 7557, www.abney-park.org.uk). Stoke Newington rail or 73, 106, 149, 243, 276, 349 bus. Open dawn-dusk daily. Visitors' centre 10am-4pm Mon-Fri.

Abney Park became London's first non-denominational cemetery in Victorian times, sparking a scandal with its hieroglyphic-adorned Egyptian-style gates. The now gloriously overgrown 32-acre site has many impressive trees, remnants of what was once the largest cemetery arboretum to be found anywhere in Europe.

Brompton Cemetery

Fulham Road, SW10 9UG (7352 1201, www.royalparks.org.uk). West Brompton tube/rail. Open Summer 8am-8pm daily. Winter 8am-4pm daily.

Laid out in formal fashion around a domed chapel, modelled on St Peter's in Rome, this well-ordered cemetery is the posthumous residence of suffragette Emmeline Pankhurst. It's a peaceful haven – except on match days at nearby Stamford Bridge.

Bunhill Fields Cemetery

38 City Road, EC1Y 1AU (7374 4127). Old Street tube/rail. Open Oct-Mar 8am-4pm Mon-Fri; 9.30am-4pm Sat, Sun; Apr-Sept 8am-dusk Mon-Fri; 9.30am-4pm Sat-Sun.

City workers in search of souls lunch in this former dissenters' burial ground, dating back to the 17th century, where the graves of William Blake, John Bunyan and Daniel Defoe can be found. A guided tour (£4) runs on Wednesdays at 12.30pm from April to September, meeting at the gardener's hut (www.citygardenswalks.com).

Hampstead Cemetery

Fortune Green Road, NW6 1DR (7527 8300). West Hampstead tube/rail. Open 8am-4.30pm Mon-Fri; 9am-4.30pm Sat; 10am-4.30pm Sun.

Opened in 1876 and now gently sliding into wonderfully photogenic decay, the 26-acre site was designed by leading landscape gardener Joseph Metson. The Llewelyn Davies boys, who were the inspiration for JM Barrie's *Peter Pan*, are buried here.

Highgate Cemetery ★

Swain's Lane, N6 6PJ (8340 1834, www. highgate-cemetery.org). Highgate tube. Open East cemetery Mar-Oct 10am-5pm Mon-Fri; 11am-5pm Sat, Sun. Nov-Feb 10am-4pm Mon-Fri; 11am-4pm Sat, Sun. Admission East cemetery £3. West cemetery tours £7. No credit cards.

Arguably Britain's finest Victorian garden cemetery, Highgate's famous inmates include Karl Marx and George Eliot. The beautiful West Cemetery, with its decaying, ivy-covered tombs, is accessible by guided tour only (book in advance).

Kensal Green Cemetery

Harrow Road, W10 4RA (8969 0152, www.kensalgreen.co.uk). Kensal Green tube/rail or 18, 23, 52, 70, 295, 316 bus. Open Apr-Sept 9am-6pm Mon-Sat; 10am-6pm Sun. Oct-Mar 9am-5pm Mon-Sat; 10am-5pm Sun.

London's oldest public cemetery was a fashionable final resting place in the 19th century, and numerous noble names adorn its

THE CITY'S HIDDEN GARDENS

The Square Mile might not seem the most obvious place to find tranquil green retreats, but it harbours a wealth of hidden garden gems, many created on the sites of buildings destroyed in the Great Fire of London and during the Blitz. Before setting off to explore, download a map at www.cityoflondon.gov.uk. Alternatively, a two-hour guided tour of the City's historic green spaces leaves from the information centre at St Paul's every Saturday and Sunday from April to September at 1.30pm (£6, 8441 1926, www.citygardenswalks.com).

The best-known garden is probably **Postman's Park**, near St Paul's tube station on King Edward Street. The small but serene memorial garden has a Victorian wall of tiles commemorating ordinary people who sacrificed their lives for others, designed by Charles Frederic Watts.

Head down the road towards Newgate Street for **Christchurch Greyfriars**, with its lovely, box-hedge bordered rose garden, a suntrap on summer afternoons, and at its best in June and July.

East of Postman's Park, another gem is the diminutive **St Mary Aldermanbury Garden** on Love Lane, with its heady-smelling camellia, knot garden and neat box and yew hedges: a bust of Shakespeare looks down on office workers eating their lunch.

A walk along London Wall will take you to the City of London's first public park, **Finsbury Circus**, tucked behind Moorgate tube. The bandstand hosts jazz performances during the City of London Festival (www.colf.org).

Finally, it's impossible to talk about the City's gardens without squeezing in a mention of the impossibly romantic **St Dunstan in the East Church Garden**, a short stroll from Monument tube. Here, creepers and wisteria weave around a tower and the ruins of a Christopher Wren-designed church, while exotic shrubs flourish in the shelter of the walls.

GOING OUT

BEAUTY

FASHION

PARTIES

FOOD

HEALTH

ECO

OUTDOORS

HOME

CHILDREN

PETS

TRANSPORT

RESOURCES

mausoleums. Here too are the graves of Isambard Kingdom Brunel, Wilkie Collins, Anthony Trollope and William Makepeace Thackeray. A guided tour runs on Sundays.

Nunhead Cemetery

Entrances on Limesford Road or Linden Grove, SE15 3LP (7732 9535, www.fonc. org.uk). Nunhead rail. Open Summer 8.30am-7pm daily. Winter 8.30am-5pm daily. Tours 2.15pm last Sun of month.
One of the lesser known but most attractive of London's Victorian cemeteries, this 52-acre site is now part nature reserve. Crumbling tombs stand amid ash and sycamore trees, while heroes of Trafalgar and Waterloo sleep beneath avenues of lime. There is a conducted tour of the cemetery on the last Sunday of every month starting at the Grove gates at 2.15pm.

Parks

For details of London's eight **Royal Parks**, visit www.royalparks.org.uk, which provides details of forthcoming events, plus sports and leisure facilities. If you fancy a game of **tennis**, *see p117.*

Best for...
Bathing

Hampstead Heath

Men & Women's ponds, Millfield Lane, N6. (7485 3873, www.cityoflondon.gov.uk/ hampstead). Gospel Oak rail. Open May-Sept 7am-8.30pm daily; varies rest of year. Mixed pond, East Heath Road, NW3. Hampstead Heath rail. Open May-Sept 7am-6.30pm daily; varies rest of year.

Who needs chlorine when you can go pond dipping instead? The heath's three bathing ponds were originally dug as reservoirs to feed the capital's water supply and have been a popular place for outdoor swimming since the 19th century. Their closure was averted in 2007 after an army of bathers, hardened by years of early morning dips, faced down the local council. Concerns about the water quality have now been resolved, and lifeguards are on duty most days. A day ticket for the ponds costs £2, a one year season ticket £102. To get opening times for winter, call ahead as times are dependent to a degree on weather. You must also be a member of the Hampstead Heath Winter Swimming Club to use the mixed pond in the winter months.

Best for...
Birdlife

St James's Park
Horse Guards Road SW1 (7930 1793, www.royalparks.org.uk). St James's Park tube. Open 5am-midnight daily.
The lake in St James's Park is home to ducks, geese, gulls, black swans and, best of all, friendly pelicans – first introduced to the park in the 15th century, as a show-stopping gift from the Russian ambassador. Daily feeding time with the wildlife officers is at 2.30pm, if you fancy joining them for lunch. Afterwards, check out what's on at the bandstand, which has a packed summer schedule.

Best for...
Dinosaurs

Crystal Palace Park
Crystal Palace Park Road, Anerley Hill & Thicket Road, SE26 (8778 9496). Crystal Palace or Penge West rail. Open 7.30am-dusk daily.
A Victorian vision of *Jurassic Park*, this series of life-size dinosaur sculptures were a world first when they were unveiled in 1854. Made of concrete and brick, they were based on the best available evidence at the time. They have since been proved far from scientifically accurate, but that doesn't detract from their

freaky charm as they loom out of the undergrowth. Following restoration work they are now protected with a Grade I listing.

Best for...
Children

Kensington Gardens
Kensington Gore, W2 2UH (7298 2141, www.royalparks.org.uk). Queensway or Bayswater tube. Open 10am-dusk daily.
As well as the famous bronze statue depicting Peter Pan and a host of friendly animals, the park's Diana, Princess of Wales Memorial Playground is inspired by the boy who never grew up, with teepees, a tree encampment and a huge pirate ship surrounded by a sandy 'beach' (*see also p171*).

Best for...
Formal gardens

Queen Mary's Rose Garden
Regent's Park, Inner Circle, NW1 4NR (7486 7905, www.royalparks.org.uk). Baker Street or Regent's Park tube. Open dawn-dusk daily.
First laid out in the 1930s, London's largest rose garden boasts some 30,000 roses of more than 400 varieties; visit in mid June to enjoy the multitude of blooms at their fragrant best. Nearby, there's the boating lake (*see p134*); after your exertions, recover in the estimable Garden Café (*see p130*).

Best for...
Kite-flying

Parliament Hill ★
Highgate Road, NW5 1QR (7332 3773, www.cityoflondon.gov.uk/hampstead). Gospel Oak or Hampstead Heath rail. Open 8am-dusk daily.
Parliament Hill has acquired the nickname Kite Hill, thanks to its popularity with aficionados of this heady pastime. Standing over 300ft high, the famous mound (on the south east side of Hampstead Heath) offers unsurpassed views of Canary Wharf's distant skyscrapers, the City and the dome of St Paul's Cathedral.

GOING OUT

BEAUTY

FASHION

PARTIES

FOOD

HEALTH

ECO

OUTDOORS

HOME

CHILDREN

PETS

TRANSPORT

RESOURCES

City Secret

A deliciously muddy low-tide scramble can be had at Deptford's **Creekside Centre** (14 Creekside, SE8 4SA, 8692 9922, www.creeksidecentre.org.uk). Clad in fetching thigh-high waders, you'll be taken on a two-and-a-half-hour expedition exploring the area's history and wildlife. Wear old togs. Tickets cost £10.

See also *Richmond Park, for Kitevibe's taster sessions, courses and lessons in power-kiting, kite buggying and kite landboarding (07866 430979, www.kitevibe.com).*

Best for…
Theatre

Regent's Park
Open Air Theatre, Inner Circle, NW1 4NR (0844 826 4242, www.openairtheatre.org). Baker Street or Regent's Park tube.
Britain's only permanent professional outdoor theatre, the Open Air Theatre has one of the largest auditoria in the capital. Its annual 15-week season is extremely popular and usually includes a children's play, plus various Sunday night comedy and concerts. It's a delightful place to take a picnic on a summer night; all the productions have specially long intervals. It can get chilly as the evening draws on, so take an extra jumper or blanket.

Best for…
Lounging

Green Park
Piccadilly, SW1 (7930 1793, www.royal parks.org.uk). Green Park or Hyde Park Corner tube. Open dawn-dusk daily.
The park's iconic green and white striped deckchairs are much sought-after on clement afternoons, so arrive early to bagsy yours, then settle down with the papers and

a picnic. The deckchairs are available next to the refreshment kiosk by the Green Park tube entrance from March to October, and cost £1.50 for an hour or £4 for three. For details of guided walks throughout the year, check the website.

Best for…
Pastoral bliss

Richmond Park
Richmond upon Thames, Surrey, TW10 5HS (8948 3209, www.royalparks.org.uk). Richmond tube/rail, then 65 or 371 bus. Open summer 7am-dusk daily Winter 7.30am-dusk daily.
Ancient woodlands, rolling hills, herds of roaming deer… it's easy to forget you're in a city at all when you visit London's largest royal park (save for the tower blocks encroaching from Roehampton). To feel truly countrified, survey it on horseback by hiring a steed from one of several local stables; call the park for details.

Best for…
Conkers

Bushy Park
Hampton Court Road, Hampton, Middlesex TW12 2EJ (8979 1586, www.royalparks. org.uk). Hampton Court, Hampton Wick or Teddington rail. Open Dec-Aug, Oct dawn-dusk daily; Sept, Nov 8am-10.30pm.
The Chestnut Avenue in Bushy Park is at its towering finest in late spring, when the trees' 'candles' are in bloom, providing a good excuse for an annual celebration in the park on the second Sunday of May. In the autumn, the horse chestnuts come into their own as a source of champion specimens for knuckle-bruising conker fights.

Wildlife & nature reserves

The **London Wildlife Trust** (www.wildlondon.org.uk) manages over 50 nature reserves across the capital,

City Secret

The **Parkland Walk** (www.parkland-walk.org.uk) is a leafy trail and nature reserve running from Finsbury Park to Highgate Wood. The four-and-a-half-mile footpath follows a series of disused railway lines, passing along atmospheric abandoned platforms and echoing tunnels en route.

with habitats ranging from woodlands and meadows to grasslands and marshes.

Camley Street Natural Park

12 Camley Street, NW1 0PW (7833 2311, www.wildlondon.org.uk). King's Cross tube/rail. Open 10am-5pm daily.
Created from an old coalyard on the banks of the Regent's Canal, this two-acre reserve squeezes in wildflower meadows, marsh woodland and reed beds. Its habitats support a rich variety of birds and butterflies.

Epping Forest

Information Centre, High Beech, Loughton, Essex IG10 4AF (8508 0028, www.cityof london.gov.uk/openspaces). Wanstead tube/ Chingford rail. Open Information Centre summer 10am-5pm daily. Winter 10am-3pm daily. Forest 24hrs daily.
Henry VIII's former hunting ground covers some 6,000 acres, from east London to just north of Epping. The majority of the forest is heavily wooded but it also encompasses meadow, parkland and ponds. And there's a grazing herd of English Longhorn cattle.

Greenwich Peninsula Ecology Park

Thames Path, John Harrison Way, SE10 0QZ (8293 1904, www.urbanecology. org.uk). North Greenwich tube or108, 161, 472, 486 bus. Open 10-5pm Wed-Sun.
Once an industrial wasteland, now returned to marshland, the park consists of an inner and outer lake – the latter open at all times. Spot cormorants and herons from the bird hides and look out for frogs, toads and newts.

Highgate Wood

Muswell Hill Road, N10 3JN (8444 6129, www.cityoflondon.gov.uk/openspaces). Highgate tube or 43, 134, 263 bus. Open 7am-dusk daily.
A 70-acre remnant of the ancient Forest of Middlesex, this oak, holly and hornbeam wood harbours foxes, bats and grey squirrels. There's a café and visitors' centre, which organises popular bat-watching walks.

London Wetland Centre

Queen Elizabeth's Walk, Barnes, SW13 9WT (8409 4400, www.wwt.org.uk). Hammersmith tube then 283 bus, Barnes rail or bus 33, 72, 209. Open Mar-Oct 9.30am-6pm daily. Nov-Feb 9.30am-5pm daily. Admission £9.95; £5.50-£7.40 reductions; £27.75 family.
This Barnes-based 100-acre Site of Special Scientific Interest celebrates its tenth anniversary in 2010. It's just four miles out of central London, but feels worlds away. Its rustling reeds and tranquil ponds are a haven for birds (including kingfishers and spoonbills) – new underwater cameras add an alternative view of the wildlife.

Railway Fields

Green Lanes, by Umfreville Road N4 1EY (8348 6005, www.haringey.gov.uk). Manor House tube or Harringay Green Lanes rail. Open 9am-5pm Mon-Fri. Phone ahead.
Mysterious wrought iron gates creak open to reveal a little-known nature reserve just off bustling Green Lanes. The two-acre site, a former railway goods yard, supports more than 200 species of wildflower.

Sydenham Hill Wood & Cox's Walk

Entrances on Crescent Wood Road & junction of Lordship Lane and Dulwich Common, SE21 (www.wildlondon.org.uk). Sydenham Hill or Forest Hill rail, or P4, 176, 185, 197, 202, 363 bus. Open dawn-dusk daily.
Once part of the Great North Wood, which stretched from Deptford to Selhurst, this woodland is home to 200 species of trees and flowering plants as well as birds, woodland creatures and rare insects.

Home

GOING OUT
BEAUTY
FASHION
PARTIES
FOOD
HEALTH
ECO
OUTDOORS
HOME
CHILDREN
PETS
TRANSPORT
RESOURCES

Art

For wealthy collectors, there's no shortage of galleries and fairs at which to part with considerable sums for art. However, there are plenty of places in the capital to source affordable artwork too.

Fairs & open studios

Unless otherwise specified, listed fairs run in late October, creating a fringe scene around the pricey **Frieze Art Fair** (www.friezeartfair.com). Look out, too, for the ad hoc annual **Keith Talent Gallery** (www.keithtalent.com) fair, where prices start at £200. It's also worth subscribing to **Art Rabbit** (www.art rabbit.com) and **New Exhibitions** (www.newexhibitions.com), both of which will alert you to new names.

Affordable Art Fair
Battersea Evolution, SW11 4NJ (8246 4848, www.affordableartfair.com). Sloane Square tube, then free shuttle bus. Admission £12.

Over 120 galleries exhibit a dizzying selection of original prints, photography, sculpture and paintings, priced from £50-£3,000. The fair takes place in March and October.

Art Car Boot Fair
146 Brick Lane, E1 6RU (www.artcarboot fair.com). Shoreditch High Street rail. Admission £4.
With past stallholders including the likes of Gavin Turk and Peter Blake, this day-long knees-up (June usually) is a great place to pick up small-scale offerings (jewellery, prints, T-shirts) from seriously collectable artists.

artLONDON
Royal Hospital Chelsea, Royal Hospital Road, SW3 4SR (7259 9399, www.artlondon.net). Sloane Square tube. Admission £12.

CRAFT COLLECTIVES

Cockpit Arts
7419 1959, www.cockpitarts.com.
Cockpit Arts' studios in Holborn and Deptford hold regular open days where you can buy direct from the designers. Expect everything from exquisite hand-woven textiles to cascading silver and glass necklaces, funky furniture and screen-printed notebooks – plus the chance to be nosy, meet the artists and have a poke around the studios.

Hidden Art London
7729 3800, www.hiddenart london.co.uk.
The Hidden Art organisation holds two annual open studio weekends,

usually in November and December. Around 50 studios take part, offering craft workshops and pieces for sale – from ceramics and glass to textiles and jewellery. The website features a useful searchable directory too.

Made in Clerkenwell
7251 0276, www.craftcentral.org.uk.
Twice a year, over 70 Clerkenwell-based designer-makers throw open their studios to the public. Snap up necklaces for £15 or inexpensive letterpress-printed cards and stationery, or invest in interiors or bespoke commissions from rising talents.

Held the week before Frieze, this lively four-day art fair attracts galleries from around the world and sells 'a little bit of everything'. Prices range from £100 to £100,000.

Chocolate Factory Open Studios

Chocolate Factory, 1 Clarendon Road, N22 6XJ (8365 7500, www.collage-arts.org). Wood Green tube. Admission free.
Over 100 artists open their studios for this annual event, held over a weekend in autumn. Pieces run the gamut from screenprints to sculpture, with plenty of items under £500.

Free Range ★

Old Truman Brewery, 91 Brick Lane, E1 6QL (7770 6100, www.free-range.org.uk). Shoreditch High Street rail. Admission free. No credit cards.
June and July sees the Truman Brewery overrun with new artistic talent, as weekly-changing exhibitions showcase the work of more than 3,000 graduate artists. With prices starting at £20 for prints, it's a great chance to scout future stars of the scene. It's open Friday to Monday: go on a Friday to nab the newest and best stock.

Great Western Studios Open Studios

65 Alfred Road, W2 5EU (7221 0100, www.greatwesternstudios.com). Westbourne Park tube. Admission free. No credit cards.
A hundred studios (Great Western moved to this new building in late 2009) are opened to the public for the first weekend in December, then one weekend in early June, selling new painting, sculpture, illustration, photography and crafts. Gift items sell for as little as £30-£50, while more serious works cost from £300.

London Art Fair

Business Design Centre, 52 Upper Street, N1 0QH (7288 6482, www.londonartfair. co.uk). Angel tube. Admission call for details.
This mammoth art fair has been going strong for more than two decades, exhibiting work from over 100 galleries. All art forms are represented, with prices from £160-£200 for screenprints and photographic prints. Held in January, it's London's first art fair of the year.

Secret Sale

Royal College of Art, Kensington Gore, SW7 2EU (7590 4186, www.rca.ac.uk/secret). South Kensington tube. Admission free.
Anonymous artworks by world-famous artists are mixed with works by the RCA's graduates at this hugely popular November sale, where 2,500 postcard-sized works are sold off for £45 each on a first come, first served basis. Be prepared for long queues and an almighty scrum on sale day. You must pre-register to purchase (this can be done online the day before) and there are also raffle tickets on sale allowing winners to be one of the first 50 people allowed in on the day.

Framing

Alec Drew

5-7 Cale Street, SW3 3QT (7352 8716, www.alec-drew.co.uk). Sloane Square tube. Open 9.15am-6pm Mon-Fri; 10am-4pm Sat.
Expect a wide choice of frames and museum-quality glass from a company that's just as happy framing the kids' doodles as that attic find that might be an original Turner. Staff can also recommend related services, such as restretching, cleaning, removing old backing and providing linen backing for posters. Alec Drew can also recommend picture-hanging services if required.

Art & Soul ★

Unit G14, Belgravia Workshops, 157 Marlborough Road, N19 4NF (7263 0421, www.artandsoulframes.com). Archway tube. Open 9am-5pm Tue-Fri; by appointment Sat.
Rebecca Bramwell aims to provide a service for customers on a budget who want quality framing. She's happy to advise on what suits the work, and her prices are very reasonable. Readymade small frames made from offcuts cost as little as £3.50.

John Jones

4 Morris Place, off Stroud Green Road, N4 3JG (7281 5439, www.johnjones.co.uk). Finsbury Park tube/rail. Open 9.30am-5.30pm Mon-Fri by appointment.

GOING OUT

BEAUTY

FASHION

PARTIES

FOOD

HEALTH

ECO

OUTDOORS

HOME

CHILDREN

PETS

TRANSPORT

RESOURCES

Clients at this well-known framing workshop include Tate and Christie's; if you want to be in such luminary company, it'll cost you. The average framing costs over £250, but for that you get impeccable quality, skilled craftsmen and the knowledge that your work has been framed by the best in the business. Note that it's open by appointment only. An installation and hanging service is also on offer.

Pendragon Fine Art Frames
1-3 Yorkton Street, E2 8NH (7729 0608, www.pendragonframes.com). Old Street tube/rail. Open 9am-5pm Mon-Fri; by appointment Sat.
Keith Andrews has been running Pendragon for almost a decade, offering advice, suggestions and patience in equal measure from his Hackney workshop, where he and a genial team of craftsmen make excellent frames at affordable prices. Galleries like the Serpentine recommend this place, and with very good reason.

Ray's Glass & Frames
120 Hackney Road, E2 7QF (7729 4727). Bethnal Green tube. Open 6am-3pm Mon-Thur; 6am-2.30pm Fri; 6am-11.30am Sat.
Pick out a frame moulding from D&J Simons & Sons next door (122-150 Hackney Road, E2 7QS, 7739 3744, www.djsimons.co.uk), then take it in to Ray's to be cut to size and joined – at a fraction of the cost of most picture framers. The minimum charge is £10.

Shops & galleries

A&D
51 Chiltern Street, W1U 6LY (7486 0534, www.aanddgallery.com). Baker Street tube. Open 10.30am-7pm Mon-Sat.
Kitsch and witty works by new artists (from £30) plus more costly limited-edition prints.

Cosh
2nd Floor, Colina House, Colina Mews, N15 3HS (8881 5605, www.coshuk.com). Turnpike Lane tube. Open 11am-6pm Mon-Sat.
Cosh offers a wide range of prints from hip young illustrators and graphic artists.

City Secret

As well as offering an excellent range of contemporary photography, online company **55 Max** (0845 056 8728, www.55max.com) can transfer your own images on to canvas, acrylic, blankets, wallpaper or roller blinds. Prices start at £40 for an 8 x 10in canvas. If you want to go all out, there's even a bespoke wallpaper service.

Degree Art
12A Vyner Street, E2 9DG (8980 0395, www.degreeart.com). Bethnal Green tube. Open by appointment Mon, Tue; noon-6pm Wed-Sun.
An impressive array of work by young artists on a key art-world street.

Flow
1-5 Needham Road, W11 2RP (7243 0782, www.flowgallery.co.uk). Notting Hill Gate tube. Open 11am-6pm Mon-Sat.
This gallery houses the work of more than 100 artists, specialising in applied art.

Greenwich Printmakers
1A Greenwich Market, SE10 9HZ (8858 1569, www.greenwich-printmakers.org.uk). Greenwich rail/DLR. Open 10.30am-5.30pm Tue-Sun.
Limited-edition lithographs, etchings and prints, with prices from £40 to £500.

Transition Gallery
Unit 25A, Regent Studios, 8 Andrews Road, E8 4QN (7254 4202, www.transitiongallery. co.uk). Bethnal Green tube. Open noon-6pm Fri-Sun.
Group shows by emerging and established artists, with prices rarely rising above £1,000.

Will's Art Warehouse
Sadler's House, 180 Lower Richmond Road, SW15 1LY (8246 4840, www.wills-art.com). Bus 22. Open 10.30am-6pm daily.
Contemporary art at keen prices (£50-£3,000).

GOING OUT

BEAUTY

FASHION

PARTIES

FOOD

HEALTH

ECO

OUTDOORS

HOME

CHILDREN

PETS

TRANSPORT

RESOURCES

GOING OUT

BEAUTY

FASHION

PARTIES

FOOD

HEALTH

ECO

OUTDOORS

HOME

CHILDREN

PETS

TRANSPORT

RESOURCES

Address Book Secrets
Abigail Ahern
Interior designer & owner of Atelier Abigail Ahern

Travel is great for inspiration but London is just so sprawling and creative. I love to champion the unusual and support emerging designers, and the capital is a great place to do both. The annual **Tent Festival** (www.tentlondon.co.uk), part of the London Design Festival, is great for seeking out new talent.

One of my favourite new designers is **Andrew Oliver** (www.mademade.co.uk) whose 'drunken tables' and 'crooked lamps' have a wonderfully wobbly appeal. I also love **Squint**'s (178 Shoreditch High Street, E1 6HU, 7739 9275, www.squintlimited.com) furniture for its fabulously contrasting colours and patterns.

In terms of beautiful furnishings, **Liberty** (Regent Street, W1B 5AH, 7734 1234, www.liberty.co.uk) is the absolute star. I also love **Caravan** (3 Redchurch Street, EC2 7DJ, 7033 3532, www.caravanstyle.com) and **Story** (4-5 Dray Walk, Old Truman Brewery, E1 6QL, 7247 3137) for quirky finds and oddities.

I love searching for vintage items too. The owners of Trois Garçons restaurant have opened a tiny but fabulous vintage shop called **Maison Trois Garçons** (45 Redchurch Street, E2 7DL, 7033 8703). The **Dog & the Wardrobe** (Unit 3B, Regent Studios, 8 Andrew's Road, E8 4QN, 07855 958741, www.thedogandwardrobe.com) is another great place for a rummage. They stock a lot of '50s and '60s items.

My top tip for style on a budget is never to overlook an attractively shaped item on the basis of its colour or material. I have a Victorian table that was a horrible brown colour when I bought it – I simply took it to my local car sprayer in Hackney and got it sprayed to a bright lacquered finish.

Another boutique I really like is Maureen Doherty's **Egg** (36 Kinnerton Street, SW1X 8ES, 7235 9315, www.eggtrading.eu). It sells wonderful homemade ceramics, clothes and jewellery with a nice, pared down aesthetic. There's a crafty feel to a lot of the items there. It isn't really my style but every time I visit, it makes me want to own the perfect white house in which to display it all.

I spent a lot of time travelling around sourcing furnishings and researching so when I'm relaxing I like to stay local. **The Towpath** (42 De Beauvoir Crescent, N1 5SB), on the canal near Kingsland Road, is a great place to unwind. It's a sweet café that serves amazing tapas (it's owned by Italian-American food writer Lori De Mori and her husband) – perfect for a summery glass of rose.

I have a dog who is a big fan of parks. While I love Hyde Park and St James's Park for their city feel, there's nothing quite like **Hampstead Heath** for escaping city life for a while. I'm busy preparing for the launch of my own range of furniture and lighting in autumn 2010 so I need to grab any downtime while I can.

Interiors

From one-off salvage yard finds to the hippest designer boutiques, the capital is brimming with interiors ideas.

Architectural salvage

Although its premises are just outside London, honourable mention must be made of the splendid **Antique Church Furnishings** (Rivernook Farm, Sunnyside, Walton-on-Thames, Surrey KT12 2ET, 01932 252736, www.church antiques.com), which specialises in prewar church fixtures and furniture (the pews and chapel chairs are of more interest to most buyers than the fonts and pulpits). Prices are a steal, and they'll deliver anywhere.

Architectural Forum
312-314 Essex Road, N1 3AX (7704 0982, www.thearchitecturalforum.com). Angel tube or 38, 56, 73, 341 bus. Open 10am-5pm Mon-Sat.
The shop sells polished-up fireplaces and interesting antiques at reasonable prices. There's also a small but vertiginously stacked outdoor yard, dominated by Belfast sinks and cast-iron radiators in various states of repair; for access, ask in the shop.

D&A Binder
101 Holloway Road, N7 8LT (7609 6300, www.dandabinder.co.uk). Highbury & Islington tube/rail. Open 10am-6pm Mon-Sat.
It's not strictly a salvage yard, but the wonderful D&A Binder specialises in vintage shop fittings. There are treasures to be found amid its dusty recesses: a 1920s mahogany shirt cabinet would be perfect for many-shirted modern-day dandies, while smaller but just as enticing pieces include mirrors, mannequins, hooks, hatstands and old advertising paraphernalia.

LASSCo
Brunswick House, 30 Wandsworth Road, SW8 2LG (7394 2100, www.lassco.co.uk). Vauxhall tube/rail. Open 10am-5pm Mon-Sat; 11am-5pm Sun.
LASSCo has three outlets displaying its vast range of architectural salvage, with a dizzying array of appealing items at any one time. The main site in Vauxhall is the one to head for if you fancy a good root around. But should you prefer to hunt from the comfort of your chair, the website is also excellent, with great search criteria and good navigation facilities.

Park Royal Salvage
Lower Place Wharf, Acton Lane, NW10 7AB (8961 3627, www.parkroyalsalvage. co.uk). Harlesden tube. Open 7.30am-4.30pm Mon-Fri. No credit cards.
Park Royal has built up an impressive collection of salvage pieces – from reclaimed bricks, beams, flooring and railway sleepers to fireplaces, sash and stained glass windows, elaborate garden statuary and lovely antique baths and sinks.

Retrouvius ★
2A Ravensworth Road, NW10 5NR (8960 6060, www.retrouvius.com). Kensal Green tube. Open 10am-6pm Mon-Sat.
Former architects Adam Hills and Maria Speake like to 'bridge the gap between destruction and construction' in their smart west London salvage business, which focuses on finding furniture and historic materials from demolition sites across the UK. The emphasis at Retrouvius is on 20th-century salvage and modern antiques, such as flooring from Heathrow Terminal 2, industrial lighting and vintage chairs.

Interior & design boutiques

Aria

Barnsbury Hall, Barnsbury Street, N1 1PN (7704 6222, www.aria-shop.co.uk). Angel tube or Highbury & Islington tube/rail. Open 10am-6.30pm Mon-Sat; noon-6.30pm Sun.
One of London's oldest independent design stores, Aria stocks all the big names (Alessi, Verner Panton, Kartell, Philippe Starck et al) in its bright and spacious Islington shop, a former music hall.

Atelier Abigail Ahern ★

137 Upper Street, N1 1QP (7354 8181, www.atelierabigailahern.com). Angel tube or Highbury & Islington tube/rail. Open 10.30am-6pm Mon-Sat; noon-5pm Sun.
This tiny interiors shop may not have a huge range, but what it lacks in quantity is more than made up for in quality. The selection is both inventive and original, with much of it from emerging international designers. Textiles are particularly strong; as well as some striking merino wool ottomans (£755), there are Impressionist paintings transposed on to linen by Argentinian-born artist Haby Bonomo (from £65). Colour ranges are muted but striking, summing up a store that's a delightful departure from the sparse lines of many design stores.

Caravan ★

3 Redchurch Street, EC2 7DJ (7033 3532, www.caravanstyle.com). Liverpool Street tube/rail. Open 11am-6.30pm Tue-Fri; noon-6pm Sat-Sun.
Stylist and author Emily Chalmers's Redchurch Street boutique is a treasure trove of cool interiors ideas, vintage finds and unusual decorative pieces. Think glossy French industrial lamps, battered leather suitcases, stunning vintage teapots, tiny cameo brooches, big black ornamental crows, woollen knitted dog toys, light-reactive singing birds and gold angel wings for decorating candles.

Casa Mexico

1 Winkley Street, E2 6PY (7739 9349, www.casamexico.co.uk). Bethnal Green tube/rail or Cambridge Heath rail. Open 10am-6pm Mon-Fri; 10am-5pm Sat, Sun.
For all things Mexican, this Bethnal Green store is a must-visit: the product list covers the usual kitchenware – from little *cazuelas* (bowls) to *chimineas* (wood-burning stoves) – lamps, rugs and blankets, and 'ranch-style' furniture (made from seasoned pine) but also features Mexican folk art, bags and baskets, ponchos and a range of handmade tiles. Of course, no Mexican outpost would be complete without a full range of Day of the Dead products, and Casa Mexico definitely doesn't disappoint.

Graham & Green

4 Elgin Crescent, W11 2HX (7243 8908, www.grahamandgreen.co.uk). Ladbroke Grove tube. Open 10am-6pm Mon-Sat; 11.30am-5.30pm Sun.
The Graham & Green chain sells an enticing mix of furniture and accessories, ranging from sweet 1950s-inspired oak chairs (£150) to more opulent pieces, such as the embossed-brass Darjeeling chest-of-drawers (£875).
Other locations *across the city.*

Lifestyle Bazaar

11a Kingsland Road, E2 8AA (7739 9427, www.lifestylebazaar.com). Hoxton rail. Open 11am-7pm Mon-Sat; noon-5pm Sun.
Bright, fresh colours and quirky modern designs in a light-filled space make this little shop a delight to explore. The French ownership ensures a strong Gallic presence, but there's much to admire from globally sourced designers too.

Mint

2 North Terrace, Alexander Square, SW3 2BA (7225 2228, www.mintshop.co.uk). South Kensington tube. Open 10.30am-6.30pm Mon-Sat.
Mint's owner Lina Kanafani has an unerring instinct for good design and a great eye for the unusual and unexpected – which means its premises in the Brompton Design District are packed with exciting furniture, beautiful

CONCEPT STORES

Anthropologie

158 Regent Street, W1B 5SW (7529 9800, www.anthropologie.co.uk). Piccadilly Circus tube. Open 10am-7pm Mon-Wed; 10am–8pm Thur; 10am-7pm Fri, Sat; noon-6pm Sun.
The elder sister of Urban Outfitters is a sight to behold. You'll find clothes, jewellery and designer collaborations alongside an impressive range of vintage-inspired homewares.

Aubin & Wills

64-66 Redchurch Street, E2 7DP (3487 0066, www.aubinandwills.com). Shoreditch High Street rail. Open 10am-7pm Mon-Sat; 11am-5pm Sun.
This boutique, gallery and cinema stocks blankets, biscuit tins, candles and a host of other interiors treats alongside stylish clothes and gifts.

Beyond the Valley

2 Newburgh Street, W1F 7RD (7437 7338, www.beyondthevalley.com).

Oxford Circus tube. Open 11am-7pm Mon-Sat; noon-5pm Sun.
This boutique stocks casual urban clothes, jewellery and accessories. On the lower-ground floor is a stylish range of interiors, including wallpaper, lighting, furniture and design books.

Dark Room

52 Lamb's Conduit Street, WC1N 3LL (7831 7244, www.darkroomlondon.com). Holborn tube. Open 11am-7pm Mon-Sat.
Dark Room's dark interior displays a carefully chosen selection of unisex fashion, accessories and interiors.

Wolf & Badger

46 Ledbury Road, W11 2AB (7229 5698, www.wolfandbadger.com). Bayswater tube. Open 10am-6pm Mon-Sat; 11am-5pm Sun.
This hip boutique stocks an edgy selection of clothing, accessories, jewellery and shoes, as well as cool homewares.

---

clocks, ceramics and lighting from both established designers and recent graduates.

Places & Spaces

30 Old Town, SW4 0LB (7498 0998, www.placesandspaces.com). Clapham Common tube. Open 10am-5.45pm Tue-Sat; noon-4pm Sun.
Laura Slack's store is full of contemporary and classic designs, from Droog's milk bottle light (£968) to Eric Jorgensen's Ox chair (£5,900). The shop offers an impressive sourcing service, as well as exclusive contracts with a number of European manufacturers.

Ryantown

126 Columbia Road, E2 7RG (7613 1510, www.misterrob.co.uk). Hoxton or Shoreditch High Street rail. Open noon-5pm Sat; 9am-4.30pm Sun.

Printmaker Rob Ryan opened this lovely gallery/shop in summer 2008. Tiles, printed tissue paper, screen-prints, paper cut-outs, cards, wooden keys, limited-edition prints, vases, Easter egg cups, even skirts and T-shirts, all bear his distinctive, fun graphics and words – with phrases such as 'The stars shine all day as well' printed on many of the covetable items.

SCP

135-139 Curtain Road, EC2A 3BX (7739 1869, www.scp.co.uk). Shoreditch High Street rail. Open 9.30am-6pm Mon-Sat; 11am-5pm Sun.
SCP is known for its beautiful yet functional pieces, with timeless classics from the likes of Jasper Morrison, Matthew Hilton and Robin Day. Smaller (and cheaper) buys include Donna Wilson's hip knitted toys

City Secret

The annual price-slashing one-day showroom sale at design store **Vitra** (30 Clerkenwell Road, EC1M 5PG, 7608 6200, www.vitra.com) is the stuff of legend. Design aficionados queue for days in the hope of taking home an Eames chair, RRP £3,194, for under £100. If you want to join in the fun, make straight for the piece you want and grab the slip attached to it to bag the sale.

(from £20) and Rob Brandt's crumpled ceramic beakers (from £4.95).
Other location 87 Westbourne Grove, W2 4UL (7229 3612).

Skandium
86 Marylebone High Street, W1U 4QS (7935 2077, www.skandium.com). Baker Street tube. Open 10am-6pm Mon-Wed, Fri, Sat; 10am-7pm Thur; 11am-5pm Sun.
Skandium is one of those shops that takes your breath away when you walk in, thanks to its quirky owl-print Iittala tableware (from £6.50), strokably smooth Artek chairs and jewel-like lighting from the likes of & Tradition, Le Klint and Louis Poulsen.
Other location 247 Brompton Road, SW3 2EP (7584 2066).

Squint
178 Shoreditch High Street, E1 6HU (7739 9275, www.squintlimited.com). Shoreditch High Street rail. Open 10am-6pm Mon-Fri; by appointment Sat; 1-5pm Sun.
Squint's products – easily recognisable by the colourful and distinctive patchwork designs – are now stocked in the likes of Harrods and Liberty, but this is its only stand-alone shop and showroom, where you can see a selection of its bespoke and the bestselling 'ready to go' Chesterfield sofas (from £4,500), iconic Egg chairs and other upholstered furniture. The beautiful coverings are made up of both contemporary and vintage textiles, and all of the pieces are handmade in England.

Suzy Hoodless
27 Chesterton road, W10 5LY (7221 8844, www.suzyhoodless.com). Ladbroke Grove tube. Open 9.30am-6.30pm Mon-Fri.
Design consultant and former *Wallpaper* interiors editor Suzy Hoodless stocks her own chic, distinctive furniture, rug and wallpaper designs alongside a finely edited selection of antiques and 20th-century homeware. The quality is high, as are the prices.

Twentytwentyone ★
274 Upper Street, N1 2UA (7288 1996, www.twentytwentyone.com). Angel tube or Highbury & Islington tube/rail. Open 10am-6pm Mon-Sat; 11am-5pm Sun.
Twentytwentyone stocks an alluring mix of vintage originals, reissued classics and contemporary designs. The main River Street showroom houses furniture, while the smaller Upper Street shop is great for gifts and accessories. It has been expanded to include a basement showroom to display lighting, as well as a few larger items.
Other location 18C River Street, EC1R 1XN (7837 1900).

Unto This Last
230 Brick Lane, E2 7EB (7613 0882, www.untothislast.co.uk). Shoreditch High Street rail. Open 10am-6pm daily.
This unpretentious Brick Lane workshop is dedicated to the small-scale manufacturing of birch plywood and laminate bookcases, cabinets, slatted chairs and beds, all at very reasonable prices. A curved coffee table, for example, costs from £95, though the intricate, undulating Nurbs table is £580.

Viaduct
1-10 Summers Street, EC1R 5BD (7278 8456, www.viaduct.co.uk). Farringdon tube/rail. Open 9.30am-6pm Mon-Fri; 10.30am-4pm Sat.
Viaduct's galleried premises showcase the finest contemporary design, with a particular focus on leading European manufacturers such as Driade, Ox and Droog. You don't have to spend a fortune to pick up a design icon, with affordable pieces such as Magis's Air chair (£80) and Flos's Tab light (£146).

Flowers & gardens

Blooming bouquets, inspiring garden centres and recommended garden designers.

Florists

Most of the major chains will send flowers abroad, including **Interflora** (0870 366 6555, www.interflora.co.uk) and **Teleflorist** (0800 083 0930, www.teleflorist.co.uk).

More and more florists now offer fairtrade flowers. **Flowe(RED)** (0845 218 1435, www.flowered.com) has a fantastic selection of bouquets available online. The **Organic Flower Company** (0845 226 0608, www.tofc.co.uk); **John Lewis** (0845 604 9049, www.johnlewis.com) also sells selected fairtrade bunches.

Columbia Road Market (Columbia Road, Bethnal Green, E2) is a must for cut flowers, shrubs and bedding plants. It runs from 8am to 2pm every Sunday, with cut-price bargains towards the end.

Angel Flowers
60 Upper Street, N1 0NY (7704 6312, www.angel-flowers.co.uk). Angel tube. Open 9am-7pm Mon-Sat; 11am-5pm Sun.
The premises may be small, but the range of bouquets is impressive, ranging from hand-tied posies (from £35) to enormous, show-stopping arrangements of hot tropicals and orchids. They're a favourite for weddings, but equally obliging if you call for a bouquet. The shop delivers to north, north-west and central London, with prices from £30.

Bloomsbury Flowers
29 Great Queen Street, WC2B 5BB (7242 2840, www.bloomsburyflowers.co.uk). Covent Garden tube. Open 9.30am-5pm Mon; 9.30am-5.30pm Tue-Fri.
Personal service is the focus here, so instead of ready-assembled bouquets, staff talk you through the options to create tailor-made seasonal bunches. Good-quality standards like roses and peonies bloom alongside more unusual choices such as scented herbs. Deliveries are in pretty, tissue-lined boxes.

Jane Packer Flowers
32-34 New Cavendish Street, W1G 8UE (7935 2673 shop, 0845 074 6000 delivery, www.janepacker.com). Bond Street tube. Open 9am-6pm Mon-Sat.
This sleek Marylebone store offers a gorgeous range of flowers at reasonable prices, with chic but quirky arrangements from around £40. Nationwide next-day delivery is offered, with a same-day service for addresses within a five-mile radius of the shop, while the website offers an array of seasonal bouquets.

Jennie Mann Floral Designs
63A Church Lane, N2 8DR (8365 2284, www.jenniemann.com). East Finchley tube. Open 9am-5pm Mon; 9am-5.30pm Tue-Fri; 9am-4pm Sat.
This talented north London florist works with seasonal and English flowers whenever possible, with the average bouquet costing around £35. Lovely arrangements feature old-fashioned blooms such as ranunculus, hyacinths and phlox, while nationwide and international delivery is offered.

La Maison des Roses
48 Webbs Road, SW11 6SF (7228 5700, www.maison-des-roses.com). Clapham South tube or Clapham Junction rail. Open 10am-6pm Mon-Sat.
For sheer romance it's hard to top this deliciously pretty – and great-smelling – florist, devoted exclusively to roses, among them headily perfumed garden roses, unusual pink-tipped dolce vita blooms and green

GARDEN DESIGNERS

The Royal Horticultural Society-affiliated **Society of Garden Designers** (*01989 566695, www.sgd.org.uk*) can provide a list of accredited members.

Creative Garden Design
07788 962735.
Stoke Newington-based Rafael Duran offers landscaping, clearance and garden maintenance. Former clients are full of praise for his work.

Lucy Sommers
07813 500327, www.lucysommers gardens.com.
Capel Manor-trained Sommers offers a full design spectrum, from lush sub-tropical to minimalist gravel and stone; her website is a great showcase for her work.

Origin Landscapes
07815 465445, www.originlandscapes.com.
Jay Osman handles construction, maintenance and full garden design, and is 'a consumate professional', according to previous customers.

Rob Bratby Gardens
07811 472799, www.robertbratby gardens.co.uk.
Rob Bratby offers landscaping, design and planting to suit any style of garden, traditional or contemporary, with particular attention paid to ecological concerns. Prices range from around £5,000 to £50,000.

Plantability
07986 542868, www.choose plantability.co.uk.
This Stoke Newington designer trained at Capel Manor and focuses on design and planting plans rather than the build. Design services, including a final plan, average around £500.

Will Nash
8365 3656, 07961 171406.
Garden enthusiast Nash will take on any size of garden in north London, and any size of job, from fencing to full landscaping, patios and ponds. He likes to realise ideas with clients, encouraging them to visit his past projects and talk to previous clients.

Ecuadorian roses. Same-day London orders arrive in smart pistachio green packaging, and there's a next-day nationwide service: delivery costs £5-£15.

Rebel Rebel ★
5 Broadway Market, E8 4PH (7254 4487, www.rebelrebel.co.uk). London Fields rail or 26, 48, 55 bus. Open 10am-6pm Tue-Fri; 10am-5pm Sat.
The proprietor of this fragrant Hackney haven is passionate about seasonal English blooms: last time we dropped in, the heady scent of stocks and lilac filled the shop. Bouquets are beautifully presented, with simple wrapping and ribbons. A delivery service (from £30 a bouquet, plus delivery) covers east, north and central London.

Robbie Honey
7720 3777, www.robbiehoney.com. Open for phone enquiries 9am-5pm Mon-Fri.
Operating out of London's flower market means hot young florist Robbie Honey can select the freshest blooms for his bouquets, starting at £45. The striking arrangements are made up wholly from flowers rather than padded out with foliage, and generally feature just one variety. The team will deliver to any London postcode (from £12.50).

Scarlet & Violet
76 Chamberlayne Road, NW10 3JJ (8969 9446, www.scarletandviolet.co.uk). Queens Park tube. Open 9am-6pm Mon-Sat.
The signature style at this Kensal Green florist is beautifully simple, romantic

bouquets. Staff are happy to make up tiny posies (£5) or bouquets (from £15), though there are ready-assembled bunches. Delivery is £5-£27.

Wild at Heart
Turquoise Island, 222 Westbourne Grove, W11 2RH (7727 3095, www.wildatheart. com). Notting Hill Gate tube. Open 8am-6pm Mon-Sat.
Wild at Heart is vibrant with peonies, delphiniums, hydrangeas and sweet peas in summer, daffs, tulips and anemones in spring. Head office is the WaH flowers and interiors shop in Pimlico, and there are also concessions in Liberty and Harrods.
Other location *54 Pimlico Road, SW1W 8LP (3145 0441).*

Garden centres

NORTH

Camden Garden Centre
2 Barker Drive, St Pancras Way, NW1 0JW (7387 7080, www.camdengardencentre. co.uk). Camden Town tube. Open Apr-Sept 9am-5.30pm Mon, Tue, Fri, Sat; 9am-7pm Wed, Thur; 11am-5pm Sun. Oct-Mar 9am-5pm Mon-Sat; 10am-4pm Sun.
Pick up a rejected perennial in need of some TLC from the bargain section by the entrance, or venture further in for a sterling selection of bedding shrubs, old-fashioned and hybrid tea roses, herbs and climbers. The Garden Services Team can be called in for anything from once-a-month upkeep to turfing, trellising and complete redesigns.

Capital Gardens
Alexandra Palace, Alexandra Palace Way, N22 7BB (8444 2555, www.capitalgardens. co.uk). Wood Green tube or Finsbury Park tube/rail, then W3 bus or Alexandra Palace rail. Open 9am-6pm Mon-Sat; 10.30am-4.30pm Sun.
London's biggest garden centre sticks to tried-and-tested favourites: plenty of bedding standards, plus verdant shrubs and climbers for those too impatient to train their own from

scratch. There are plenty of accessories too, from barbecues to children's gardening kits.

Clock House Nursery
Forty Hill, Enfield, Middlesex EN2 9EU (8363 1016, www.clockhousenursery.co.uk). Enfield Town rail, then 191 bus. Open 9am-5pm daily.
From the profusion of garden centres dotted around Enfield, Clock House is one of the biggest and best. Its high-quality flowers and shrubs are sold almost at wholesale prices, as most are grown on site – a godsend if you're planning a major overhaul.

North One Garden Centre
The Old Button Factory, 25A Englefield Road, N1 4EU (7923 3553, www.n1gc. co.uk). Essex Road rail or 76, 141 bus. Open Apr-Dec 9.30am-6pm Mon-Wed, Fri-Sun; 9.30am-7pm Thur. Jan-Mar 9.30am-5pm Mon-Wed, Fri-Sun; 9.30am-7pm Thur.
With its chic garden accessories and furniture, this diminutive, award-winning garden centre is pitched at style-savvy urbanites. Plants are displayed in artfully assembled displays, making it easy to see what will work together.

EAST

Growing Concerns
2 Wick Lane, at Cadogan Terrace, E3 2NA (8985 3222, www.growingconcerns.org). Bus 8, S2. Open Summer 10am-6pm Tue-Sun. Winter 8am-4pm Tue-Sun.
Tucked between the Hertford Union Canal and Victoria Park, this tranquil, prettily laid-out community garden centre is staffed by an enthusiastic team. Prices are competitive, with perennials from £4.50 and enormous shrubs for around £60. Ice-cream is a welcome sideline.

SOUTH

Dulwich Garden Centre
20-22 Grove Vale, SE22 8EF (8299 1089, www.dulwichgardencentre.co.uk). East Dulwich rail. Open 9am-5.30pm Mon-Sat; 10am-4pm Sun.

Stock ranges from showy climbers and shrubs to seeds, planters and perennials. Herbs are a speciality, with plenty of unusual offerings (bergamot, hyssop, marsh mallow) and numerous varieties of better-known herbs: 20 species of thyme, ten mints and ten lavenders at the last count. In summer, look out for boxes of lettuce and corn seedlings.

Fulham Palace Garden Centre

Bishop's Avenue, SW6 6EE (7736 2640, www.fulhamgardencentre.com). Putney Bridge tube. Open 9.30am-5.30pm Mon-Thur; 9.30am-6pm Fri, Sat; 10am-5pm Sun.
Profits at this friendly, countrified garden centre go to the charity that runs it, Fairbridge, which supports socially and economically alienated young people. There's a flourishing array of bedding plants and shrubs, and helpful staff.

WEST

Clifton Nurseries

5A Clifton Villas, W9 2PH (7289 6851, www.clifton.co.uk). Warwick Avenue tube. Open Apr-Sept 8.30am-7pm Mon-Sat; 10.30am-4.30pm Sun. Oct-Mar 8.30am-5.30pm Mon-Sat; 10.30am-4.30pm Sun.
Founded in 1851, Clifton Nurseries boasts a sophisticated palm house stocked with exotic specimens and an impressive topiary-dotted outdoor space. Along with a comprehensive array of high-quality indoor and outdoor plants, the nursery offers garden design and maintenance services, including useful one-off 'garden tidies'.

C Rassell

80 Earl's Court Road, W8 6EQ (7937 0481). High Street Kensington tube. Open Jan-Mar, mid July-Sept 9am-5.30pm Mon-Wed, Fri, Sat; 9am-6.30pm Thur. Apr-mid July, Oct-Dec 9am-5.30pm Mon-Wed, Fri, Sat; 9am-6.30pm Thur; 11am-5.30pm Sun.
The deliciously old-fashioned Rassell's is ideal for novices. A board outside suggests what to plant in the month ahead, while each species has an informative, handwritten label. There are bedding plants of every hue, as well as plenty of specimens for shady spots.

Ginkgo Garden Centre

Railway arches, Ravenscourt Avenue, off King Street, W6 0SL (8563 7112, www.ginkgogardens.co.uk). Ravenscourt Park tube. Open Mar-Dec 9am-6pm Mon-Sat; 10am-5pm Sun. Jan, Feb 9am-5pm Mon-Sat; 10am-5pm Sun.
Glamorous Ginkgo sits beside Ravenscourt Park, so pulls in fair-weather gardeners with its grandiloquent clipped box and bay trees and gorgeous climber and burgeoning cottage-garden perennials. It's also strong on Mediterranean splendour for the sunny terrace; olives that would do well in big planters, little citrus trees and architectural spiky agaves give instant impact.

Petersham Nurseries ★

Church Lane, off Petersham Road, Petersham, Richmond, Surrey TW10 7AG (8940 5230, www.petershamnurseries.com). Richmond tube/rail. Open 9am-5pm Mon-Sat; 11am-5pm Sun.
There isn't a corner of this celebrated nursery that isn't ravishing, especially in its flowery summer garb. Idyllically set amid Petersham's pastures, there are big blowsy dahlias and planters full of sweet peas and nasturtiums in high season, fruit trees and bushes for autumn planting and bulbs, conifers and evergreens for winter interest. It really is a feast for the eyes – and the stomach too, as Petersham Nurseries is home to Skye Gyngell's fantastic café.

City Secret

If garden centres are just a bit too grubby for your liking, check out a garden boutique instead. Blackheath's **Hortus** (26 Blackheath Village, SE3 9SY, 8297 9439, www.hortus-london.com) and Hampstead's **Judy Green's Garden Store** (11 Flask Walk, NW3 1HJ, 7435 3832) both offer functional but beautiful garden equipment, plants, flowers and an excellent professional service.

GOING OUT
BEAUTY
FASHION
PARTIES
FOOD
HEALTH
ECO
OUTDOORS
HOME
CHILDREN
PETS
TRANSPORT
RESOURCES

Restoration

Make do and mend – with a little expert assistance.

Clocks

The Clock Clinic
85 Lower Richmond Road, SW15 1EU (8788 1407, www.clockclinic.co.uk). Putney Bridge rail/tube. Open 9am-6pm Tue-Fri; 9am-1pm Sat.
Clocks, barometers and musical boxes will be returned to their former glory at this south-west London godsend.

Robert Loomes Clock Repair
168c Marlborough Road, N19 4NP (7477 2224, www.dialrestorer.co.uk). Open by appointment only.
This antique watch and clock repairers and restorers offers quality workmanship, with a 12-month guarantee on work undertaken.

Fabrics & upholstery

Consult the **Association of Master Upholsterers** (029 2077 8918, www.upholsterers.co.uk) for a directory of members, a list of upholstery courses and lots of information and advice.

Atomic Antiques
125 Shoreditch High Street, E1 6JE (7739 5923, www.atomica.me.uk). Shoreditch High Street rail. Open 11.30am-5.30pm Tue-Sun.
This mid-century modern furniture shop specialises in re-upholstering chairs and sofas from the same period.

Austrian Bedding Company
205 Belsize Road, NW6 4AA (7372 3121). Kilburn Park tube. Open 10am-5pm Mon-Sat.
This specialist will turn your old lumpy duvet into a thing of beauty, cleaning and topping up the down, then packing it into a brand-new cover ready for a great night's sleep.

JE Norris
7A Tranquil Passage, SE3 0BJ (8852 8725). Blackheath rail. Open 10am-1pm Mon-Sat.
Upholstering East End furniture since 1945, this reliable family business offers on-site consultations and free estimates.

John Lewis
300 Oxford Street, W1A 1EX (7629 7711, www.johnlewis.com). Oxford Circus tube. Open 9.30am-8pm Mon-Wed, Fri; 9.30am-9pm Thur; 9.30am-7pm Sat; noon-6pm Sun.
If a much-loved piece of furniture needs a good stuffing, a gentle reshaping or a whole new look, John Lewis can help. On selection of an appropriate fabric, they will come to you and give you a free estimate for the job.

Keys
Stephenson Road, Clacton on Sea, Essex CO1 4XA (01255 432518, www.bedlinen centre.co.uk). Open 9am-4.30pm Mon-Sat.
If your favourite eiderdown or duvet is looking a bit down, Keys will supply a bag into which you pack it off to them for restuffing – they can even turn two skinny ones into one fat one. Duvets cost from £185, eiderdowns from £355.

Textile Services Association
8863 7755, www.tsa-uk.org.
The trade association for launderers and dry-cleaners can suggest specialist cleaners in your area for everything from antique fabrics to continental quilts.

William Fountain & Co
68A Cobden Road, E11 3PE (8558 3464, www.williamfountain.com).

Leytonstone tube. Open 8am-6pm Mon-Fri. No credit cards.

This east London family business offers upholstery and re-upholstery, loose covers, and furniture and antique repairs.

Glass & tableware

Blue Crystal
7278 0142, www.bluecrystalglass.co.uk.
Chipped glasses, damaged chandeliers and even cloudy glasses can be repaired.

Bouke De Vries
07765256660.
Specialist in repairing chipped and broken ceramic pieces, whether it be replacing the handle of a favourite teapot or repairing a broken vase; rates start at £40 per hour.

Chinasearch
01926 512402, www.chinasearch.co.uk.
Chinasearch holds thousands of patterns from over 40 glass, cutlery and dinnerware manfacturers, so if you've broken a favourite cup, there's a good chance you'll find it here.

Facets
107 Boundary Road, E17 8NQ (8520 3392, www.facetsglass.co.uk). Leyton tube. Open by appointment only.
If it has glass in it, Facets can probably fix it. The range of services is mind-boggling; antique and modern glass can be restored, hair and clothes brushes rebristled, silver cutlery replated and hourglasses refilled.

Tablewhere?
8361 6111, www.tablewhere.com.
Tablewhere? keeps more than a million pieces of discontinued china, so finding vintage crockery, sourcing missing pieces or extending a dinner service should be a doddle. Prices are reasonable.

Specialist services

If you're looking to restore a treasured antique to its former glory, a really good starting point is the **Conservation Register** (www.conservation register.com). The database allows you to search through hundreds of categories and will provide the names of relevant experts.

Hossack & Gray
Studio 10, 9E Queensyard, White Post Lane, E9 5EN (8986 3345, www.hossack andgray.co.uk). Hackney Wick rail. Open 9.30am-6.30pm Mon-Fri; by appointment Sat.
Antique restoration, expert leather-staining, wood-turning and bespoke furniture.

W Sitch & Co
48 Berwick Street, W1F 8JD (7437 3776, www.wsitch.co.uk). Oxford Circus, Piccadilly Circus or Tottenham Court Road tube. Open 9am-5pm Mon-Fri; 9am-1pm Sat. No credit cards.
W Sitch has occupied this Soho townhouse since 1776. The business buys and sells period lights and can make replicas of lights too. A repair and restoration service is also available on request.

Tile restoration

Mosaic Restoration Company
Verwood House, High Street, West Haddon, Northamptonshire NN6 7AP (01788 510000, www.mosaicrestoration.co.uk). Open 8.30am-5.30pm Mon-Fri.
Gary Bricknell and his team will travel anywhere to deal with mosaic-tile cleaning, polishing or restoration projects. They also offer a bespoke service for Victorian and Edwardian-style geometric floors, pre-fabricated in their workshop.

Tiled Perfection
01920 871555, www.tiledperfection.com.
Established in the 1990s, Tiled Perfection specialise in laying and restoring Victorian tiled floors. Past customers include the V&A, but mere mortals looking to get their garden path spruced up or their entrance hall retiled are also welcomed.

GOING OUT
BEAUTY
FASHION
PARTIES
FOOD
HEALTH
ECO
OUTDOORS
HOME
CHILDREN
PETS
TRANSPORT
RESOURCES

Useful services

Essential services, tradesmen and contacts.

Cleaning

If you need a serious spring clean or end of tenancy clean-up, or can't face the post-party carnage, a specialist cleaning company could be your salvation.

For carpets and windows, the best starting points are the **National Carpet Cleaners Association** (0116 271 9550, www.ncca.co.uk) and the **Federation of Window Cleaners** (0161 432 8754, www.f-w-c.co.uk), both of which will direct you to members in your area. **Jeeves of Belgravia** (*see p67*) also offers rug, carpet and curtain cleaning.

Absolutely Spotless
8932 7360, www.absolutelyspotless.co.uk.
Absolutely Spotless specialises in house-moving and spring cleans. Armed with an industrial hoover, its teams of cleaners guarantee a gleaming finish – and will come back if they've missed anything. Prices start from £90 for a studio apartment. Window cleaning is also offered (£20-£30 for a two-bedroom property if you're having your house cleaned at the same time; from £90 for window-cleaning only), while carpet cleaning is good value at a pound per square yard.

Anyclean
0800 195 1215, www.anyclean.co.uk.
Anyclean undertakes almost any kind of cleaning, including rugs, and house-moving cleans. Domestic cleaning starts at £9 (plus VAT) an hour for a vetted, insured cleaner; contracts are flexible, ranging from weekly three-hour cleans to fortnightly visits.

Cadogan Company
8960 8020.
Cadogan will collect, clean and rehang curtains and fabric blinds (£6.50 per square yard). It also steam cleans carpets, rugs and upholstery (from £30 for an armchair).

Clean'N'Gone
0800 075 7800, www.cleanngone.co.uk.
Clean'N'Gone specialises in cleaning rugs, upholstery and mattresses (£24 for a bedroom carpet), along with regular and one-off domestic cleaning. It charges by the job, so can give you costs upfront; a two-bedroom end of tenancy clean, for example, is £143 (plus VAT and the cost of cleaning materials).

Oven Cleaning Company

01428 717174, www.theovencleaningco.com.
This company tackles one of the nastiest of chores: restoring your encrusted oven to shiny perfection. Non-caustic, non-toxic products are used, with prices from £28 (ex VAT) for a built-in single oven; the average spend is £60.

Perfect Clean

0800 195 7848, www.perfectclean.co.uk.
Post-party blitzes, spring cleans and regular contracts are undertaken, along with carpet and upholstery cleaning. Hourly rates are reasonable: £11 for the spring clean or £12 for the after-party service, say, with a minimum of three hours per visit. You'll pay extra if you don't provide cleaning products.

Computer repair

If you've got an Apple laptop, it's worth knowing about the free one-on-one **Genius Bar** sessions – call 0800 048 0408 to book an appointment.

Geeks on Wheels

0800 107 4110, www.geeks-on-wheels.com. Appointments 8am-9pm Mon-Fri; 9am-5pm Sat, Sun.
Guaranteeing a no fix, no fee service, the 20 technicians who make up Geeks on Wheels aren't cheap at £75 for the first hour, then £37.50 per half hour, but they are British-Standard accredited and get glowing reviews from previous customers. There's a 10% discount for pensioners, nurses and students.

Geek Squad

0800 049 4335, www.geeksquad.co.uk. Appointments 7.30am-8pm Mon-Fri; 9am-5pm Sat, Sun.
We like the *Men in Black* nature of Geek Squad, whose techs dress like FBI agents and solve some problems remotely, taking control of your PC via the net. Home visits start at £100 to fix one problem, regardless of how long it takes; charges for dealing with extra problems then range from £25-£80. The Geeks also have a no fix, no fee guarantee.

Honeylight

54 Moreton Street, SW1V 2PB (7821 0670, www.honeylight.co.uk). Pimlico tube. Open 9am-5.30pm Mon-Fri.
Dealing with PCs and Macs, Honeylight offers free estimates for data recovery and repairs if you take your computer into the shop (it takes a week) and a while-you-wait emergency service, plus call-out engineers who'll come anywhere within the M25 (from £85/hr plus VAT). It's accredited by both Apple and ISO 9002 quality systems, so you're in safe hands.

Mac Daddy

Unit 10, ZLR Studios, West Heath Yard, 174 Mill Lane, NW6 1TB (3393 5098, www.mac-daddy.co.uk). West Hampstead tube. Open by appointment 10am-5pm Mon-Fri. No credit cards.
Mac Daddy's Apple-certified engineers run a Mac Clinic and offer a range of services, including an annual freelance contract (£375) that includes a yearly check-up, priority in the workshop, telephone support and a discounted call-out rate. The pay-as-you-go rate is £70 per hour for business customers and £50 for residential, with a sliding call-out fee based on London zones, and there's a 24-hour repair/upgrade rate of £90 per hour. Prices are exclusive of VAT.

Mike Will Fix It

0776 264 7547, www.mikewillfixit.com. Appointments 9am-9pm Mon-Sat. No credit cards.
The first port of call for any PC owner should be Mike. At just £25 per hour for labour, capped at £90 (for home users) irrespective of job, time or distance, his prices beat most bigger companies hands down. He'll travel to most of London (some areas of north and east London aren't covered) and can usually be there within 24 hours. As a certified Windows support service with years of experience, he should be able to solve any problem. And if he can't, he won't charge you.

PureMacintosh

07956 288958, www.puremacintosh.com. Open 10am-6pm. Mon-Fri. No credit cards.

GOING OUT

BEAUTY

FASHION

PARTIES

FOOD

HEALTH

ECO

OUTDOORS

HOME

CHILDREN

PETS

TRANSPORT

RESOURCES

GOING OUT

BEAUTY

FASHION

PARTIES

FOOD

HEALTH

ECO

OUTDOORS

HOME

CHILDREN

PETS

TRANSPORT

RESOURCES

CONCIERGE SERVICES

You don't need a six-figure salary to use a concierge service these days, thanks to a new breed of companies aimed at Londoners on less lavish budgets. Instead of demanding eye-wateringly expensive yearly membership, they charge by the hour – and the range of services is also broader that you might think. While they can sort out parties, holidays and other delicious frivolities, they can also step in to tackle more tedious everyday tasks, like waiting in for a delivery on your behalf, or organising your paperwork and bills.

Buy:time
0870 486 2624, www.buy-time.co.uk.
Want to organise a surprise party, sort out your bills and long-neglected admin or get the errands you never have time for done in one fell swoop? Buy:time promises to organise your life by the hour, by the day, or via a bespoke plan. There are no joining fees, just an hourly rate of £39, which

is reduced if you buy blocks of time; 20 hours, for example, is charged at £29 per hour (ex VAT).

Cushion the Impact
7704 6922, www.cushion theimpact.co.uk.
If it's legal, moral and feasible, Cushion the Impact will be happy to help. Whether it's organising unpaid bills and unfilled tax returns or tackling time-consuming chores, they'll take it off your hands. The hourly fee is £40, although the more hours you buy, the cheaper the rates then become.

Life's Too Short
7100 3456, www.lifes2short.co.uk.
Lifestyle management comes in at just £29 an hour for regular users of Life's Too Short, or £40 for one-off projects, whether it be finding and booking tradesmen, researching a holiday, getting your filing up to date or helping you move house.

Specialising in Macs and covering all of London, Chris Essex-Hill and Alan Drew of PureMacintosh have over 35 years' combined experience of Macs, dealing with software, hardware, networking, buying advice, upgrades and maintenance. Call-outs cost £75 an hour, though they are also very happy to discuss full- and half-day rates if required.

Scooter Computer
1 Putney Bridge Approach, SW6 3JD (7384 5949, www.scootercomputer.co.uk). Putney Bridge tube. Open 9am-5.30pm Mon-Fri; by appointment Sat. No credit cards.
Happy dealing with both Macs and PCs, Scooter Computer charges an hourly fee of £85 including VAT for the first hour, then a half-hourly rate.

Electricians

Also check out **Home Jane** and **020 Handyman** (*see p161*).

Electrical Contractors' Association
7313 4800, www.eca.co.uk.
This nationwide trade association can provide you with a list of contractors.

National Inspection Council for Electrical Installation Contracting
0870 013 0382/www.niceic.org.uk.
The NICEIC is a regulatory body issuing strict rules to its members; use the online Find an Electrician feature to locate your nearest registered electrician. It also offers an independent complaints procedure, if work doesn't meet its standards.

RJ Electrical

8599 2841/mobile 07836 677836.
Richard James is a general electrician who knows his stuff, returns your calls, and is warmly recommended by former clients. He does rewiring, call-outs and cooker repairs, and is based in north-east London.

Glaziers

The **Glass & Glazing Federation** (0870 042 4255, www.ggf.org.uk) provides a directory of local glaziers.

In addition to the companies listed below, **Ray's Glass & Frames** (*see p145*) takes on domestic glazing jobs and repairs broken windows, charging a £60 call-out fee, plus glass and labour costs.

Absolute Glass

0800 298 1488, www.absoluteglass.net.
Open 7am-4.30pm Mon-Fri.
Undertakes emergency window repair, and fits all types of glass and windows.

Elite Sash Window Company

8275 0770, www.elitesash.com.
Open 9am-5pm Mon-Fri.
The Classic Window Company specialises in overhauling and repairing sash windows.

Sash Window Workshop

0800 597 2598, www.sashwindow.com.
Open 8.30am-5pm Mon-Thur; 8.30am-4.30pm Fri.
A team of joiners, craftsmen and painters can restore, replace, draught-seal, double-glaze and soundproof sash or casement windows.

Handymen

Online forums such as **Rated People** (*see p164*) are a good place to find reliable handymen.

A Woman's Touch ★

7167 2124, www.awomanstouch.org.uk.
Kerrie Keeling and her team are highly recommended for their decorating work, but also take on construction and renovation jobs, from electrical and plumbing jobs through to extensions and loft conversions.

Handyman for Hire

07515 875061,
www.handymanforhire.co.uk.
All kinds of DIY is offered (bar working with gas appliances, or major electrical works), from hanging paintings to custom-building furniture. Most work is costed by the half-day (£175) or day (£275), but there are also hourly rates (£60/first hour, then £25/30mins) and fixed quotes for larger jobs.

Home Jane

0845 832 3639, www.home-jane.co.uk.
From handywomen to plasterers, painters and plumbers, Home Jane offers vetted, fully qualified and insured female home helpers.

Johnny Cashman

07776 231949.
As well as being a great general handyman, Johnny Cashman is a CORGI- registered plumber who can handle both gas central heating and plumbing work.

Kensington Maintenance Company

0845 838 2928, www.k-m-c.co.uk.
Owen Muir at KMC specialises in odd jobs, whether it be getting you into your house when you've locked yourself out, painting and decorating or fixing a leaking tap.

0800 handyman

0800 426396, www.0800handyman.co.uk.
Open 8am-6pm Mon-Fri; 10am-2pm Sat.
The team at 0800 can take on everything from sash window cord replacement to plumbing in sinks, all for a half-hourly rate of £20, plus a £20 call-out charge (ex VAT). 'Prompt, unpatronising and trustworthy,' enthuses one regular user.

020 Handyman

8358 3847, 07881 524592 mobile,
www.020handyman.com.
020 Handyman charges £40 for the first half hour, then £40 for each subsequent hour, up to a maximum daily rate of £240 (labour

GOING OUT

BEAUTY

FASHION

PARTIES

FOOD

HEALTH

ECO

OUTDOORS

HOME

CHILDREN

PETS

TRANSPORT

RESOURCES

costs only, ex VAT). All staff handling plumbing and gas jobs are CORGI-registered and all electricians fully accredited.

Junk collection

In addition to the services listed below, think about donating unwanted items to charity or find out if they can be recycled (see p124); another option is giving them away on **Freecycle** (www.freecycle.org).

Most local councils offer a collection service for bulky goods such as fridges, ovens and furniture – it's often free, or costs around £15-£20 for a pick-up.

Any Junk?
0800 043 1007, www.anyjunk.co.uk.
Any Junk? will take pretty much anything you want to get rid of – and promises to recycle or reuse over a third of it. Prices are based on load size and start at around £50, which includes the services of a two-man team. There's an extra charge for disposing of computer monitors and fridges.

Clutter Clinic
07834 338568, www.clutterclinic.co.uk.
If you're swamped with clutter and need impartial advice on what to get rid of and how to maximise storage space, the Clutter Clinic can help. An initial consultation costs £50 per hour, then it's £60 an hour for the clearing. The company can also help streamline and reorganise your wardrobe, or help you unpack after moving house.

Ecojunk
0800 043 0432, www.ecojunk.com.
Ecojunk collects junk and garden waste, then recycles as much of it as possible. Prices start at £51, though extra charges are levied for collections made outside business hours and disposing of fridges and computer monitors.

Eco Rubbish Clearance Company
0800 988 3061, www.ecorubbish clearance.co.uk.
Another eco-aware operation, which sends a two-strong team and van to collect your junk

– and promises to sweep up afterwards. Prices start at £45 (but do head upwards of this too so confirm by phone) and labour included for the first two hours. There's also a free scrap car collection service.

Locksmiths & keyholding companies

The **Master Locksmiths Association** (0800 783 1498, 01327 262255 non-emergencies, www.locksmiths.co.uk) can also help you to find a qualified locksmith in your area.

Delta Security
181 Dalston Lane, E8 1AL (8985 1855, www.deltasecurity.net). Hackney Downs rail. Open 8am-5pm Mon-Fri.
As well as offering all manner of locks and security systems, Delta will get you into your house if you're locked out. The call-out and labour charge is around £65, not including the cost of a new lock, if required.

Farringdon Locksmith & Tool Supplies
29 Exmouth Market, EC1R 4QL (7837 5179). Angel tube. Open 8am-5.30pm Mon-Fri; 8am-5pm Sat.
This helpful locksmith offers emergency lock services across London, with charges starting at around £65, plus the cost of a replacement lock.

SpareKeys
0870 069 5397, www.sparekeys.com.
SpareKeys will hold on to a set of your car, office and house keys; if you then lock yourself out, you can call them 24/7 and they'll get you back in. The annual membership fee is £39, with a £20-£30 charge for each call out: more expensive than relying on neighbours, but more reliable too.

Tony Andrews
299 Mill Hill, NW7 2QL (8444 7300, www.tonyandrews.net). Open 8.30am-6pm Mon-Sat; 11am-5pm Sun.

This long-established local locksmiths provides a good emergency call-out service.

Plumbers

Two trade bodies cover plumbing, the **Association of Plumbing & Heating Contractors** (0121 711 5030, www.competentpersonsscheme.co.uk) and the **Institute of Plumbing & Heating Contractors** (01708 472 791, www.plumbers.org.uk). Both can provide lists of contractors.

All Go Plumbing
0800 083 2215, www.allgoplumbing.co.uk.
Alan Good and his team cover a wide range of plumbing jobs, from bespoke bathrooms to humble blocked loos.

Aqua-Care
0800 389 2238, www.24hrlondon plumber.co.uk.

A CORGI-registered emergency specialist offering a one-hour service with no call-out fee.

Dyno
0800 000999, www.dyno.com.
Part of British Gas, Dyno offers a fast, reliable service and friendly staff.

Kate Churchill
07733 333727.
A dependable, fairly priced service, covering selected areas of north London.

Leakbusters
0800 328 8125, www.leakbusters.net.
Plumbers whose work comes in under the original quote due to unexpected savings are hard to find: this is a north London gem.

Mainbreak Plumbing
07917 108876.
Craig and Simon are CORGI-registered to carry out gas boiler work, but also take on tiling jobs and complete bathroom refits.

FLATPACK ASSEMBLY

Em FlatPack
8861 0889, www.emflatpack.co.uk.
The 23-strong team offers a set rate for most jobs and reasonable hourly rates; £35 for the first hour, then £20 for each subsequent hour.

Fearless Mike
01273 711166, www.fearlessmike.com.
Can't bear the thought of queuing for that IKEA wardrobe, never mind assembling it? IKEA specialists Mike Ear and his team will buy, deliver and assemble it for you. Delivery costs from £25, assembly from £30 per hour for a one-man job.

Put 'Em Up
8427 0054, www.putemup.co.uk.
This Harrow-based company is a dab hand at assembling everything from

kitchens to garden sheds. A telephone quote is available for most items: a chest of drawers, for example, is £40.

Screwdriver
0800 454828, www.screwdriver-flatpack.co.uk.
Screwdriver charges a fixed rate if the item you need assembling is in its database, so you know exactly what you'll pay. Other items are charged by the hour (£48), then £10 per 15 minutes. If you're moving house, staff can dismantle furniture too.

Unflatpack Company
7460 2600, www.unflatpack.com.
John Griffin's company assembles pretty much any piece of furniture that comes in a box. It costs £7/15mins, with a £20 call out charge and a minimum of an hour's work required.

GOING OUT
BEAUTY
FASHION
PARTIES
FOOD
HEALTH
ECO
OUTDOORS
HOME
CHILDREN
PETS
TRANSPORT
RESOURCES

GOING OUT

BEAUTY

FASHION

PARTIES

FOOD

HEALTH

ECO

OUTDOORS

HOME

CHILDREN

PETS

TRANSPORT

RESOURCES

Rosie Riley
8692 3375, 07932 566039.
Rosie Riley covers south-east London for all types of plumbing work, but will travel further afield for major work.

Removals

The **British Association of Removers** (01923 699480, www.bar.co.uk) represents over 500 removal and storage companies, all of them covered by its Office of Fair Trading-approved code of practice; search online for London-based firms.

Register with the excellent (and free) **www.iammoving.com**, who will inform a personalised list of companies, such as utilities, of your new address. **The Post Office** (0845 722 3344, www.postoffice.co.uk) can redirect mail to your new address, charging from £7.64 for a month.

Cadogan Tate Moving & Storage
0800 988 6011, www.cadogantate.com.
This long-established firm is one of London's smartest: there are personal move planners and special crates for delicate items.

Fast Forward
8888 1050, www.ffg123.com.
Fast Forward will move anything anywhere in the UK.

Movers Not Shakers
7630 9005, www.moversnotshakers.co.uk.
Movers Not Shakers caters for all sizes of job, from a simple 'man-with-a-van' service (from £40/hr) to big international moves.

Nifty Shifty ★
0800 1777 213, www.niftyshifty.co.uk.
Nifty Shifty's team is brilliant, say past users: professional, organised, reliable and calm.

Roger's Removals
8953 6777, www.rogersremovals.co.uk.
This reliable Finchley firm has been in the removals business for almost 40 years.

Shirley's Removals
7254 5580.
Originally specialising in moving house for the gay community, this small but well-run removals firm promises to treat your possessions with care and move them swiftly.

Tool hire

HSS Hire
www.hss.com.
This fairly-priced tool-hire company has outlets across London.
Other locations *across the city.*

Tool Chest
68 Iffley Rd, W6 0PB (8748 7912, www.toolchesthire.co.uk). Hammersmith tube. Open 8am-5pm Mon-Fri; 9am-2pm Sat.
This Hammersmith-based tool and plant hire company will deliver, or you can go along to the shop. Prices are competitive: a cordless drill costs a tenner to use for a 24-hour period.

Trade associations & useful contacts

A number of websites offer directories of tradesmen with user-generated reviews, allowing you to read previous customers' comments on all kinds of companies, from plumbers to interior designers. Sites include **Problem Solved** (www.problemsolved.co.uk) and **HomePro** (0870 734 4344, www.homepro.com). At **Rated People** (0870 220 8810, www.ratedpeople.co.uk), you're asked to submit a description of the job, then tradespeople submit quotes – but you can still check comments from former customers.

It's best to employ a member of a trade association that demands adherence to a strict code of practice. If you have legal concerns, contact the **Office of Fair Trading** (0845 722 4499, www.oft.gov.uk), or consult its Shoppers' Rights, which explains your legal rights as a consumer.

Children

GOING OUT

BEAUTY

FASHION

PARTIES

FOOD

HEALTH

ECO

OUTDOORS

HOME

CHILDREN

PETS

TRANSPORT

RESOURCES

Activities

We've scoured London for the very best crafty, creative, musical and messy children's activities – all used by real parents.

Drop-in activities

There are hundreds of drop-in activities in London, and most museums offer crafts at weekends. For under-fives there's also an extensive network of one o'clock clubs, many with structured activities; check with your local council. And on public holidays, all sorts of unlikely venues teem with workshops.

ARTS & CRAFTS

Art 4 Fun
172 West End Lane, NW6 1SD (7794 0800, www.art4fun.com). West Hampstead tube/rail. Open 10am-6pm Mon, Wed, Thur, Sat, Sun; 10am-8pm Tue; 10am-10pm Fri. Fees £5.95/day plus materials; workshops call for details.
Kids can learn how to make a mosaic, or decorate various wood, glass, fabric or ceramic items (from £3.50) with non-toxic paints; if you've opted for ceramics, staff will glaze and fire your masterpiece. Workshops for six- to 11-year-olds, covering all kinds of art techniques, run in school holidays.

Artsdepot
5 Nether Street, N12 0GA (8369 5454, www.artsdepot.co.uk). West Finchley or Woodside Park tube. Open 9am-5.30pm Mon-Fri; 10am-5.30pm Sat, Sun. Session times vary; call for details. Fees from £7/session.
The glorious Messy Play sessions at this stylish community arts centre allow pre-schoolers (ten months to three years) the chance to get down and dirty with tubs full of paint. There are also term-long art,

dance and drama courses for kids aged three or over, plus children's shows every Sunday in the theatre.

Geffrye Museum ✈
136 Kingsland Road, E2 8EA (7739 9893, www.geffrye-museum.org.uk). Hoxton rail. Open 10am-5pm Tue-Sat; noon-5pm Sun. Fees free.
The first Saturday of the month brings workshops for five- to 16-year-olds, including wig-making, lotion-mixing (using lavender from the beautiful herb garden), silhouetting and more. The museum also runs family-friendly Summer Sunday events and free half-term workshops for three- to 15-year-olds covering everything from trifle-making to puppet design.

V&A Museum of Childhood
Cambridge Heath Road, E2 9PA (8983 5200, www.vam.ac.uk/moc). Bethnal Green tube. Open 10am-5.45pm daily. Fees free.
Art activities at the V&A are well thought out and substantial, with parent and toddler workshops most Fridays and special holiday activities for over-fives. Kids can also follow a gallery trail through the museum's awesome collection of toys, filling in the clues to track down a missing toy.

COOKING

La Cucina Caldesi
118 Marylebone Lane, W1U 2QF (7487 0750, www.caldesi.com). Baker Street or Regent's Park tube. Open 10.30am-12.30pm Sat. Fees £40/session.
Not content with having a great restaurant in Marylebone, the Caldesi family also built a small cookery school around the corner. It offers children's classes one Saturday a

month and in the school holidays, with sessions aimed at different age groups (six to 12s and teenagers). The courses aim to teach kids how to prepare a menu based on healthy seasonal ingredients, while the teenagers' courses are targeted at budding chefs who already have some experience.

Kids Cookery School

107 Gunnersbury Lane, W3 8HQ (8992 8882, www.thekidscookeryschool.co.uk). Acton Town tube. Open Office 9am-5.30pm Mon-Fri. Fees School hols £15/75mins; £30/2.5hrs; £50/5hrs. No credit cards.
Acton's Kids' Cookery School (a registered charity) has purpose-built kitchens that exist primarily to teach the principles of healthy cooking and eating to children. During term time, the centre concentrates on local schoolkids, but throughout the holidays cookery sessions for children of three and above are offered on a bookable basis. Sessions vary in length according to what's on the menu and fees are low considering all ingredients are included in the price. Assisted places are available for those on low incomes.

CREATIVE WRITING

Children's Writers & Illustrators in South London

cwislenquiries@hotmail.com.
Send this enterprising group of authors an email and they will reply with regular newsletters, advertising everything from poster illustration workshops (threes to 12s) to intensive writing courses for over-eights. The activities are Lambeth-based and held on an ad hoc basis, but are well worth looking out for; the writers involved have a real talent for inspiring youngsters.

DANCE & MUSIC

East London Dance

Stratford Circus, Theatre Square, E15 1BX (8279 1050, www.eastlondondance.org). Stratford tube/rail. Classes times vary; phone for details. Fees free.
This East End dance centre runs free hip hop and street dance classes for children aged

City Secret

The crowning glory at the **Horniman Museum** (100 London Road, SE23 3PQ (8699 1872, www.horniman. ac.uk) is its magnificent aquarium, refurbished in 2006. It houses over 200 species of aquatic life in 14,000 litres of water, divided into seven distinct zones, but it's the superb interactive displays and wonderful live exhibits – including mesmerising jellyfish and British seahorses – that make this place such a treat. When he died, the museum's eponymous Victorian founder bequeathed it to the people of London, so entrance is absolutely free.

eleven and above. Led by professionals, sessions are exhilarating (and exhausting).

Handel House Museum

25 Brook Street, W1K 4HB (7495 1685, www.handelhouse.org). Bond Street tube. Open 10am-6pm Tue, Wed, Fri, Sat; 10am-8pm Thur; noon-6pm Sun. Admission £5; £2-£4.50 reductions, free under-5s.
Family-friendly musical events take place on selected weekends. Although most workshops are aimed at older kids, toddlers are allowed. The museum's curators are passionate about spreading a love of classical music to children.

It's a Kid's Thing

279 Magdalen Road, SW18 3NZ (8739 0909, www.itsakidsthing.co.uk). Earlsfield rail. Open 9am-6pm daily. Fees £2-£5.
This family-run venue is loved by parents because of its healthy café, party rooms and indoor play zone. The music and dance classes (including Baby Ballet and Sing & Sign) are popular. Other activities include baby massage and messy art. Book ahead.

Jackson's Lane

269A Archway Road, N6 5AA (8341 4421, www.jacksonslane.org.uk). Highgate tube.

GOING OUT

BEAUTY

FASHION

PARTIES

FOOD

HEALTH

ECO

OUTDOORS

HOME

CHILDREN

PETS

TRANSPORT

RESOURCES

Open 10am-10pm Tue-Sat; 10am-5pm Sun.
Fees from £5/session.

The studios in this arts centre are always buzzing with some kind of workshop. For older kids, street dance (nine to 15s) is popular. The venue is also home to a good café, a toddler group and children's theatre productions. Classes change sporadically, so check the website.

NATURE

Oasis Children's Nature Garden ★
Larkhall Lane, SW4 2SP (7498 2329, www.oasisplay.org.uk). Stockwell tube. Open Term-time 3.30-5.30pm Wed-Fri; 10am-3.30pm Sat. School hols 10am-3.30pm Mon-Fri. Admission £1-£2.

A riotous little patch of the countryside in inner London, Oasis runs a Saturday Nature Club, charging £2 per child. Children of all ages are welcome, though under-fives must be supervised. The digging pit (a patch of mud that kids are allowed to dig and water without bothering seedlings) and the heavily populated frog pond are the big draws.

SPORT & YOGA

Albert & Friends' Instant Circus
St Alban's Church Hall, Margravine Road, W6 8HJ (8237 1170, www.albertandfriends instantcircus.co.uk). Barons Court tube. Classes times vary; phone for details. Fees £8.50/session.

These Saturday morning sessions are great fun, with general circus skills classes for three to sevens and eight to 16s kicking off the day, then more specialised lessons such as static trapeze and corde lisse in the afternoon.

Triyoga
6 Erskine Road, NW3 3AJ (7483 3344, www.triyoga.co.uk). Chalk Farm tube. Class times vary; check website for details. Fees £6.50.

Triyoga starts 'em young with its popular pregnancy yoga sessions, post-natal 'Mummy & Me' yoga classes, before moving on to sessions for kids (for ages four to eight, and eight to 13 respectively). Drop-in is available for most classes. There are baby massage sessions too.

City farms & zoos

Admission to the following farms and zoos is free, unless otherwise specified, but donations are always appreciated.

Battersea Park Children's Zoo
Queenstown Road, Battersea Park, SW11 4NJ (7924 5826, www.batterseazoo.co.uk). Sloane Square tube, then 19, 137 bus/ Battersea Park or Queenstown Road rail/ 156, 345 bus. Open Summer 10am-5.30pm daily. Winter 10am-4pm daily. Admission £7.50; £6-6.50 reductions; free under-2s; £25 family.

Tiny things for tiny tots are the order of the day at Battersea's zoo, as playful otters, lively meerkats, a mouse doll's house and a wide range of other friendly critters keep the little ones delighted for hours.

Freightliners City Farm
Paradise Park, Sheringham Road, off Liverpool Road, N7 8PF (7609 0467, www.freightlinersfarm.org.uk). Caledonian Road or Holloway Road tube/Highbury & Islington tube/rail. Open Summer 10am-4.45pm Tue-Sun. Winter 10am-4pm Tue-Sun. No credit cards.

In the heart of Islington, this farm teems with a wide variety of animal activity. The inhabitants range from cows, sheep, geese, cockerels and bees to impressively sized rare breeds, like the super-sized giant Flemish rabbits. You can buy hen and duck eggs of all hues in the shop, along with own-grown fruit and veg for tea.

Hackney City Farm
1A Goldsmiths Row, E2 8QA (7729 6381, www.hackneycityfarm.co.uk). Cambridge Heath Road rail, then 26, 48, 55 bus. Open 10am-4.30pm Tue-Sun, bank hols.

Set against the urban backdrop of Hackney Road, this popular farm is a genuine urban oasis. A wide array of animals, including rare-breed pig Bella the saddleback, delight

GOING OUT

BEAUTY

FASHION

PARTIES

FOOD

HEALTH

ECO

OUTDOORS

HOME

CHILDREN

PETS

TRANSPORT

RESOURCES

the throngs. Frizzante Café is another draw, along with regular pottery and craft classes for adults and children.

Kentish Town City Farm ★
1 Cressfield Close, off Grafton Road, NW5 4BN (7916 5421, www.ktcityfarm.org.uk). Chalk Farm tube/Kentish Town tube/rail/ Gospel Oak rail. Open 9am-5pm daily. No credit cards.
London's oldest city farm stretches into pasture and well-tended vegetable gardens by the railway line. A pond with a dipping platform is full of frogs, and a riding school is the scene of weekend pound-a-go pony rides.

Mudchute City Farm
Pier Street, E14 3HP (7515 5901, www.mudchute.org). Crossharbour, Mudchute or Island Gardens DLR. Open 9am-5pm daily. No credit cards.
London's biggest city farm offers a surreal experience: standing in a meadow full of sheep while taking in the skyscrapers of Canary Wharf. You're allowed to feed many of the animals (goats, geese and horses).

Spitalfields City Farm
Buxton Street, off Brick Lane, E1 5AR (7247 8762, www.spitalfieldscityfarm.org).
Whitechapel tube. Open Summer 10am-4.30pm Tue-Sun. Winter 10am-4pm Tue-Sun. No credit cards.
This spick-and-span community farm features geese honking about in a lovely space, where poultry, gardeners and livestock produce free-range eggs, seasonal vegetables and manure (respectively).

Stepney City Farm
Stepney Way, at junction with Stepney High Street, E1 3DG (7790 8204, www.stepney cityfarm.org). Stepney Green tube. Open times vary, phone for details.
A full complement of farmyard creatures hunker down next to old railway carriages full of straw bales, all rubbing along together nicely in the shadow of St Dunstan's Church.

Surrey Docks Farm
South Wharf, Rotherhithe Street, SE16 5ET (7231 1010, www.surreydocksfarm.org.uk). Canada Water tube, then 381, C10 bus. Open 10am-5pm Tue-Sun. No credit cards.
The riverside location, a yard patrolled by naughty goats (it pays to keep your chocolate out of sight), paddocks filled with farmyard animals and a resident blacksmith all combine to make Surrey Docks Farm a firm favourite.

Vauxhall City Farm

165 Tyers Street, SE11 5HS (7582 4204/ www.vauxhallcityfarm.info). Vauxhall tube/ rail/2, 36, 44, 77 bus. Open 10.30am-4pm Wed-Sun. No credit cards.
You can't miss this charming, community-staffed farm as you get off the train, as your senses are assailed by the unmistakeable farmyard byre aroma. Inhabitants include chickens, rabbits, goats, horses and some very friendly pigs.

ZSL London Zoo

Outer Circle, Regent's Park, NW1 4RY (7722 3333/www.zsl.org). Baker Street or Camden Town tube, then 274 or C2 bus. Open Mar-June, Sept, Oct 10am-5.30pm daily. Nov-Feb 10am-4pm daily. Last entry 1hr before closing. Admission (including £1.70 voluntary contribution) £19.80; £18.30 reductions; £16 3-15s; free under-3s; £65 family (2+2 or 1+3).
The biggest and arguably the best of the capital's animal encounters, this is where you can meet uncaged monkeys, feed the penguins, watch dramatic birds of prey displays and learn all about buglife. Don't miss the steamy, tropical Blackburn Pavilion bird house.

Playgrounds

On sunny days, you can't beat **Coram's Fields** (*see p176*); if the weather's too wet for its petting zoo, sandpits and

---

AFTER-HOURS ADVENTURES

Book your place and pack your toothbrush: several of London's most famous attractions now offer children (and their parents) the rare opportunity to stay the night.

Monthly Science Night Sleepovers at the **Science Museum** (Exhibition Road, SW7 2DD, 7942 4747, www.sciencemuseum.org.uk) are action-packed. For £35 per person (the smallest group size is one adult and five children), you can take part in an evening of science shows, hands-on workshops and an IMAX 3D film. Next morning it's up bright and early for breakfast, a drawing contest and, finally, prize-giving. Phew.

History buffs might prefer to sleep among the statues in the **British Museum** (Great Russell Street, WC1B 3DG, 7323 8000, www.british museum.org) – a rare treat held three or four times a year for Young Friends of the BM and guests of existing members (membership is £20/yr) and book well in advance. Pitching camp in the Egyptian sculpture galleries is an unforgettable experience, and there's a different theme at each event (emperors, pre-history, the Olympics).

For anyone who fancies themselves as the next David Attenborough, Dino Snores at the **Natural History Museum** (Cromwell Rd, SW7 5BD, 7942 5000, www.nhm.ac.uk) is the hot ticket (£45). Visitors are taken by torch-light into the darkest depths of the museum, discovering clues along the way to solve a nature puzzle. Explorers can recover from their adventure by watching a film, or a show by leading naturalists before falling asleep under the watchful eye of the 150-million-year-old Diplodocus, in the iconic Central Hall.

Would-be pirates, meanwhile, can enlist as crew members aboard the **Golden Hinde** (Pickfords Wharf, Clink Street, SE1 9DG, 0870 011 8700, www.goldenhinde.com). Dressed as sailors, children aged six to 12 take part in actor-led workshops on barber surgery, navigation, and anchor-raising, scoff stew from pewter plates and round off the night with a mock battle before kipping on the gun deck.

swings, great indoor alternatives include **It's a Kid's Thing** (*see p167*).

Diana, Princess of Wales' Memorial Playground
Near Black Lion Gate, Broad Walk, Kensington Gardens, W8 2UH (7298 2117, 7298 2141 recorded information, www.royal parks.gov.uk). Bayswater tube/70, 94, 148, 390 bus. Open times vary, phone or check website for details. Over-12s must be accompanied by a child.
Dominated by a huge pirate ship surrounded by white sand, this is a wonderland for tinies. Other attractions include a tepee camp, tree-house encampment and the swingiest baby swings in town. In summer, there's a paddling pool with plugs, so that children can change the water flow, plus free school holiday entertainment. Much of the equipment is accessible to children with special needs.

Glamis Adventure Playground
Glamis Road, E1W 3DQ (7702 8301, www.glamisadventure.org.uk). Shadwell DLR. Open Term-time 3.15-7pm Mon (girls only); 3.15-7pm Tue-Fri; 10am-4pm Sat. School holidays 10am-5.30pm Mon-Fri. Times may vary, phone for details.
As well as massive play structures, swings and slides, this award-winning adventure playground has a vegetable garden and den-building area. Designed for children aged eight and over, it also runs summer sleepovers and barbecues.

Highgate Wood & Queen's Wood
Muswell Hill Road, N10 3JN (8444 6129, www.cityoflondon.gov.uk/openspaces). Highgate tube. Open 7.30am-dusk daily.
This under-12s playground is well equipped for wheelchair users, with accessible swings and a sensory bridge. Old favourites include the sandpit, rope slides and pyramid, while the adjoining Queen's Wood has swings strung from the trees.

Kidspace
Colonnades, 619 Purley Way, Croydon, Surrey CR0 4RQ (8686 0040, www.kidspace adventures.com). Waddon rail/119, 289 bus.

Open Term-time 10am-7pm Mon-Thur; 10am-8pm Fri; 9am-8pm Sat; 9am-7pm Sun. School hols 9am-7pm Mon-Thur, Sun; 9am-8pm Fri, Sat. Admission Adults £2.75-£5.50; children £5.50-£8.95; free under-1s.
Rather than the usual indoor soft play structures, Kidspace's giant climbing frames are made from sustainable timber, with parents encouraged to climb in too. The resulting atmosphere is joyous. A soft play area for toddlers, go-karts, mini-golf and a 27-foot climbing wall make this kid (and dad) heaven. It's for under-13s only.

Parsloes Park
Parsloes Avenue/Gale Street, Dagenham, Essex RM9 5QP (8595 4155, www.lbbd. gov.uk). Becontree tube. Open dawn-dusk daily.
A teen area has joined the established children's playground, with tubular slides, a two-person skyway and rodeo board. Natural rock seating, mounds and 29 newly planted trees keep this playground green.

Queens Park
Kingswood Avenue, NW6 6SG (8969 5661, www.cityoflondon.gov.uk/openspaces). Queens Park tube/rail. Open Park 7.30am-dusk daily. Zoo Sumer 11am-7pm Mon-Fri; 1-5pm Sat, Sun. Winter 11am-6pm Mon-Fri; 1-5pm Sat, Sun.
This north London playground has a colossal sandpit, a paddling pool (filled in May, which is earlier than most pools) and a small children's zoo. There are separate areas for under-fives and fives to 12s.

St Giles-in-the-Fields
60 St Giles High Street, WC2H 8LG (7240 2532, www.stgilesonline.org). Open Summer 7am-dusk daily. Winter 8.30am-dusk daily.
Tucked behind Shaftesbury Avenue Odeon, this West End playground is an essential piece of London parent knowledge. It's a basic affair with swings, a roundabout and two slides – nothing groundbreaking, but fantastic for your kids to let off some steam after a hard morning spent trawling the shops of Covent Garden or Oxford Street.

GOING OUT
BEAUTY
FASHION
PARTIES
FOOD
HEALTH
ECO
OUTDOORS
HOME
CHILDREN
PETS
TRANSPORT
RESOURCES

Address Book Secrets
Karen Hastings
Founder of Cupcake members' club and spa

I created **Cupcake** (10 Point Pleasant, SW18 1GG, 8875 1065, www.cupcakemum.com) because I wanted to make a place where mums-to-be and mums could get the support they need – and also indulge themselves from time to time. Membership includes the whole family, so dads are welcome, too – and we have classes and spa treatments tailored to men as well as women. The **Treatment Rooms** at Cupcake are open to non-members too – we've won awards for our pregnancy treatments, so they're well worth a try. We offer a host of antenatal and birth preparation classes at Cupcake.

We also really like **Baby Confidence** (8605 9125, www.babyconfidence.co.uk), which runs some great classes around London to help new mothers with the challenges of the early weeks.

There are lots of lovely designs around for babies and toddlers. **Petit Bateau** (73 Ledbury Road, W11 2AG, 7243 6331, www.petit-bateau.com) is a reliable choice. I also really like **Lush Baby** (www.lushbaby.co.uk). They stock Olive & Moss (www.oliveandmoss.com) – it offers a welcome departure from all of the pink and blue clothes you normally see.

Feather & Stitch (54 Hill Street, TW9 1TW, 8332 2717, www.featherandstitch.com) has some really good clothes for pregnant women – and not all of it is officially 'maternity' either. **JoJoMamanBébé** (68 Northcote Road, SW11 6PL, 7228 0322, www.jojomamanbebe.co.uk) is brilliant too.

A wonderful resource for interacting with local mums and other pregnant women is **Nappy Valley Net** (www.nappyvalleynet.com). It's especially useful for first-time mums to connect with others. That's one of the reasons I started Cupcake. But if you can't come to the club, I definitely recommend connecting online with women who are at the same stage of life. And to help get organised before the baby comes, I recommend **Wizz2U** (www.wizz2u.com). I have been using them for years and they're a godsend!

For relaxation, the Cupcake spa is fantastic (especially the Warm Wishes massage and facial). But I also love a run around **Clapham Common** (www.claphamcommon.org) to unwind. Another outdoor space I adore is **Cannizaro Park** (www.cannizaropark.org.uk) in Wimbledon – it's relatively undiscovered too.

I love **Borough Market** (Southwark Street, SE1 1TL, 7407 1002, www.boroughmarket.org.uk) but it's definitely not a secret! It gets really crowded, so those with children are better off visiting on Thursdays.

The **Museum of London in Docklands** (West India Quay, E14 4AL, 7001 9844, www.museumindocklands.org.uk) is great for children. They have specific sessions for toddlers with stories, music sessions and creative play. It's free too. I also like the **Museum of Childhood** (Cambridge Heath Road, E2 9IA, 8983 5200, www.vam.ac.uk/moc).

Eating out

Good food for kids can be hard to find. The eateries below not only have excellent menus, but are places where families can happily hang out for an afternoon.

Restaurants & cafés

From the big chains, our favourites are **Wagamama** (noodles, rice dishes and fresh juices), **Pizza Express** (the Piccolo menu offers three courses for £6.10) and **Carluccio's** (exceedingly tot-friendly). **Park cafés** are generally very child-friendly too, *see p130*.

CENTRAL

Rainforest Café
20 Shaftesbury Avenue, W1D 7EU (7434 3111, www.therainforestcafe.co.uk). Piccadilly Circus tube. Meals served noon-10pm Mon-Fri; 11.30am-8pm Sat; 11.30am-10pm Sun. ££.
Children are thrilled by the animatronic animals, jungle noises and waterfalls, but another big plus is that the menu here has been approved both by the Soil Association and Allergy UK. Items are marked for their absence of gluten, dairy or egg – so you can order gluten-free sausage and mash, or egg-free pasta with organic salmon and vegetables. At £11.95 for two courses it isn't cheap, but that's par for the course in the centre of town.

Tate Modern Café: Level 2 ★
2nd floor, Tate Modern, Sumner Street, SE1 9TG (7401 5014, www.tate.org.uk). Southwark tube/Blackfriars or London Bridge tube/rail. Meals served 10am-5.30pm Mon-Thur, Sun; 10am-9.30pm Fri; 10am-7.30pm Sat. £-££.
The Tate Modern Café prides itself on the sourcing of its menu; catch of the day from Newlyn boats, real Lancashire cheesecake

and fresh Dorset crab might feature. Children are given crayons and activity sheets, and can choose smaller portions from the adult menu for £6.95. There's also a children's menu, served between 11am and 3pm for £5.10.

NORTH

Camden Arts Centre Café
Arkwright Road, NW3 6DG (7472 5516, www.camdenartscentre.org). Finchley Road tube/Finchley Road & Frognal rail. Meals served noon-4pm Tue, Thur-Sun; noon-7pm Wed. £.
This serene café is one of the loveliest spots to lunch in north London, especially if you bag a table on the lavender-planted terrace. There's plenty of room for buggies, plus books and puzzles to keep children busy. The menu ranges from sourdough and granary sandwiches to child-friendly light bites (own-made houmous with pitta, bruschetta) and mini portions of the daily special.

That Place on the Corner
1-3 Green Lanes, N16 9BS (7704 0079, www.thatplaceonthecorner.co.uk). Highbury & Islington tube/rail or Canonbury rail, or 21, 73, 141, 276, 341, 476 bus. Meals served 9.30am-6.30pm Mon-Thur; 9.30am-8pm Fri; 9.30am-8.30pm Sat; 9.30am-6pm Sun. £.
Parents here have no worries about annoying their table neighbours – adults aren't allowed in unless they're with a child. There's a biggy park by the door, an inviting play area and daily music, arts and crafts sessions. The children's menu is a run-down of old favourites like sausage and mash, pasta, pizza, burgers and cottage pie, all own-made

GOING OUT

BEAUTY

FASHION

PARTIES

FOOD

HEALTH

ECO

OUTDOORS

HOME

CHILDREN

PETS

TRANSPORT

RESOURCES

GOING OUT

BEAUTY

FASHION

PARTIES

FOOD

HEALTH

ECO

OUTDOORS

HOME

CHILDREN

PETS

TRANSPORT

RESOURCES

and served with a portion of vegetables. Babies are also catered for with a daily organic vegetable purée. For grown-up customers there are cakes and good coffee.

EAST

Mudchute Kitchen

Mudchute Park & Farm, Pier Street, E14 3HP (7515 5901, www.mudchute kitchen.org). Crossharbour, Mudchute or Island Gardens DLR/D6, D7, D8 bus. Open 9am-5pm Tue-Sun. Meals served 9am-4pm Tue-Sun. £.

Overlooking the stables and open from breakfast until teatime, the café at London's largest city farm is a wonderfully homespun affair. Almost everything on the seasonal, daily-changing menu is sourced on the farm, including goose smoked in the on-site smokehouse. Children can choose half portions from the main menu or tuck into a selection of nursery favourites.

SOUTH

Bodean's

169 Clapham High Street, SW4 7SS (7622 4248, www.bodeansbbq.com). Clapham Common tube. Meals served noon-3pm, 6-11pm Mon-Fri; noon-11pm Sat; noon-10.30pm Sun. £-££.

ICE-CREAM PARLOURS

Gelateria Danieli

16 Brewers Lane, Richmond, Surrey TW9 1HH (8439 9807, www.gelateria danieli.com). Richmond tube/rail. Open 10am-8pm Mon-Wed; 10am-10pm Thur-Sat; 11am-10pm Sun. Times may vary; call to check.

Connoisseurs of all ages flock to this Richmond hole-in-the-wall to sample the superlative ice-creams and sorbets, made with fresh fruit and minimum additives. Flavours range from cinnamon and plum or *dulce de leche* to classic raspberry ripple; scoops are an absolute steal at £2 each.

Other locations *across the city.*

Marine Ices

8 Haverstock Hill, NW3 2BL (7482 9003, www.marineices.co.uk). Chalk Farm tube. Open noon-11pm Tue-Sat; noon-10pm Sun.

Generations of children have scoffed chocolate sauce-slathered banana splits, peach melbas and sundaes at this sweetly old-fashioned gelateria, opened by the Mansi family in 1930. If you're en route to Primrose Hill, order a cone at the takeaway hatch.

Morelli's at Harrods

Harrods Food Halls, 87-135 Brompton Road, SW1 7XL (7893 8959, www. morellisgelato.com). Knightsbridge tube. Open 9am-9pm Mon-Sat; noon-6pm Sun.

For truly show-stopping sundaes, this is the place to come. With 24 hours' notice you can commission your own bespoke flavour to take home, for £14.45 per litre plus the cost of your chosen ingredients.

Oddono's

14 Bute Street, SW7 3EX (7052 0732, www.oddonos.com). South Kensington tube. Open 11am-11pm Mon-Thur, Sun; 11am-midnight Fri, Sat.

Truly top-notch ingredients (Valrhona chocolate, Piedmont hazelnuts, Madagascan vanilla pods) mean even the simplest *gelati* taste sublime here, though grown-ups may be tempted by more sophisticated combinations such as chocolate and cognac.

Parlour Restaurant

Fortnum & Mason, 181 Piccadilly, W1A 1ER (7734 8040, www.fortnum

Ice hockey on the TV and plastic cows gazing down keep juniors occupied while waiting for their meal of chicken, burger or ribs with mash or fries at this cheery barbecue joint. At this branch (and the Fulham outpost) kids eat free with a paying adult every day between noon and 5pm.

Other locations *across the city.*

Crumpet ★

66 Northcote Road, SW11 6QL (7924 1117, www.crumpet.biz). Clapham Junction rail. Meals served 9am-6pm Mon-Sat; 9.30am-6pm Sun. £.

Set in the middle of south London buggy territory, this café is intimate with the needs

andmason.co.uk). Green Park or Piccadilly Circus tube. Open 10am-7.30pm daily.

For sheer indulgence, Fortnum's first-floor ice-cream parlour is hard to beat. The children's menu offers sumptuous sundaes for £8 or dual scoops for £6, while adult options include fantastic bellini sorbets and wonderfully innovative sundaes, starring unusual ingredients such as stem ginger and honeycomb or marmalade and lemon curd.

Scoop

40 Shorts Gardens, WC2H 9AB (7240 7086, www.scoopgelato.com). Covent Garden tube. Open 11am-9.30pm daily. Times may vary; call to check.

This Italian-run gelateria offers a sublime array of flavours: kids will love the creamy, hazelnut-studded *bacio*, while the other 23 flavours include heady amaretto or ricotta and caramelised figs. Sorbets, such as passion fruit, melon and blackberry, contain real fruit. Gluten- and sugar-free ices are available, as are nifty takeaway coolboxes.

of its well-heeled clientele and their offspring. There's a well-stocked play corner and bookshelf, space for pushchairs and a bathroom with free nappies and a child-size loo. Proper tea, scones, imaginative sandwiches and cakes are a speciality.

WEST

Le Cercle

1 Wilbraham Place, SW1X 9AE (7901 9999, www.lecercle.co.uk). Sloane Square tube. Lunch served noon-3pm, dinner served 6-11pm Tue-Sat. £££.

All credit to this smart Sloane Square establishment for reaching out to families with its 'Petits Gourmets' dégustation menu. At lunchtimes, the five-course menu is free for under-12s accompanied by an adult eating à la carte. Beleaguered parents might be amazed, but dishes such as pumpkin with star anise slip down remarkably well.

Giraffe

270 Chiswick High Road, W4 1PD (8995 2100, www.giraffe.net). Turnham Green tube. Meals served 8am-11pm Mon-Fri; 9am-11pm Sat; 9am-10.30pm Sun. £-££.

Numerous parents have recommended Giraffe – and this branch, adjacent to Chiswick Common, was singled out for particular praise. Staff fuss over youngsters, presenting them with a balloon at the door, while the well-balanced kids' menu (£4.75 for a main course and a drink) always goes down a treat.

Other locations *across the city.*

Gracelands

118 College Road, NW10 5HD (8964 9161, www.gracelandscafe.com). Kensal Green tube. Meals served 8.30am-5pm Mon-Fri; 9am-5pm Sat; 9.30am-3pm Sun. £.

The regularly changing kids' menu (£3.50) at Gracelands features the likes of pasta with own-made pesto or bolognese and sausage and mash. Main menu options run from splendid quiches to salads and ciabatta, but many parents pop in just to chat over coffee while toddlers investigate the play corner.

GOING OUT

BEAUTY

FASHION

PARTIES

FOOD

HEALTH

ECO

OUTDOORS

HOME

CHILDREN

PETS

TRANSPORT

RESOURCES

GOING OUT

BEAUTY

FASHION

PARTIES

FOOD

HEALTH

ECO

OUTDOORS

HOME

CHILDREN

PETS

TRANSPORT

RESOURCES

Parties

The following entertainers and venues have been recommended by parents (and children) who have used them. Relax and enjoy.

Entertainers

Jenty the Gentle Clown
07957 121764, www.jentythegentle clown.com.
Specialising in parties for the under-threes, Jenty can also hype it up with a disco and limbo dancing for kids up to 11. Traditional games, face painting. magic and singalongs with the banjo are all part of the fun. Jenty charges £145 for one hour, £195 for two.

Jigsaw
8447 4530, www.jigsaw-arts.co.uk.
For smooth-running themed parties, call in this north London stage school's teachers, who moonlight as entertainers. Spellbinding takes the children (from three to 12 years) through wizard school, while would-be pirates can go treasure hunting. Prices start at £120 for an hour.

Juggling John
0845 644 6659, www.jugglingjohn.com.
Circus skills (with a fair amount of juggling, naturally), magic, escapology and edge-of-the-seat storytelling keep even fidgety guests enraptured. Prices start at £185 for an hour.

Karma Drama
07956 932561, www.karmadrama.co.uk.
Karma Drama can arrange anything from simple singalongs for toddlers (£120/ 90mins) to all-singing, all-dancing 'MTV Star' parties. Drama and West End musical-themed events are also fun. A two-hour extravaganza with props and costumes, led by four staff, costs around £500.

Lily Lou Entertainment ✷
07763 911061, www.fairyparty.co.uk.

Lily Lou Entertainment's fairy parties (pirate and circus parties and glitter discos also available) come highly recommended by children and grown-ups alike. Sussex-based, they travel to London for an additional £50 fee (a standard two-hour fairytale party comes in at £170) and will have little ones mesmerised with a mixture of balloon animals, magic, songs, stories and prizes.

Venues

Chislehurst Caves
Old Hill, Chislehurst, Kent BR7 5NB (8467 3264, www.chislehurstcaves.co.uk). Chislehurst rail.
Little gremlins can enjoy a spooky tour of the caves, with ghost stories and a bat-shaped cake. Packages cost from from £60 (for a maximum of 20 children and four adults), plus £4.50 a head for food.

Colour House Children's Theatre
Merton Abbey Mills, Watermill Way, SW19 2RD (8542 5511, www.colourhousetheatre. co.uk). Colliers Wood tube.
Your party gets front seats for the show at this delightful children's theatre, ending with the cast singing *Happy Birthday* to the blushing birthday boy or girl. Once the rest of the audience has left, the empty theatre is yours. Prices for the show and venue hire, with no extras, start at £110 for ten guests.

Coram's Fields ✷
93 Guilford Street, WC1N 1DN (7837 6138, www.coramsfields.org). Russell Square tube. Open 9am-dusk daily.
A party at this lovely, centrally located playground is a steal: you can hire a room, complete with kitchen, for £70 an afternoon.

Discover

383-387 High Street, E15 4QZ (8536 5555,
www.discover.org.uk). Stratford tube/rail/DLR.
Dedicated to creating stories, this is a perfect
party venue, and a Story Builder
accompanies the children. You bring the food,
so prices come in at £6.50-£8.50 per guest.

Little Dinosaurs

The Actual Workshop, The Grove,
Alexandra Park, N22 7AY (8444 1338,
07957 457771, www.littledinosaurs.co.uk).
Alexandra Palace rail.
Unlike many indoor adventure play centres,
Little Dinosaurs is a thoroughly pleasant
venue for all the family. You'll find the usual
playframe set up with slides and tunnels, but
the venue not only has windows, it's also in
the middle of a lovely park. Parties (£12 per
child) include your own dinosaur host, 45-60
minutes on the playframe, a party tea and
party bags.

IN THE CLUB

Forget playspaces in giant retail parks
and grimy church halls. For a price
(and many parents swear it doesn't
work out to be much more pricey than
the cost of their children's usual
weekly activities) you and your brood
can join a members' club for families
and recline (or play) in super-stylish
environs feeling very pleased with
yourselves indeed.

Cupcake

10 Point Pleasant, SW18 1GG (8875
1065, www.cupcakemum.com).
Wandsworth Town rail. Open 9am-9pm
Mon-Thur; 9am-6pm Fri, Sat. Fees
£1,250/yr; £125/mth.
Cupcake caters to mums-to-be and
families with young children with a
great café and a host of classes
(included in the fees), activities and
spa treatments. There are antenatal
classes, yoga, pilates, spa treatments
and baby showers. For children there
are fantastic play equipment and
classes including baby massage,
cookery, art and toddler football. Mums
and dads can get stuck into fitness
sessions (bootcamp, pilates or 'daddy
karate', perhaps), chill out in the spa or
enlist Cupcake's nanny-finding service.

Maggie & Rose

58 Pembroke Road, W8 6NX (7371
2200, www.maggieandrose.com).
West Kensington tube. Open 9am-
6pm Mon-Fri; 10am-5pm Sat, Sun.
Fees £500/yr; £200/term; £120-
£280/class.
Members of Kensington-based Maggie
& Rose have access to a softplay
area, cinema, playroom and café.
There are also a host of classes,
including ballet, art and cookery, and
spaces available for birthday parties.

Purple Dragon

Alexandra Avenue, SW11 4FN (7801
8688, www.purpledragonplay.com).
Clapham Junction rail. Open 9am-
6pm. Fees vary; phone for details.
This swanky members' club for
families offers (for a substantial
price) state-of-the-art play facilities
and activities tailored to different
age groups, a host of classes (in
everything from art, music and
cookery to languages, pilates and
yoga; additional fees charged),
a reading room, science lab, art
zone and water pod, after-school
and homework clubs. There's also
a garden, a terrace and a restaurant
and café serving locally sourced,
organic food. For adults there's free
Wi-Fi, plenty of space to relax, spa
treatments and a drop-off service for
those needing to get on with chores
elsewhere. A new venue is planned
in Chelsea in late 2010.

GOING OUT

BEAUTY

FASHION

PARTIES

FOOD

HEALTH

ECO

OUTDOORS

HOME

CHILDREN

PETS

TRANSPORT

RESOURCES

Shopping

For the complete lowdown on children's shops in London, consult Time Out's annually updated *London's Best Shops* guide: the following are a few of our favourite smaller boutiques.

All-rounders & gifts

Bob & Blossom
140 Columbia Road, E2 7RG (7739 4737/ www.bobandblossom.com). Hoxton rail. Open 9am-3pm Sun.
Bob & Blossom sells retro knitted toys and rattles, guitars, spinning tops, and its own-label stripey Ts and cheeky slogan hats.

Born
168 Stoke Newington Church Street, N16 0JL (7249 5069, www.borndirect.com). Bus 73, 393, 476. Open 9.30am-5pm Tue-Fri; 9.30am-5.30pm Sat; noon-5pm Sun.
Natural, organic and fair trade pregnancy products, baby equipment and clothes fill the shelves, from babygros and cotton nappies to sturdy scooters and brightly painted toys. Practical gear includes Ergo's organic cotton

baby carrier and sleek buggies from the likes of Phil & Teds and Bugaboo. There's ample space for children to play, and a sofa for breastfeeding mothers.

Green Baby ★
345 Upper Street, N1 0PD (7359 7037, www.greenbaby.co.uk). Angel tube/Highbury & Islington tube/rail. Open 9.30am-5.30pm Mon-Fri; 10am-5pm Sat; 11am-5pm Sun.
Founded in 1999, Green Baby remains a first port of call for eco-conscious parents, selling organic cotton baby basics (from £5.50 for a short-sleeved bodysuit) and a sterling selection of washable nappies, along with Tushies gel-free disposables, nursery equipment and strokably soft sheepskins.
Other locations *5 Elgin Crescent, W11 2JA (7792 8140); 52 Greenwich Church Street, SE10 9BL (8858 6690).*

Igloo
300 Upper Street, N1 2TU (7354 7300, www.iglookids.co.uk). Angel tube/Highbury & Islington tube/rail. Open 10am-6.30pm Mon-Wed; 10am-7pm Thur; 9.30am-6.30pm Fri, Sat; 11am-5.30pm Sun.
A one-stop shop for everything from sweet melamine tableware and hobby horses to Anne Claire Petit's quirky crocheted toys. The clothes (newborn to eights) include Mini-A-Ture's delicate dresses and smocks and No Added Sugar's bold, slogan-print Ts.
Other locations *80 St John's Wood High Street, NW8 7SH (7483 2332); 227 King's Road, SW3 5EJ (7352 4572).*

JoJo Maman Bébé
68 & 72 Northcote Road, SW11 6QL (7228 0322 maternity, 7223 8510 baby & children, www.jojomamanbebe.co.uk).

City Secret

There are lots of good reasons to visit a toy library and saving money and space at home are just two of them. They tend to stock specialist and educational toys, games and puzzles and lend them out for up to six weeks at a time. They usually provide drop-in play sessions for the local community too. Membership rules vary from library to library, but fees are always kept low. For a list of toy libraries in your area, contact the **National Association of Toy & Leisure Libraries** (7428 2288, www.natll.org.uk).

CHIC MATERNITY SHOPS

It's impossible to cover maternity wear without a mention of the mighty **Topshop** (214 Oxford Street, W1W 8LG, 7636 7700, www.topshop.com), whose ground-floor maternity department offers chic, affordable styles, plus a small, adorable range of baby togs (girls only – sorry, chaps).

Blossom Mother & Child

164 Walton Street, SW3 2JL (7589 7500, www.blossommotherandchild. com). South Kensington tube. Open 10am-6pm Mon-Sat; noon-5pm Sun.
Blossom's owners have a gift for sourcing pregnancy-friendly pieces from hot designers; the Clements Ribeiro range is a store exclusive, and there are specially adapted jeans from hip names like J Brand. The own-brand line includes cocktail frocks (from £325) and perfectly cut trousers (£149). **Other locations** *69 Marylebone High Street, W1U 5JJ (7486 6089). Harrods, 4th Floor, 87-135 Brompton Road, SW1X 7XL (7730 1234).*

Crave Maternity

4 Duke Street, TW9 1HP (8940 8255, www.cravematernity.co.uk). Richmond tube/rail. Open 10am-6pm Tue-Sat; 11am-5pm Sun.
Filling a much-needed niche between high street and high fashion, Crave's designs range from boyfriend jeans (£69) to sweet summer dresses and elegant black frocks (from £65).

9 London by Emily Evans

8 Hollywood Road, SW10 9HY (7352 7600, www.emilyevansboutique.com). Earl's Court tube. Open 10am-6pm Mon-Sat.
Head here for amazingly flattering day and evening dresses and you'll be following in the footsteps of a whole host of celebrities. You'll pay around £65 for a deliciously pretty sundress; more for opulent silk evening attire.
Other locations *Harrods, 4th Floor, 87-135 Brompton Road, SW1X 7XL (7730 1234).*

Clapham Junction rail. Open 9.30am-5.30pm Mon-Sat; 11am-5pm Sun.
Best known as a catalogue retailer of all things child-related, JoJo's also has a mini-chain of stores in London's nappy valleys (Putney, Turnham Green, Finchley and Dulwich). Friendly staff and a strong ethical trading ethos add to the appeal.
Other locations *across the city.*

Mini Kin

22 Broadway Parade, N8 9DE (8341 6898). Bus 41, W7. Open 9.30am-5.30pm Mon-Sat; 10.30am-4.30pm Sun.
As well as Burt's Bees toiletries, accessories and clothes from the likes of Imps & Elfs, Mini Kin has a hairdressing salon out back. Animal chairs, colourful decor and friendly staff help coax reluctant tots into the hot seat; cuts cost from £10.95.

Trotters

34 King's Road, SW3 4UD (7259 9620, www.trotters.co.uk). Sloane Square tube. Open 9am-7pm Mon-Sat; 10.30am-6.30pm Sun.
A shop of many parts, Trotters sells clothes, books, toys and accessories, as well as running a hairdressing station. The shoe concession, staffed by expert fitters, runs a loyalty card scheme for regulars.
Other locations *throughout the city.*

Clothes & shoes

Biff

41-43 Dulwich Village, SE21 7BN (8299 0911, www.biffkids.co.uk). North Dulwich rail/P4 bus. Open 9.30am-5.30pm Mon-Fri; 10am-6pm Sat.

GOING OUT
BEAUTY
FASHION
PARTIES
FOOD
HEALTH
ECO
OUTDOORS
HOME
CHILDREN
PETS
TRANSPORT
RESOURCES

With separate areas devoted to footwear, childrenswear and babies' clothes, Biff makes head-to-toe shopping pleasantly painless for harassed parents and their offspring.

Olive Loves Alfie ★
84 Stoke Newington Church Street, N16 0AP (7241 4212, www.olivelovesalfie.co.uk). Finsbury Park tube/rail, then 106 bus, or

73, 393, 476 bus. Open 10am-5.30pm Mon-Fri; 10am-6pm Sat; 10am-5pm Sun.
Gorgeous prints and colourful stripes dominate this sweet boutique, which steers clear of anything pink and frilly or plastered in logos.

One Small Step One Giant Leap
3 Blenheim Crescent, W11 2EE (7243 0535, www.onesmallsteponegiantleap.com). Ladbroke Grove tube. Open 10am-6pm Mon-Fri; 9am-6pm Sat; 11am-5pm Sun.
Part of an expanding mini-chain, this airy, attractive shoe shop and its cheery staff offer top-notch British and European brands, covering everything from back-to-school sensibles to delicate ballet pumps.
Other locations *across the city.*

Petit Aimé
34 Ledbury Road, W11 2AB (7221 3123, www.aimelondon.com). Notting Hill Gate tube. Open 10am-6.30pm Mon-Sat.
The children's offshoot of French womenswear boutique Aimé (next door at no.32) is the epitome of Gallic chic, with understated, deliciously stylish dresses and separates for newborn to ten-year-olds.

So Tiny London
64 Great Titchfield Street, W1W 7QH (7636 2501, www.showroom64.com). Oxford Circus tube. Open 11am-6pm Mon-Fri.
A great source of presents for new babies, So Tiny London stocks a small but well-edited array of labels (newborn to tens, though the emphasis is on younger children). We love Dandy's retro T-shirts, Maria Collins' old-fashioned bonnets and Bonnie Baby's cashmere and cotton knits.

Soup Dragon
27 Topsfield Parade, Tottenham Lane, N8 8PT (8348 0224, www.soup-dragon.co.uk). Finsbury Park tube/rail, then W7 bus. Open 9.30am-6pm Mon-Sat; 11am-5pm Sun.
Gorgeous – and affordable – clothes. Expect lesser-known labels and contemporary styles – we love the clover-print PJs (from £9.50).
Other locations *106 Lordship Lane, SE22 8HF (8693 5575).*

PARTY BAGS

Happy Green Earth
0845 388 0931, www.happygreen earth.com.
Heart- or robot-shaped organic chocolate lollies and wooden toys and puzzles prove going green needn't be dull and worthy: the wooden pirate pop guns (£2) and wool purses (£2.50) are particularly sweet.

Letterbox
0844 557 5263, www.letterbox parties.co.uk.
Letterbox's website offers almost 100 party bag gems, from parent-friendly french knitting sets and paper aeroplane kits to child-pleasing noisy putty and bog-eyed bugglies. Many cost under £2.

Little Cherry
01784 470570, www.little cherry.co.uk.
Little Cherry's eco ethos means its party bags are filled with lovely wooden toys (from spinning tops or skipping ropes to chunky beads). Pre-filled bags start at under £4.

Party Party
For listings, *see p75.*
Most of Party Party's traditional party bag fillers cost under a pound. Fortune-telling fish can be yours for 20p a throw, while whoopee cushions are a mere 75p.

Pets

Whether you need a parlour to groom your pooch to perfection or a replacement gerbil in a hurry, there are tried-and-tested options below.

Dog-friendly pubs

Brown Dog
28 Cross Street, SW13 0AP (8392 2200, www.thebrowndog.co.uk). Barnes Bridge rail or bus 209. Open noon-11pm Mon-Sat; noon-10pm Sun.
Aptly, the logo at this laid-back local is a chap walking his dog: well-behaved pets are welcome in the cosy bar and dining area, or pretty beer garden. The gastropub fare is accomplished and, this being Barnes, even the dog treats are a cut above: pigs' ears and bones are generally available (some free, some not), while resident mutt Willow looks on from his basket.

Grapes
76 Narrow Street, E14 8BP (7987 4396). Westferry DLR. Open noon-3pm, 5.30-11pm Mon-Wed; noon-11pm Thur-Sun.
This ancient, beam-filled riverside pub remains popular with east London pet owners. After a pint of ale, and an equally refreshing bowl of water or ice cubes for your dog, head across the road for a brisk walk in Ropemakers' Field.

Hope
1 Bellevue Road, SW17 7EG (8672 8717, www.thehopepub.co.uk). Wandsworth Common rail. Open noon-11pm Mon-Wed, Sun; noon-midnight Thur-Sat.
The smartly turned-out Hope is well placed to cater for dog-walkers heading to the common, and has made a virtue out of doing so. A nearby pottery has been commissioned to cast personalised bowls for the pub's regulars, while jars of treats await in the doggy snack area. It's an exceedingly pleasant spot to while away an afternoon,

with an impressive range of international beers and obscure draught ales available.

Mucky Pup ★
39 Queen's Head Street, N1 8NQ (7226 2572, www.myspace.com/muckypupn1). Angel tube. Open 4pm-1am Mon-Sat; 1pm-midnight Sun.
A sign on the door reading 'strictly no under-18s unless they've got four legs' sets the tone at this earthy, unpretentious boozer. Staff are happy to provide dogs with bowls of water and free snacks, while Wi-Fi and a free jukebox add to the appeal for their owners.

Prince's Head
28 The Green, Richmond, Surrey TW9 1LX (8940 1572). Richmond tube/ rail. Open 11am-11pm Mon-Sat; noon-10.30pm Sun.
The management at this Fuller's pub stock up on chews and biscuits on a weekly basis – offered free of charge, along with water – and dogs are warmly welcomed. Choose from the sterling range of real ales (ESB, Chiswick, London Pride) that can be enjoyed at one of the outdoor tables overlooking Richmond Green.

Spaniards Inn ★
Spaniards Road, NW3 7JJ (8731 8406, www.thespaniardshampstead.co.uk). Hampstead tube/210 bus. Open noon-11pm daily.
Conveniently located for walks on the heath, the Spaniards is the only pub we know with its own semi-automated dog wash on the premises; buy a token from the bar for a shampoo, rinse and dry. Dog biscuits are on sale and pooches are allowed anywhere on the premises – although there's a strict leads policy because of the cats in the garden.

PET SITTERS

Dogs & Kisses
8244 5377, 07837 952553,
www.dogsandkisses.co.uk.
Doggie daycare and home-from-home
boarding. Fees from £30 a day.

Cats, Dogs & Peace of Mind
100 Clements Road, SE16 4DG
(7394 8319, www.cdpom.com).
Cats and other small pets are looked
after in your home (from £11.87 a
visit). Dog-walking is available (from
£13.57 a visit), as is daycare for dogs
and overnight boarding (from £30).

Elaine Hicks
07788 934280
Elaine walks dogs in Shoreditch and
Highbury. Prices are £10 per hour for
your first dog; second or extra dogs
can be walked at the same time for
£5 each. Elaine can also pet-sit for
you (price on application).

London Cattery
456 Hornsey Road, N19 4EF (7272
3354, www.londoncattery.com).
Prices at this cattery start at £7.32
per day (more for larger cages and
Christmas or bank holiday bookings).

Silverdale Boarding Kennels
& Cattery
Bedfont Road, Feltham, TW14
8EE (8890 1784, www.silverdale-
kennels.com).
Cats boarding starts at £9.76 a day;
dogs from £13.62 (both + VAT).

Grooming parlours

A good groomer should be happy to let
you see the salon's facilities, and talk you
through procedures. He or she should be
able to carry out scissor/clipper work, plus
hand stripping (plucking out the dead coat)
and anal gland, teeth, nail and skin care.
Cats should be groomed away from dogs.

In addition to the salons listed below,
Primrose Hill Pets (*see p186*) and
Mutz Nutz Dog Spa (*see p186*) offer
excellent grooming services.

Dog About Town
196 Bellenden Road, SE15 4BW (7358
9709). Peckham Rye rail. Open 9.30am-5pm
Tue-Sat. No credit cards.
This is a no-nonsense cat and dog grooming
parlour of 40 years' standing. Small dogs are
clipped fom £30; larger varieties from £50.

Dogs Delight
4 Station Parade, Burlington Lane, W4 3HD
(8995 4040, www.dogs-delight.net). Chiswick
rail. Open 10.30am-4.30pm Mon-Sat.

Run by a mother-and-daughter team, Dogs
Delight offers a doggy day crèche and
boarding, dog walking and cat sitting, in
addition to professional grooming services.
Prices for cats start at £50, while dogs depend
on the size and breed. Pre-book, unless it's for
a quick walk-in treatment (from £8).

Top Dog Grooming
598 Kingston Road, SW20 8DN (8542
9449, www.topdoggrooming.co.uk). Raynes
Park rail. Open 9am-4pm Mon-Fri; 9am-
1pm Sat. No credit cards.
Bathing costs from £20, grooming and
clipping from £30, while prices for a quick
nail-trim or ear-clean start at £6. Top Dog
also caters for sensitive skins, and can treat
for fleas and various skin conditions.

Waggin' Tails
366 Fulham Road, SW10 9UU (7823 3111,
www.waggintailsonline.com). Fulham
Broadway tube. Open 10am-5pm Mon, Sat;
10am-6pm Tue, Wed, Fri; 10am-7pm Thur.
This friendly Fulham cat and dog grooming
salon offers everything from pedicures to
reflexology and aromatherapy baths (clips

from £30, treatments cost from £7). Cats' 'bed and breakfast' is available at £12 a night, while doggy day care costs from £6 per hour.

Pet shops

Animal Fair of Kensington
17 Abingdon Road, W8 6AH (7937 0011, www.animal-fair.co.uk). High Street Kensington tube. Open 9.30am-6pm Mon-Sat; 11am-5pm Sun.
This deceptively large Kensington outlet has been a local institution for more than 50 years, selling fish, hamsters, gerbils, rats, guinea pigs and rabbits. There's a wide selection of food and accessories for pets of all kinds, including radio-controlled mice for frustrated felines. The shop also offers a dog grooming service (from £30).

Aquatic Design Centre
109 Great Portland Street, W1W 6QG (7580 6764, www.aquaticdesign.co.uk). Portland Street tube. Open 10am-8pm Mon-Thur; 10am-7pm Fri; 10am-6pm Sat; 11am-5pm Sun.
One of the world's leading bespoke fish tank designers, with clients including Harrods and Selfridges, Aquatic Design promises to turn your underwater dreams into reality. Its central London store also stocks a good range of more standard equipment, as well as more than 300 tanks full of an astonishing array of marine, tropical and coldwater fish, starting from just 95p.

Canonbury Veterinary Practice
226-228 Essex Road, N1 3AP (7359 3888, www.canvet.com). Essex Road rail. Open 8am-7pm Mon-Fri; 9am-5pm Sat; 10am-2pm Sun.
This small but well-stocked pet shop sells treats, toys, food, litter, bedding and assorted pet paraphernalia. It's attached to a vet's surgery, which checks and approves all of the products that are stocked, so quality is high and there's nothing gimmicky. Puppy socialisation and basic training classes run on Tuesday evenings, costing £15 for the first two sessions, then £5 a time.

Chiswick Pets
32-34 Devonshire Road, W4 2HD (8747 0715, www.chiswickpet.co.uk). Turnham Green tube. Open 9am-6pm Mon-Sat; 11am-4pm Sun.
Husband-and-wife team Eileen and Raymond pride themselves on offering customers personalised, expert advice. As well as a full range of foods and accessories for all pets, including birds, the shop stocks small mammals such as rabbits, guinea pigs, hamsters and rats, along with reptiles (including lizards and tortoises) and coldwater and tropical fish. They're also very careful about selling to responsible owners – so staff won't sell fish without ensuring that their new tanks will be fitted with the correct filters, for example.

Holly & Lil ★
103 Bermondsey Street, SE1 3XB (3287 3024, www.hollyandlil.co.uk). London Bridge tube/rail. Open 11.30am-6.15pm Tue, Wed; 11.30am-7pm Thur; 10.30am-6.15pm Fri; 10.30am-5pm Sat.
Holly & Lil's dog collars and leads are all handmade, luxurious and on-trend; there are limited-edition collections – the winning Toto in the BBC's *Over the Rainbow* wore the Rainbow collar, while the calf leather Cross of St George was a must-wear for the 2010 World Cup – in all materials (leather, tartan, Harris tweed) and all styles ('charm collars' are adorned with beads, tiny multicoloured dice, or semi-precious stones). Prices start at around £40, rising to £120 for the heavily adorned Boho models. The shop also sells a range of harnesses and charity collars (for a cause), and cats get a look in too with their own line of collars.

Kings Aquatic & Reptile World
26 Camden High Street, NW1 0JH (7387 5553, www.kingsreptileworld.co.uk). Mornington Crescent tube. Open 10am-6pm Mon-Sat; 10am-2pm Sun.
Reptile expert Simon King set up this exotic pet shop, supplying arachnids, snakes, amphibians, invertebrates and reptiles, in 1997. Any squeamish readers out there can relax, though – all the creatures are safely

GOING OUT

BEAUTY

FASHION

PARTIES

FOOD

HEALTH

ECO

OUTDOORS

HOME

CHILDREN

PETS

TRANSPORT

RESOURCES

GOING OUT
BEAUTY
FASHION
PARTIES
FOOD
HEALTH
ECO
OUTDOORS
HOME
CHILDREN
PETS
TRANSPORT
RESOURCES

ensconced in their cages. Prices vary widely depending on the rarity of the specimen; a tarantula will set you back between £10 and £200, lizards go for £8 to £800 and baby corn snakes are £45. King also breeds rare monitor lizards and runs a handy pet-sitting service. Crickets, locusts and frozen mice are for sale for pets' snacks, and there are all sorts of cages on offer too.

Mungo & Maud

79 Elizabeth Street, SW1W 9PJ (7467 0820, www.mungoandmaud.com). Sloane Square tube or Victoria tube/rail or 11 bus. Open 10am-6pm Mon-Sat.

A boutique with a touch of French sophistication, this is the ultimate 'dog and cat outfitters'. Fed up with her dog's outmoded accessories clashing with her modern home, dog-lover Nicola Sacher decided to design her own range to fill the niche. Stylish and minimalist, pooch products include the likes of washable dog beds, collars and leads, and the Petite Amande shampoo and fragrance range (from £18.50), which can be used by dogs and humans alike; for kitty, there's the likes of catnip and some lovely embroidered wool cat blankets.

Mutz Nutz

221 Westbourne Park Road, W11 1EA (7243 3333, www.themutznutz.com). Ladbroke Grove or Westbourne Park tube. Open 10am-6pm Mon, Fri, Sat; 10am-7pm Tue-Thur; noon-5pm Sun.

As the name suggests, the treats from this attractive boutique will drive cats and dogs (or their owners) crazy. On the shelves you'll find toys, leads, handmade jewel-encrusted collars (£50-£200), organic nibbles, toothbrushes – even dog nappies. There are also special dog car seats and, bizarrely, wedding dresses with veils. Cats are equally well catered for, with catnip spray and a three-sided 'scratch lounge'. The nearby same-owned Dog Spa (22 Powis Terrace, W11 1JH, 7243 3399) offers Italian baths: pets are tended to by personal groomers and leave fully coiffed, perfumed and ribbon clad.
Other locations *Mutz Nutz Dog Spa, 22 Powis Terrace, W11 1JH (7243 3399).*

Primrose Hill Pets

132 Regent's Park Road, NW1 8XL (7483 2023, www.primrosehillpets.co.uk). Chalk Farm tube. Open 9am-6pm Mon-Sat; 11am-5pm Sun.

MISSING PETS

If your pet goes missing, contact local police stations, vets and animal rescue centres (*see p187*); to find your local police station, visit www.met.police.uk. The **RSPCA** also recommends ringing its cruelty and advice line (0300 123 4999) – open 24 hours a day, seven days a week. You should also call the animal warden at your local council (normally within the environmental health division), who has responsibility for registering strays.

    Battersea Dogs & Cats Home (*see p187*) also has a lost dogs and cats line (0901 477 8477) for Londoners, while the **Missing Pets Bureau** (0870 199 9999, www.pets bureau.com) operates a national

missing pets register and has links to over 12,000 rescue centres and other organisations. You should also make your own posters and put them up in the local area.

    To safeguard your pet, register it with the **UK National Missing Pets Register** (www.nationalpetregister. org), who'll provide you with a unique ID that can be engraved on your pet's collar. You should also get your pet microchipped, so that if found, it can be identified; it costs £15-£30. This generally includes membership of **Petlog** (0844 4633 999, www.petlog. org.uk), which holds your address details alongside the ID number and runs a 24-hour reunification service.

The UK's finest quality leads and collars are available here (Hunter, Fox & Hounds, Up Country), as well as some very swish numbers from Germany and the US (Timberwolf): they come in all sizes, in leather, fabric or nylon, plain or diamanté. There is also a range of coats (all sizes, some exclusive), beds (faux suede, vet bed), airline-approved pet carriers (Vari-Kennel and Sherpa) and a range of grooming products (including ones for sensitive skins and allergies), plus there's a treatment services for cats and dogs (by appointment). Informed staff give advice on diets, food, supplements and treats and they'll readily point you in the direction of local breeders and shelters.

Rescue centres

All of the organisations below require an interview and a home visit before you adopt an animal. The **RSPCA** (0300 123 4555, www.rspca.org.uk) also runs rescue centres across London. For your nearest, check the website. If you're looking for a specific breed of rescue dog, the **Kennel Club** (0844 463 3980, www.the-kennel-club.org.uk) publishes a directory of different dog breed rescue centres.

Battersea Dogs & Cats Home
4 Battersea Park Road, SW8 4AA (7622 3626, www.battersea.org.uk). Battersea Park rail.
Battersea Dogs & Cats Home is the largest dogs' home in the UK, with up to 500 animals on site, around a fifth of which are cats. Rescue dogs cost £95, cats £60; a waiting list may apply for puppies and kittens.

Cats Protection
North London Adoption Centre, 135 Junction Road, N19 5PX (7272 6048, www.northlondon.cats.org.uk). Archway tube.
The UK's leading feline welfare charity has up to 7,000 cats available for re-homing at any one time through its nationwide network of local adoption centres, such as this one in Archway.

Celia Hammond Animal Trust
151-153 Barking Road, E16 4HQ (7474 8811, www.celiahammond.org). Canning Town tube/rail.
Founded by '60s model Celia Hammond, the trust runs two London clinics. Each operates a 24-hour rescue service, with website photos of recently rescued dogs, cats and kittens (re-homed in pairs, or with their mother).
Other locations *233-235 Lewisham Way, SE4 1UY (8694 6545).*

Dogs Trust West London
Highway Farm, Harvil Road, Harefield, Uxbridge UB9 6JW (0845 076 3647, www.dogstrust.org.uk).
The west London branch of this national charity has 75 kennels, and cares for around 1,600 dogs a year. The website has a photo gallery of dogs currently needing a home.

Mayhew Animal Home
Trenmar Gardens, NW10 6BJ (8969 0178, www.mayhewanimalhome.org). Kensal Green tube.
The Mayhew was set up over 100 years ago as a home for 'the lost and starving dogs and cats of London', and now cares for up to 175 moggies and 50 dogs. There's a set fee of £120 to buy dogs and £75 for cats, which includes vaccinations.

Wood Green Animal Shelters
601 Lordship Lane, N22 5LG (0870 190 4440, www.woodgreen.org.uk). Wood Green tube.
Cats adopted from this north London shelter, first opened in 1924, come with four weeks' free pet insurance. A £85 donation is suggested when you take one home.

Vets

To locate your nearest vet, use the postcode finder on the **Royal College of Veterinary Surgeons'** website at www.rcvs.org.uk; the RCVS also investigates complaints against vets.

If you're on a low income or receiving benefits, your pet may qualify for

GOING OUT

BEAUTY

FASHION

PARTIES

FOOD

HEALTH

ECO

OUTDOORS

HOME

CHILDREN

PETS

TRANSPORT

RESOURCES

City Secret

Freebie magazine **London Dog Tails** (www.londondogtails.com) is a mine of information for canine owners in the capital, from product and pub reviews to tried-and-tested walks and details of upcoming events; pick up a copy from vets and pet shops around town, or check it out online.

reduced-price neutering and subsidised clinics. **Cats Protection** and the **RSPCA** (*see p186*) both offer voucher schemes for low-cost neutering, as do most rescue centres. The **Beaumont Animals' Hospital** (*see below*) offers a subsidised neuter clinic for cats and dogs, while the **Blue Cross** (Sheppard House, 1-5 Hugh Street, SW1V 1QQ, 7932 2370, www.bluecross.org.uk) runs an appointments-only service offering low-cost veterinary care and vaccinations to low-income south and east Londoners.

The **Mayhew Animal Home** (*see p187*) also offers cheap neutering to all pet owners, charging from £22-£25 for cats and £50-£85 for dogs, along with a low-cost vaccinations clinic on Wednesday, Saturday mornings. Call for details.

Abbey Veterinary Clinic

84 Dalston Lane, E8 3AH (7254 1362). Dalston Kingsland rail. Open 9-10am, 1-2pm, 5-7pm Mon-Thur; 1-2pm, 5-7pm Fri; 2-5pm Sat.
Sparklingly clean, and sandwiched in a row of shops on Dalston Lane, Abbey has a loyal local following. The staff are unfailingly efficient, and can usually offer a same-day appointment with the vet. The consultation fee is £32.70.

Beaumont Animals' Hospital

The Royal Veterinary College, Royal College Street, NW1 0TU (7387 8134, www.rvc.ac. uk). Mornington Crescent tube or Camden Road rail. Open 9am-7.30pm Mon-Fri; 9am-1.30pm Sat.

Opened in 1932, the Beaumont is the Royal Veterinary College's practice. Nurses' clinics offer everything from nail-clipping to microchipping.

Brockwell Veterinary Surgery

224-228 Railton Road, SE24 0JT (7737 2526, www.brockwellvets.co.uk). Herne Hill rail. Open 8am-7pm Mon, Tue, Thur, Fri; 8am-8pm Wed; 8.30am-4pm Sat.
A relaxed local that offers reliable service at fair prices: regulars praise the friendly staff. The surgery also runs an out-of-hours advisory line and a cat boarding service.

Dragon Veterinary Clinic

496 Hornsey Road, N19 4EF (7272 3354, www.dragonvets.co.uk). Archway tube or Finsbury Park tube/rail. Open 9am-7pm Mon-Fri; 9am-4pm Sat.
Cats are a particular area of expertise at this cheery local practice, headed by partners Mary Nicoll and James Caspar, and represent a major chunk of the team's caseload (though they see a fair few dogs too). An onsite laboratory means fast test results, and there's a popular cattery at the back; book well ahead.

Portman Veterinary Clinic

86 York Street, W1H 1QS (7723 2068, www.portmanvetclinic.co.uk). Marylebone tube/rail. Open 9am-noon, 3pm-5.45pm Mon-Fri.
Run by Bruce Fogle, a bestselling author and former vet at London Zoo, the Portman is a smart establishment of some 30 years' standing. It's not the cheapest, but your pet is in safe hands. The clinic is affiliated with the Emergency Veterinary Clinic (55 Elizabeth Street, SW1W 9PP, 7730 9102), which deals with out-of-hours emergencies.

Westside Veterinary Clinic

2 Burland Road, SW11 6SA (7223 7003, www.westsidevets.co.uk). Clapham Junction rail. Open 9am-7pm Mon-Fri; 9am-noon Sat.
Family pets are the mainstay at this supremely friendly clinic. Staff take time to get to know your pet – and remember their names, according to one local.

Transport

Airports

Check-in on time with the fastest – and cheapest – ways to reach London's closest airports, by coach, rail and car.

By coach & rail

We've given standard adult fares for rail and coach services: ask for details of railcard reductions and child fares.

Gatwick Airport

0844 335 1802, www.gatwickairport.com. About 30 miles south of central London, off the M23.

From Victoria, the Gatwick Express (0845 850 1530, www.gatwickexpress.co.uk) takes 30 minutes and runs 3.30am to 12.30am daily. Tickets cost £16.90 for a single, £28.70 for an open return. Far cheaper (and only five to ten minutes slower) is the Southern service (0845 748 4950, www.southernrailway.com), with trains every five to ten minutes (or every 30 minutes between 1am and 4am); a single costs £11.30, an open return £23.60. Alternatively, take the Thameslink (0845 748 4950, www. firstcapitalconnect.co.uk) from London Bridge, Blackfriars, Farringdon or King's Cross for £8.90 single, £17 open return. With National Express (0871 781 8178, www.national express.com), the coach takes 80-90 minutes; tickets cost from £7.50 for a single. Cheaper still is the easyBus (www.easybus.co.uk) to/from Earl's Court, with advance tickets from £3.99, taking 65-80 minutes. A taxi costs around £100 and takes just over an hour.

Heathrow Airport

0844 335 1801, www.heathrowairport.com. About 15 miles west of central London, off the M4.

The Heathrow Express (0845 600 1515, www. heathrowexpress.co.uk) runs from Paddington 5.10am to 11.12pm daily, and takes 15-20 minutes. Tickets cost £16.50 single, £32 return (£1 cheaper if you book online, £2 more if you buy on board). The Heathrow Connect (0845 678 6975, www.heathrowconnect.com) runs from Paddington via Ealing Broadway, West Ealing, Hanwell, Southhall and Hayes. The trains run every half-hour, with stops at two stations at Heathrow: one serving Terminals 1, 2 and 3, and the other serving Terminal 4. To get from the T4 station to Terminal 5, you must return to the T1, 2 and 3 station. The journey from Paddington takes 25-30 minutes and costs £7.90; an open return is £15.80. At £4.50, the tube (7222 1234, www.tfl.gov.uk) is cheaper, but takes around an hour into central London on the Piccadilly Line. Tubes run from 5am until 11.57pm daily (6am to 11pm on Sundays); at night, the half-hourly N9 bus takes over. National Express (0871 781 8181, www.nationalexpress.com) coaches take 90 minutes and run half-hourly from Victoria, between 5am and 9.35pm daily: a single costs £5. A taxi into town costs £40-£70 and takes from 40-60 minutes, depending on traffic.

London City Airport

7646 0000, www.londoncityairport.com. About 9 miles east of central London.

On the Docklands Light Railway (DLR), the journey from Bank to London City Airport takes around 20 minutes; trains run from 5.30am to 12.30am Monday to Saturday, 7.30am to 11.30pm Sunday. A taxi into central London costs around £30.

Luton Airport

01582 405100, www.london-luton.com. About 30 miles north of central London, J10 off the M1.

Luton Airport Parkway Station is close to the airport, but not in it: there's a five-minute shuttle-bus ride. The Thameslink service (0845 748 4950, www.firstcapitalconnect.co. uk), calling at five central London stations (including St Pancras and London Bridge), takes 35-45 minutes. Tickets cost £13.50 single, £23 return, and trains run at least hourly through the night. Luton to Victoria takes 60-90 minutes by coach: Green Line (0870 608 7261, www.greenline. co.uk) also runs a 24-hour service, with singles at £14, returns £19. With easyBus (www.easybus. co.uk), advance singles start at £2. A taxi costs upwards of £70, and takes around 90 minutes.

Stansted Airport

0844 335 1803, www.stanstedairport.com. About 35 miles north-east of central London, J8 off the M11.

The Stansted Express (0845 748 4950, www. stanstedexpress.com) from Liverpool Street takes 40-45 minutes. Trains leave every 15-45 minutes; tickets cost £19.80 single, £28.70 return. The half-hourly Airbus (0871 781 8181, www.nationalexpress.com) coach from Victoria takes at least 80 minutes and runs 24 hours; a single is £10, a return £17. EasyBus (www.easybus.co.uk) runs from Baker Street, and takes a similar length of time; singles from £2-£10. Terravision (01279 662931, www. terravision.eu) runs shuttle services to Victoria (around 75 minutes) and Liverpool Street (around 55 minutes) at £9 one way, £14 return. A taxi is around £100, and takes an hour.

Motorbike taxis

For speedy journeys or airport dashes, weave through packed-solid traffic perched on the back of a motorbike.

All of the companies listed have a minimum £25 charge, and offer fixed airport rates; bikes are equipped with panniers, and can carry small to medium suitcases. You pay a premium for the thrill though: central London to Gatwick currently costs £110-£120.

Passenger Bikes *0844 561 6147, www.passengerbikes.com.*

Taxybikes *7255 4269, www.addisonlee.com/services/taxybikes.*

Virgin Limobike *3126 3998, www.virginlimobike.com.*

Parking

Rates for airport parking vary depending on your length of stay, but booking ahead is invariably far cheaper than turning up on the day. For details, contact:

Gatwick *0844 335 1000, www.gatwickairport.com.*

Heathrow *0844 335 1000, www.heathrowairport.com.*

London City Airport *7646 0000, www.londoncityairport.com.*

Luton *01582 405100, www.london-luton.com.*

Stansted *0844 335 1000, www.stanstedairport.com.*

VALET PARKING

For minimum stress, and to avoid carting heavy luggage and tired children from the car park to the terminal, book valet parking. After meeting you at departures, the driver takes your car to a secure car park, then delivers it back to the terminal when you land. It costs around £20-£40 on top of standard parking fees: book ahead for the best deals. Check www.baa. com for prices at Gatwick, Heathrow and Stansted, or try **BCP** 0871 360 2924, www.parkbcp.co.uk) or **Purple Parking** (0845 605 1831, ww.purpleparking.com).

GOING OUT

BEAUTY

FASHION

PARTIES

FOOD

HEALTH

ECO

OUTDOORS

HOME

CHILDREN

PETS

TRANSPORT

RESOURCES

Cabs & taxis

Black cabs, green cabs and more.

Black cabs

To book a black cab, call the 24-hour **Taxi One-Number** (0871 871 8710). A £2 booking fee applies, along with a 12.5% administration charge if you're paying by credit card.

Any complaints regarding black cabs should be made to the **Public Carriage Office** (0845 602 7000, www.tfl.gov.uk/pco); note the cab's five-digit number, shown in the passenger compartment and on the back bumper.

Not sure how much a cab journey might cost? Type your starting point and destination postcodes into the ingenious **www.worldtaximeter.com**, which will calculate a rough estimate of the journey time and price.

Eco-friendly cabs

The following minicab firms use hybrid petrol and electric-powered Toyota Prius cars, and offset their carbon emissions. **Radio Taxis** (7272 0272, www.radiotaxis.co.uk) also offsets carbon emissions from its black cab fleet and offers its drivers the option of using biofuel.

Climatecars
7350 5960, www.climatecars.com.
Newspapers, magazines and Belu mineral water come as standard, while bike racks allow cyclists who've had a tipple or got caught out by the rain to hitch a ride home.

Ecoigo ★
0800 032 6446, www.ecoigo.com.
Ecoigo offers a 24-hour service; carbon emissions are offset by the World Land Trust.

Green Tomato Cars
8568 0022, www.greentomatocars.com.
Green Tomato's fleet of sleek silver Priuses operates across town, offering competitive prices and a reliable service.

Minicabs

You can check if a cab company or driver is licensed at the Transport for London website (www.tfl.gov.uk). To find a licensed minicab, call the 24-hour information line (7222 1234) or use the **Cabwise** service: text the word HOME to 60835 and you'll be sent telephone numbers for two licensed minicab operators in the area, along with a taxi operator. It costs 35p, plus your standard text message rate.

The following minicab companies have female drivers:

Ladybirds *8295 0101.*

Ladycabs *7272 3300.*

Ladycars *8558 8510.*

City Secret

To arrive in style, call a **Karma Kar** (8964 0700, 07770 693979, www.karmakabs.com). Available to hire by the hour (from £50), Tobias Moss's imported Indian Ambassador cars are wonderfully opulent: think shiny, bejewelled interiors, liberally studded with sequins and suffused with incense and raga music. They're particularly popular for weddings and Fashion Week events.

Cycling

Get on your bike and beat the traffic.

Bike hire

We've given daily rates, but deals are often available for longer hire periods. Worth checking out too is Transport for London's **Barclays Cycle Hire**, see p193.

City Bike Service

2 Fairchild Place, EC2A 3EN (7247 4151, www.citybikeservice.co.uk). Old Street tube/rail. Open 8am-7pm Mon-Fri; 9am-5pm Sat. Hire £15/day. Deposit £150.
Seven-speed hybrid bikes, with helmet and lights included in the hire price.

Go Pedal!

07850 796320, www.gopedal.co.uk. Open 8am-8pm daily. Hire £20-£40/day. Deposit £150.
Rates drop over longer hire periods, or for several bikes. Delivery and collection are included, along with helmet, lights and locks.

London Bicycle Tour Company

1A Gabriel's Wharf, 56 Upper Ground, SE1 9PP (7928 6838, www.londonbicycle.com).
Southwark tube or Waterloo tube/rail. Open 10am-6pm daily. Hire £3.50/hour; £20/day. Deposit £180 cash; £1 by credit card.
Bikes, tandems and rickshaw hire. Lights are included, but helmets and panniers are extra.

Velorution

18 Great Titchfield Street, W1W 8BD (7637 4004, www.velorution.biz). Oxford Circus tube. Open 8.30am-6.45pm Mon-Fri; 10.30am-6.30pm Sat. Hire £20/day.
Choose between a Brompton with the 'Rent-a-Folder' scheme: for £20, local delivery is included (deliver is now £5 extra).

Bike shops & repairs

In addition to the following shops, **Velorution** (see above) also offers good repair services.

If you're miles from home and in need of help, try the **Mobile Cycle Service** (0800 321 3303, www.mobilecycle service.co.uk), whose mechanics will come to the rescue for surprisingly reasonable rates.

FREE CYCLE HIRE

Join Transport for London's **Barclays Cycle Hire** (www.tfl.gov.uk) scheme online (non-members can use a credit card at docking stations for hire too) for access to some 5,000 cycles (soon to be more) at docking stations across London. Once you've paid £3 for your membership key and an access fee (£1/day; £5 for seven days; £45 annually) trips up to 30 mins in length are free. Longer trips incur an escalating fee (£1/hr; £50/24hrs) in an attempt to encourage users to stick to short hops (if you want to hire a bike for two or more hours, it may be cheaper to choose one of the companies listed under **Bike hire** (see above). Once you've paid the access fee you can pick up other bikes as often as you like in that period (as long as you wait five minutes between hires).

GOING OUT
BEAUTY
FASHION
PARTIES
FOOD
HEALTH
ECO
OUTDOORS
HOME
CHILDREN
PETS
TRANSPORT
RESOURCES

Bicycle Workshop

27 All Saint's Road, W11 1HE (7229 4850, www.bicycleworkshop.co.uk). Westbourne Park tube. Open 10am-2pm, 3-6pm Tue-Fri; 9am-5pm Sat (earlier for repair drop-offs).

You can book in for repairs on weekdays, but will have to join the queue for the Saturday no-bookings workshop: doors open at 7.30am in summer and 8.30am in winter. This place has an excellent reputation, and places soon fill up.

Bikefix

48 Lamb's Conduit Street, WC1N 3LJ (7405 1218, www.bikefix.co.uk). Russell Square or Holborn tube. Open 8.30am-7pm Mon-Fri; 10am-5pm Sat.

The shop sells classic city bikes, fold-ups, recumbents and accessories galore: nip round the back for the workshop (closed Saturdays). Word-of-mouth has built up a loyal following, but there are no appointments, so get there early.

Bikemech ★

Castle Climbing Centre, Green Lanes, N4 2HA (07762 270616, www.bikemech.co.uk). Manor House tube. Open 9am-7pm Mon-Thur; 10am-5pm Sat.

Jon Chapel's skills as a mechanic come highly recommended, along with his wheel-building skills (a hard thing to find in London). At £35 plus parts, a general service is great value, while brake replacement starts at a mere £5.

Brick Lane Bikes

118 Bethnal Green Road, E2 6DG (7033 9053, www.bricklanebikes.co.uk). Shoreditch High Street rail. Open 9am-7pm Mon-Fri; 11am-6pm Sat; 11am-5pm Sun.

With its sleek frames and elegant custom builds, this track and fixed gear specialist is, according to one admirer, 'like a sex shop for fixed gear bike nuts'. Brick Lane Bikes also offers hybrid and city bikes, plus vintage town bikes (£80-£120). The workshop offers a quick turnaround, and is also open on Sundays; a full service is £35.

Brixton Cycles

145 Stockwell Road, SW9 9TN (7733 6055). Brixton tube/rail. Open 9am-6pm Mon-Wed, Fri-Sat; 10am-7pm Thur.

This place is known for its knowledgeable, friendly staff; buy a bike, and get a year's free servicing (parts not included). The workshop offers a same-day service, and there's also a daily walk-in emergency repair service during the first hour of opening; get here early.

Cycle Surgery

44 Chalk Farm Road, NW1 8AJ (7485 1000, www.cyclesurgery.com). Chalk Farm tube. Open 9am-6pm Mon, Wed, Fri; 8am-7pm Tue, Thur; 9am-6pm Sat; 11am-5pm Sun.

Prices are fair (£49 for a service), and staff members are helpful and clued-up. All repairs must be booked in advance at the weekdays-only workshop.

Other locations *across the city.*

London Bicycle Repair

Units 2-3 Benson House, Hatfields, SE1 8DQ (7928 6898, www.londonbicycle.com). Southwark tube. Open 9am-6pm Mon-Fri.

Regulars praise this cheap, efficient repair centre, where owner Rob Graham aims to fix your bike within eight hours. His team will take on anything from a clapped-out £5 bike to a £3,000 road racer; services start at £44.

London Fields Cycles

281 Mare Street, E8 1PJ (8525 0077, www.londonfieldscycles.co.uk). London Fields or Hackney Central rail or Bethnal Green tube, then 106, 253, D6 bus. Open 8am-6pm Mon-Fri; 10am-6pm Sat; 11am-5pm Sun.

The shop offers an excellent selection of bikes and accessories, while workshop services include a £30 tune-up, wheel-building and an 8am drop-in service for minor repairs. Queues start forming early, as only six repairs are taken each morning.

Two Wheels Good

165 Stoke Newington Church Street, N16 0UL (7249 2200, www.twowheels good.co.uk). Stoke Newington rail. Open 8.30am-6pm Mon-Fri; 9am-6pm Sat.

Bike brands include Puky, Pashley and Gary Fisher, while the workshops in both branches are Shimano Service Centres, with Cytech-trained mechanics just as happy to do a custom-build as a £45 service. Staff will do their best to undertake emergency repairs on the spot.

Other location *143 Crouch Hill, N8 9QH (8340 4284).*

Maintenance

For free advice and minor repairs, seek out a **Dr Bike** clinic. The 'doctor' is generally a mechanic from a local bike shop or a cycling enthusiast, often setting up shop at cycling or green events to check bike safety and carry out repairs out of the goodness of his or her heart. Various **London Cycling Campaign** (*see p196*) groups also run regular Dr Bike sessions; for details, see the website.

The following LCC groups also run regular cycle maintenance workshops, often charging a nominal fee to cover their running costs.

Greenwich Cyclists

Armada Centre, 21 McMillan Street, SE8 3EZ (www.greenwichcyclists.org.uk). Deptford rail.

Weekly two-hour classes (£5-£10) cover different areas of bike maintenance.

Hackney Cyclists

Kings Centre, Frampton Park Baptist Church, Frampton Park Road, E9 7PQ (07940 121513, www.hackney-cyclists.org. uk/workshop.htm). Bethnal Green tube, then 106, 254 bus or Hackney Central rail.

Twice-monthly workshops are led by a team of volunteers, running from 7pm to 9pm on the first and third Tuesday of every month. Ring the bell to gain entrance.

Islington Cyclists Action Group

Sunnyside Community Centre, corner of Sunnyside Road & Hazellville Road, N19 3LX. (7272 3522, 07810 211902). Archway tube or Crouch Hill rail.

Workshops are held 7-9.30pm on the fourth Wednesday of every month, bar August and December. You're asked to contribute £1.

Tower Hamlets Wheelers

Limehouse Town Hall, 646 Commercial Road, E14 7HA (07903 018970, www.towerhamletswheelers.org.uk). Limehouse DLR/rail.

These friendly, free sessions are held on the last Saturday of the month (11am-3pm). Tools, advice, tea and cakes are all on offer and there are even a few spare parts available. While it's free, donations are always welcome. Don't arrive late if you've got plenty to do.

GOING OUT

BEAUTY

FASHION

PARTIES

FOOD

HEALTH

ECO

OUTDOORS

HOME

CHILDREN

PETS

TRANSPORT

RESOURCES

GOING OUT
BEAUTY
FASHION
PARTIES
FOOD
HEALTH
ECO
OUTDOORS
HOME
CHILDREN
PETS
TRANSPORT
RESOURCES

Second-hand bikes

Avoid **Brick Lane** market, where the
shiny sets of wheels suggest owners
and cycles may not have parted ways
willingly: instead, buy stolen bikes
recovered by the police at **Frank G
Bowen** (253 Joseph Ray Road, E11 4RE,
8556 7930, www.frankgbowen.co.uk).
Auctions are held every other Thursday,
starting at 11am: viewing is the day
before. Expect up to 120 bikes, ranging
from £5 for beat-up frames to £500 for
gleaming racers.

For a full list of shops that sell second-
hand bikes, visit www.lcc.org.uk.

Bob's Bikes

*9 John Ruskin Street, SE5 0NS (7708 0599,
07961 102072). Kennington tube. Open
9am-5.30pm Mon-Sat.*
Bob sells a small range of second-hand bikes
from around £40, which are serviced by him
and come with a month's guarantee. Sellers
must show three forms of ID.

Camden Cycles ★

*251 Eversholt Street, NW1 1BA (7388
7899, www.camdencycles.co.uk). Camden
Town tube. Open 9am-7pm Mon-Fri; 9am-
6pm Sat; 11am-5pm Sun.*
There's a great selection of bikes here, from
around £60. Sellers must give two forms of ID,
and the shop keeps a stolen bicycle database.
Bikes come with a one-month warranty.

Edwardes

*221-225 Camberwell Road, SE5 0HG
(7703 5720). Elephant & Castle tube, then
12, 40, 35, 45, 68, 148, 171, 176, 468 bus.
Open 8am-6pm Mon-Sat.*
Around 20 second-hand bikes go from £50
upwards every week at Edwardes, with a
good range of makes on offer.

Everything Cycling

*530 Forest Road, E17 4NB (8521 5812).
Walthamstow Central tube/rail. Open 10am-
5.30pm Mon-Wed, Fri; 9.30am-5.30pm Sat.
No credit cards.*

Prices for second-hand bikes (bought from
verified owners) start at around £49.

Recycling

*110 Elephant Road, SE17 1LB (7703 7001,
www.re-cycling.co.uk). Elephant & Castle
tube. Open 10am-7pm Mon-Fri; 9am-6pm
Sat; 11am-5pm Sun.*
Second-hand wheels cost from £69, with an
emphasis on old-fashioned models such as
Mayfairs, and there's a 10% discount if you
pay in cash. All bikes are guaranteed for a
month after purchase.

Smith Brothers

*14 Church Road, SW19 5DL (8946 2270).
Wimbledon tube. Open 9.30am-5.30pm
Mon-Sat.*
Second-hand buys are guaranteed for up to a
year. Prices range from £89 to £300, and as
most bikes are acquired via part exchange
you've no need to worry about their history.

Training

It's not widely known, but most London
boroughs offer heavily subsidised or free
cycle training to adults who live, work or
study in the borough, in addition to in-
school cycle training for children. What's
on offer varies: in Hackney, for example,
anyone aged over 11 is entitled to two
hours' free training. Find out what you're
eligible for by checking on your local
authority's website, or calling your local
training officer: see www.tfl.gov.uk/
cycletraining for a full list.

Useful contacts

The **London Cycling Campaign**
(www.lcc.org.uk) is an essential resource,
providing information on everything
from regular rides to theft and insurance.
Meanwhile, **Transport for London**
(www.tfl.gov.uk) offers a printable
route-finder for cyclists, along with 14
free cycling maps of various areas and
information on subsidised cycle training.

Driving

From congestion charging to car clubs.

Congestion charge

Driving into central London any time between 7am and 6pm Monday to Friday incurs an £8 fee, payable online at www.tfl.gov.uk, by phone on 0845 900 1234, or at shops and petrol stations displaying the congestion charging sign or paypoint logo.

The area is defined as within King's Cross (N), Old Street roundabout (NE), Aldgate (E), Old Kent Road (SE), Elephant & Castle (S), Vauxhall, Chelsea, South Kensington (SW), Kensington, Holland Park, North Kensington, Bayswater, Paddington (W), Marylebone and Euston (N). For a map see www.tfl.gov.uk. You can pay during the day of entry, or until midnight on the next charging day after you entered the zone – but the charge goes up by £10.

Expect a £50 fine if you fail to pay (rising to £100 if you delay payment). For a map of the current congestion charge zone, see www.tfl.gov.uk. The charge doesn't apply on public holidays, or between Christmas Day and New Year's Day.

Lift shares

Save money as well as the environment by sharing lifts. **Transport for London** have set up a journey match-up service at www.londonliftshare.com for lift-seekers and providers, where options range from cost-sharing on regular commutes, to one-off trips to Brighton, Bristol and beyond. Always use your common sense, and follow recommended safety precautions. For **Liftshare**, see www.liftshare.com.

Parking

For parking in central London, visit www.westminster.gov.uk/parking, which has a map of parking bays plus details of car parks and special offers. Westminster Council also produces a handy, free **Park Right** guide, available on its website.

Another useful resource is www.park-up.com: type in a London street name and postcode for a map marked with car parks and street parking, along with charges and maximum parking times.

STREET PARKING

Parking on double yellow lines and red routes is illegal at all times, but in the evening (from 6pm or 7pm in much of central London) and at various times at weekends, parking on single yellows is legal and free. If you find a clear spot on a single yellow line during the evening, look for a sign explaining the regulations for that area.

Meters also become free at certain times during evenings and weekends; otherwise, they cost from £1 for 15 minutes, and are

> ## City Secret
>
> If that one after-work drink spiralled and you're in no fit state to get behind the wheel, call on the nifty **Scooterman** (0333 666 1999, www.scooterman.co.uk) service. A chauffeur will arrive on a foldaway scooter, which he'll stow away in the boot of your car before driving you safely home.

GOING OUT BEAUTY FASHION PARTIES FOOD HEALTH ECO OUTDOORS HOME CHILDREN PETS TRANSPORT RESOURCES

JOIN THE CLUB

Being a full-time car owner in London is often more hassle than it's worth – which is where car clubs come in. You get to use a car whenever you want, without any of the worries about insurance, MOTs and parking permits.

The major car clubs are **City Car Club** (0845 330 1234, www.citycarclub.co.uk), **Streetcar** (0845 644 8475, www.streetcar.co.uk) and **Zipcar** (7940 7499, www.zipcar.co.uk). Deals vary, but most clubs charge a joining fee or annual membership fee, then charge around £5 an hour for car usage: you book the nearest car, swipe your card to unlock it, then drive off.

The only disadvantage is that you have to return cars to the designated space you picked them up from – so one-way trips aren't an option.

To see which club has the most cars available in your area, check out www.carclubs.org.uk.

If you had more glamorous motoring in mind, sign up for a supercar club and get behind the wheel of sleek, shiny Lamborghinis and Aston Martins. **Ecurie25** (7278 3010, www.ecurie25.co.uk) charges a joining fee of £1,750 and annual membership of £11,000, for an average 40 days' driving.

---

generally limited to two hours. In central London, meters are being phased out in favour of a new pay by phone service (7005 0055, www.westminster.gov.uk): after registering your car licence plate, you can make payments over the phone, using a credit or debit card.

CAR PARKS

It's worth noting that Vauxhall Bridge Road, Grosvenor Place and Park Lane are a designated congestion zone through-route – which means certain car parks are also outside the charging zone. **Mayfair Car Park** (Park Lane, W1K 7AN, 7499 3725) charges £17 for four hours, while at **Masterpark Park Lane** (Park Lane, W1K 7AN, 0800 243348), prices start at £6 for two hours; take care to exit the right way to avoid entering the zone.

Elsewhere in town, London's major car park operators include:

Masterpark 0800 243348, *www.westminster.gov.uk/carparks.*

NCP 0845 050 7080, *www.ncp.co.uk.*

Transport for London *0845 330 9880, www.tfl.gov.uk.*

Parking tickets & clamping

If you feel you've been given an unlawful parking ticket, contact the **Parking & Traffic Appeals Service** (7747 4700, www.parkingandtrafficappeals.gov.uk) to register an appeal.

If your car has been clamped, a notice will tell you which payment centre you need to phone or visit. You'll have to stump up a £80 release fee and show a valid driver's licence. The payment centre will de-clamp your car within four hours, but won't say exactly when. Wait by your car: if you don't move it at once, it might get clamped again.

If your car has disappeared, it's probably been taken to a car pound. A release fee of £200 is levied, plus £40 per day from the first midnight after removal. To add insult to injury, you'll also probably get a parking ticket of £60-£100 when you collect the car (which will be reduced by a 50 per cent discount if paid within 14 days). To find out how to retrieve your car, call the 24-hour TRACE service hotline (7747 4747).

River services

River trips aren't just for tourists.

For commuters, **Thames Clippers** (0870 781 5049, www.thamesclippers. com) runs a regular, reliable service between Embankment Pier and Royal Arsenal Woolwich Pier; stops include Blackfriars, Bankside, London Bridge, Canary Wharf and Greenwich. A standard day roamer ticket (valid 10am-5pm) costs £12, while a single from Embankment to Greenwich is £5.30, but Oyster travelcard holders get a third off. **Thames Executive Charters** (www.thamesexecutivecharters.com) also offers travelcard discounts on its River Taxi between Putney and Blackfriars, calling at Wandsworth, Chelsea Harbour, Cadogan Pier and Embankment, meaning a £4.50 standard single becomes £3. **Westminster Passenger Service Association** (7930 2062, www.wpsa.co.uk)

runs a scheduled daily service from Westminster Pier to Kew, Richmond and Hampton Court from April to October. At £12 for a single it's not cheap, but it is a lovely – and leisurely – way to see the city, and there are discounts of between 30 and 50% for travelcard and Freedom Pass holders.

Thames River Services (www. westminsterpier.co.uk) operates from the same pier, offering trips to Greenwich, Tower Pier and the Thames Barrier. A trip to Greenwich costs £9.50, though £13 buys you a Rivercard, which allows you to hop on and off whenever you like. There's also a third off for those who are travelcard holders.

For all commuter service timetables, plus a full list of leisure operators and services, see www.tfl.gov.uk.

GOING OUT

BEAUTY

FASHION

PARTIES

FOOD

HEALTH

ECO

OUTDOORS

HOME

CHILDREN

PETS

TRANSPORT

RESOURCES

Tube & bus

See the city from a scenic bus route, or avoid the tube's worst interchanges.

Bikes on the tube

You can take folding bikes on the tube at any time, but standard bikes are only allowed on certain sections of the line, outside peak times (7.30-9.30am, 4-7pm, Monday to Friday). A map showing where cycles are allowed is available online at www.tfl.gov.uk, or by calling 7222 1234.

Interchanges to avoid

Bank/Monument: Central – Circle
Few interchanges match the confusion and length of the Bank to Monument changeover.

Hammersmith: District, Piccadilly – Hammersmith & City
The change involves a flight of stairs, ticket hall and shopping mall, across two pedestrian crossings, and another station.

Paddington: Circle, District, Bakerloo – Hammersmith & City
Two stations made into one back in 1947 mean a very long walk from one to the other.

Shepherd's Bush/Shepherd's Bush Market: Central – Hammersmith & City
An escalator, a six-minute walk, a four-road junction and a set of stairs.

Lost property

Lost property found on tubes and buses is generally held locally for a couple of days before being sent to Transport for London's main **Lost Property Office**

(200 Baker Street, NW1 5RZ, 7918 2000, www.tfl.gov.uk), open from 8.30am to 4pm Monday to Friday. A small fee is made for reuniting you with your lost property: from £1 for a brolly to £20 for a laptop.

Underground times

Tube trains run daily from around 5.30am (except Sunday, when they start an hour or two later, depending on the line). The only exception is Christmas Day, when there is no service. Generally, you should not have to wait more than ten minutes for a train. Times of last trains vary, though they're usually around 11.30pm to 1am every day except Sunday, when they finish 30 minutes to an hour earlier. Other than on New Year's Eve, when the tubes run all night, the only all-night public transport is by night bus. For details of last first and last trains for each line, and night bus route maps, visit www.tfl.gov.uk.

When to walk

Lovely as Harry Beck's tube map is, it's not designed to show the distances between stations – so you're often better off walking between certain stations, as all smug Londoners know.

The classic is, of course, **Charing Cross** to **Embankment**: a mere skip down Villiers Street. **Covent Garden** is a short stroll from **Charing Cross**. From **Covent Garden**, it's a quick flit along Long Acre to **Leicester Square**. Another easy amble is **Cannon Street** to **Mansion House** or **Monument**.

GOING OUT

BEAUTY

FASHION

PARTIES

FOOD

HEALTH

ECO

OUTDOORS

HOME

CHILDREN

PETS

TRANSPORT

RESOURCES

Events

London's smaller, lesser-known events reflect the quirky, the idiosyncractic and – sometimes – the downright weird side of life in the capital.

JANUARY-MARCH

London International Mime Festival
Various venues across London (7637 5661, www.mimefest.co.uk). Date mid-late Jan.
Established and edgy companies from across the globe perform innovative shows that, thankfully, don't involve people pretending to be trapped behind a sheet of glass.

Chinese New Year Festival
Around Gerrard Street, W1, Leicester Square & Trafalgar Square, WC2 (7851 6686, www.londonchinatown.co.uk). Leicester Square or Piccadilly Circus tube. Date late Jan/early Feb.
In 2011, the Year of the Rabbit takes over from the Year of the Tiger, an event that will be celebrated through Chinatown with a colourful children's parade, traditional dances and spectacular firework displays. Expect dense crowds.

Great Spitalfields Pancake Race
Dray Walk, Brick Lane, E1 6QL (7375 0441, www.alternativearts.co.uk). Shoreditch High Street rail. Date Shrove Tuesday.
If you like the idea of flipping a pancake or two for charity as part of a four-strong relay team, call in advance to register. If you're simply in need of some silliness and cheer, just turn up on the day.

London Lesbian & Gay Film Festival
BFI Southbank, Belvedere Road, SE1 8XT (7928 3232, www.llgff.org.uk). Embankment tube or Waterloo tube/rail. Date late Mar.
The UK's third-largest film festival is still going strong after 20-plus years, screening an evocative, sometimes provocative mix of films from around the globe.

APRIL-JUNE

Spring Loaded
The Place, 17 Duke's Road, WC1H 9PY (7121 1100, www.theplace.org.uk). Euston tube/rail. Date from early Apr-early May.
This renowned festival celebrates the best British-based contemporary dance talent.

East End Film Festival
Various venues (www.eastendfilmfestival. com). Date mid-late Apr.
Founded in 2001, the East End Film Festival is dedicated to new film-making, often exploring cinema's potential to cross social and political divides.

Camden Crawl
Various venues (www.thecamdencrawl.com). Camden Town tube. Date early May.
A two-day showcase of around 80 new bands, most of them wielding jangly guitars, in a dozen venues around Camden. Buy a one- or two-day pass and see as many as you can.

Alternative Fashion Week
Spitalfields Traders Market, Crispin Place, Brushfield Street, E1 6AA (7375 0441, www.alternativearts.co.uk). Liverpool Street tube/rail. Date 3rd wk Apr.
Check out London's new generation of design talent. Catwalk shows are held at 1.15pm every day and feature more than 70 original collections, from the sublime to the surreal.

London Marathon
Greenwich Park to the Mall via the Isle of Dogs, Victoria Embankment & St James's Park (7902 0200, www.london-marathon. co.uk). Blackheath or Maze Hill rail or Charing Cross tube/rail. Date mid-Apr.

Apply by October if you want to be one of the 35,000 starters. If admiring from the sidelines is more your cup of tea, the front runners usually reach the halfway point near the Tower of London at around 10am.

Moonwalk London
Starts & ends Hyde Park, W1 (01483 741430/www.walkthewalk.org). Date mid-May.
Raise funds for breast cancer causes by power walking through the night in your best brassière: choose from either the marathon or half-marathon route.

Jazz Plus
Victoria Embankment Gardens, Villiers Street, WC2R 2PY (7375 0441, www. alternativearts.co.uk). Embankment tube or Charing Cross tube/rail. Date June.
Lunchtime concerts from contemporary jazz musicians take place in the gardens on Tuesdays and some Thursdays between 12.30pm and 2pm. Entry is free.

Coin Street Festival
Bernie Spain Gardens, (next to Oxo Tower Wharf, SE1 9PH (7021 1600, www.coinstreet.org). Southwark tube or Waterloo tube/rail. Date June-July.
Free live music events, plus a sprinkling of theatre and dance performances, are a lovely way to while away a sunny afternoon.

Watch This Space Festival
Outside the National Theatre, SE1 9PX (7452 3400, www.nationaltheatre.org.uk). Waterloo tube/rail. Date June-Sept.
This lively theatre festival brings an eclectic array of performances to Theatre Square in front of the National Theatre.

Spitalfields Festival
Various locations across east London (7377 1362/www.spitalfieldsfestival.org.uk). Date mid-late June, 2nd wk Dec.
Spitalfields comes to musical life with a wide mix of concerts and events, with everything from classical music in churches to electronica in the market – or even a spot of bell-ringing.

Open Garden Squares Weekend
Various venues (www.opensquares.org). Date early-mid June.
Almost 200 private gardens, squares and roof gardens are opened to the public for one weekend a year, from secret 'children-only' play areas to prison gardens.

World Naked Bike Ride
Hyde Park, W1 (www.worldnakedbikeride. org). Hyde Park Corner tube. Date June.
Bicycles and nudity come together as part of a protest against oil dependency and car culture. Meet at 3pm on the day near the Achilles Statue off Broad Walk, Hyde Park, and prepare to bare.

Meltdown
South Bank Centre, Belvedere Road, SE1 8XX (0844 847 9910, www.southbank centre.co.uk). Embankment tube or Waterloo tube/rail. Date June.
Londoners get as excited about the line-up of this brilliantly unpredictable music festival as the rest of the country does about Glasto. Previous directors have included Richard Thompson, Lee 'Scratch Perry, Massive Attack, David Bowie and Patti Smith.

Pride London
Parade from Oxford Street to Victoria Embankment (0844 884 2439, www.pride london.org). Hyde Park Corner or Marble Arch tube, or Charing Cross tube/rail. Date late June/early July.
The colourful parade is preceded by Festival Fortnight, a mix of performances and cultural events around the city. The central section of the parade route, around Soho and Leicester Square, is the best place to head on the day, with cabaret, dance stages and a food festival.

Greenwich & Docklands International Festival
Various venues in Greenwich & Docklands (8305 1818, www.festival.org). Date late June-early July.
An innovative blend of free and family-friendly theatrical, musical and site-specific events. Community projects are mixed with large-scale and often visually stunning events.

GOING OUT

BEAUTY

FASHION

PARTIES

FOOD

HEALTH

ECO

OUTDOORS

HOME

CHILDREN

PETS

TRANSPORT

RESOURCES

London Festival of Architecture

Various venues (www.lfa2012.org).
Date late June-early July.
This biannual festival offers over two weeks of architecture-themed installations, events, film screenings, workshops, cycle rides and guided walks.

JULY-SEPTEMBER

London Lit Fest

Southbank Centre, Belvedere Road, SE1 (www.londonlitfest.com). Waterloo tube/rail. Date July.
This literature festival brings some of the world's finest writers to the Southbank Centre for two weeks of talks, debates and events. Attendees have included the likes of Bret Easton Ellis, Jeanette Winterson and Ben Goldacre, among others.

Somerset House Summer Series

Somerset House, Strand, WC2 ILA (7845 4600, www.somersethouse.org.uk/music). Temple tube or Charing Cross tube/rail. Date July.
The courtyard at Somerset House provides an impressive outdoor setting for live music; 2010's headliners included Corinne Bailey Rae, Gil-Scott Heron, the XX and Florence and the Machine.

Rushes Soho Shorts Festival

Various venues in Soho (7851 6207/ www.sohoshorts.com). Date late July.
Free screenings of short films and videos.

Dance Al Fresco

Regent's Park, NW1 (www.dancealfresco. org). Regent's Park tube. Date Aug.
This weekend of alfresco dance offers a chance to ballroom dance (usually on the Saturday) or tango (Sunday) in the great outdoors to your heart's content. The dancing runs from 2pm to 6pm; novices can join the lessons at 1pm.

Carnaval del Pueblo

Floats from Elephant & Castle to Burgess Park; festival at Burgess Park, SE5 (www. carnavaldelpueblo.co.uk). Date 1st wk Aug.
Europe's largest Latin American festival features colourful floats, bull riding, food and dancing, while past all-star performers have included Oscar D'León and Willie Colón.

Notting Hill Carnival

Around Notting Hill (7727 0072, www. thenottinghillcarnival.com). Bayswater, Notting Hill Gate, Queensway or Westbourne Park tube. Date Sun & bank hol Mon Aug.
London's most famous and flamboyant carnival takes over Notting Hill for two days every year; expect giant floats, pounding drums, exotic dancing and lots of food.

Portobello Film Festival

Various venues around Portobello Road (8960 0996, www.portobellofilm festival.com). Date Sept.
The Portobello Film Festival celebrated its 15th anniversary in 2010. Screening over 800 new films from around the world, Europe's largest indie film festival also hosts talks from top directors; best of all, entrance to every event is free.

Regent Street Festival

Regent Street, Soho & Mayfair, W1B 4JN (7038 3718, www.regentstreetonline.com). Oxford Circus or Piccadilly Circus tube. Date late Sept.
This annual themed event (fashion was the focus for 2010) sees the horribly busy shopping street closed to traffic for the day to make room for fairground rides, theatre, street entertainers, storytelling and music.

Mayor of London's Sky Ride

Across the city (www.goskyride.com). Date early Sept.
A one-day celebration of all things cycling, the Mayor of London's Skyride sees thousands of cyclists turning central London into a huge car-free festival of entertainment, picnics and stalls.

Great River Race

River Thames, from Ham House, Richmond, Surrey, to Island Gardens, E14 (8398 9057, www.greatriverrace.co.uk). Date late Sept.

Around 300 vessels, from Chinese dragon boats to Viking longboats, vie for victory in this 21-mile 'traditional' boat race. The prime viewing points are Richmond, Hungerford, Millennium and Tower Bridges.

Spitalfields Show & Green Fair
Allen Gardens & Spitalfields City Farm, Buxton Street, E1 (7375 0441, www. alternativearts.co.uk). Whitechapel tube. Date mid Sept.
This annual horticultural shindig brings bucolic displays of home-grown produce and handicrafts, plus stalls offering fairtrade goods and promoting green living.

Mayor's Thames Festival
Between Westminster & Tower Bridges (7983 4100, www.thamesfestival.org). Blackfriars or Waterloo tube/rail. Date mid Sept.
Celebrating the Thames, this free two-day festival gets more spectacular by the year. Festivities culminate on Sunday with an illuminated night carnival, a lantern procession and a dazzling firework finale.

Open House London
Various venues (3006 7008, www.open-city.org.uk). Date 3rd wkd Sept.
Peek behind doors that are usually closed with Open House London weekend, which gives free access to over 500 private buildings, from historic palaces to cutting-edge office spaces. Apply for a guide from the end of August and book ahead for certain buildings.

OCTOBER-DECEMBER

Raindance
Various venues across the West End (7287 3833, www.raindance.co.uk). Date late Sept-early Oct.
Britain's largest independent film festival has been running for over a decade and a half. Check the website for screenings and events.

Diwali
Trafalgar Square, WC2 (7983 4100, www.london.gov.uk). Charing Cross tube/rail. Date Oct.

London's Hindu, Jain and Sikh communities celebrate the annual Festival of Light with sumptuous fireworks, food, music and dance. Everyone's welcome to join the festivities.

London Film Festival
BFI Southbank, Belvedere Road, SE1 8XT (7928 3535, www.lff.org.uk). Embankment tube or Waterloo tube/rail. Date Oct.
A stellar array of actors and directors attends the LFF, which screens around 180 new British and international features.

London Jazz Festival
Various locations (www.londonjazzfestival. org.uk). Date mid Nov.
This renowned ten-day jazz festival joins the dots between trad jazz and the avant-garde, and between America, the West Indies and Africa, attracting a splendid line-up.

Christmas on Cheshire Street
Cheshire Street, E2. Shoreditch tube. Date early Dec.
Forget the Oxford Street scrum, and save your festive shopping for Cheshire Street's Christmas late nights. On a selected Thursday and Friday in early December, the street's shops open until 9pm for browsing, buying, mulled wine and mince pies. Think bags from Mimi (*see p52*), homewares from Labour & Wait and much more.

Great Christmas Pudding Race
Covent Garden Market (07918 608499, www.xmaspuddingrace.org.uk). Covent Garden tube. Date early Dec.
This relay of runners carrying Christmas puddings on trays is always good for a laugh. Organised in aid of Cancer Research UK it celebrates its 30th year in 2010. Creative costumes win prizes, with the overall winner getting a Christmas pudding-themed trophy.

Santa Run
Greenwich Park (7424 5533, www.doitfor charity.com). Greenwich rail. Date early Dec.
Join some 2,000 Santas for this annual festive 5K run through Greenwich Park. You get a free Santa costume when you sign up and, of course, it's all for charity.

GOING OUT

BEAUTY

FASHION

PARTIES

FOOD

HEALTH

ECO

OUTDOORS

HOME

CHILDREN

PETS

TRANSPORT

RESOURCES

Websites

The city in cyberspace.

BLOGS

www.diamondgeezer.blogspot.com

London's most interesting blogger has been posting since 2002 – and is a worthy online successor to the likes of Pepys and Ackroyd.

londonist.com

Describing itself as 'a website about London and everything that happens in it', Londonist takes a lively look at what's going on in the capital, covering everything from politics to club nights. Don't miss the map of free Wi-Fi spots; new suggestions are always welcome.

www.londonreviewofbreakfasts. blogspot.com

Deliciously entertaining and unfailingly astute reviews of breakfast establishments across the city. It's worth a gander just for the testers' pseudonyms (HP Seuss, Hashley Brown et al).

www.london.thewayweseeit.org

This inspired collaborative photo blog showcases contributors' snaps of selected parts of London. Head out with your camera and join the fun.

www.london-underground. blogspot.com

The best blogs have a tinge of obsession about them, and Annie Mole's tender paean to the biggest underground transport system in the world has it in spades.

www.onionbagblog.com

Mr Onionbag takes some lovely shots of obscure corners of London, and has a wonderfully engaging written style. His tales of woe from south London always make our sorrows feel as nought.

pigeonblog.wordpress.com

A unique blog, purportedly written by a pigeon, with some great pictures and a surreal 'pigeon that looks like' section – squint hard enough and the most unlikely of resemblances really do start to emerge.

www.sub-urban.com

Snoop around the city's underground complexes (storm drains, tunnels, sewers) and derelict buildings with daredevil Londoners Jondoe and Stoop.

COMMUNITIES

www.gumtree.com

Originally founded as a community site to welcome new arrivals to London (in particular, Aussies, Kiwis and South Africans), Gumtree has become a mecca for flatshare-seekers – and a rich source of sold-out gig tickets.

www.kudocities.com

Members of this close-knit site pose questions about London life – such as where to eat in Chinatown, or the best place to woo a first date – which other users then answer.

www.urban75.org

This Brixton-based, non-profit community site is strong on protests and activism, with bulletin boards and listings for upcoming marches, talks and rallies.

GOING OUT

www.dirtydirtydancing.com

Alistair Allan spends his evenings at some of London's hippest club nights and fashion gatherings, snapping his fellow party people. Gawp (and sometimes giggle) at the beautiful people and their after-dark attire.

www.gingerbeer.co.uk

A vibrant guide to lesbian London, listing everything from bars to book launches, plus a guide to the capital's 'Gaybourhoods'.

www.londonisfree.com

A godsend for impecunious Londoners, this useful site lists free exhibitions, events and activities across town. It's particularly good for finding live radio and TV recordings and free instore gigs.

www.run-riot.com

This fast-paced, blog-style guide is excellent for hunting out alternative events. It grew from an informal text-only bulletin and is popular with London's creative types.

www.scene-out.org

An online community of London's gay clubbers, the site offers news, listings and photos of previous nights' debauchery, plus user reviews of music, film and theatre.

HISTORY

www.classiccafes.co.uk

Pay your respects to the capital's inimitable vintage caffs. The blog features some superb photography, and reviews of the old stalwarts that are still going strong.

www.derelictlondon.com

Paul Talling's huge and deservedly popular online album documents the city's fast-disappearing past, with an amazing photo-catalogue of dereliction and decay.

www.pepysdiary.com

Get a daily dose of Pepys at web consultant Phil Gyford's pet project, in which the great man's diary entries are presented in real time, starting in 2003. We approve.

www.untoldlondon.org.uk

This impressive site delves into the archives to document the history of the capital's ethnic and cultural groups – so you might find a multimedia record of the Greek Cypriot community next to a talk by ICA director Ekow Eshun on growing up in '70s London.

LONDON LIVING

www.fixmystreet.com

Report neighbourhood nuisances such as abandoned fridges and missing paving slabs, and the team at this inspired website will pass your complaint on to the relevant authorities, and file updates on the outcome.

www.london2012.com

The official website of the London 2012 Olympic and Paralympic Games has ticket information, a countdown, and information on the upcoming grand sporting event.

www.timeout.com/london

Head here for all things relating to the Big Smoke. The search facility helps you find out what's on, fast, from classical concerts to kooky cabaret nights or family-friendly events.

www.walkit.com/london

This user-friendly site encourages Londoners to get walking. Enter the start and end points for your journey and it'll give you a map, full directions and an estimated journey time – and tell you how many calories you'll burn.

SHOPPING & SERVICES

www.lynku.com

Thrifty types will love Lynku, which lists designer fashion and furniture sales across London. It offers free weekly update emails and alerts on sales and promotions.

www.mypropertyspy.co.uk

Property sale prices in London, some dating back to 2000, make for compulsive reading: now you can find out exactly how much your dream house went for when it was gazumped.

www.propertysnake.co.uk

First-time buyers take note: this site charts falling prices across town. Homeowners may find it makes for rather depressing reading.

www.streetsensation.co.uk

Offering a a virtual tour of London's busiest shopping streets, with photos and links to more than 3,500 shops, restaurants and bars.

GOING OUT

BEAUTY

FASHION

PARTIES

FOOD

HEALTH

ECO

OUTDOORS

HOME

CHILDREN

PETS

TRANSPORT

RESOURCES

Notes

Notes

GOING OUT
BEAUTY
FASHION
PARTIES
FOOD
HEALTH
ECO
OUTDOORS
HOME
CHILDREN
PETS
TRANSPORT
RESOURCES

Notes

GOING OUT

BEAUTY

FASHION

PARTIES

FOOD

HEALTH

ECO

OUTDOORS

HOME

CHILDREN

PETS

TRANSPORT

RESOURCES

Notes

Notes

Notes

Notes

GOING OUT

BEAUTY

FASHION

PARTIES

FOOD

HEALTH

ECO

OUTDOORS

HOME

CHILDREN

PETS

TRANSPORT

RESOURCES

Advertisers' Index

Please refer to relevant sections for addresses/telephone numbers

GOING OUT

BEAUTY

FASHION

PARTIES

FOOD

HEALTH

ECO

OUTDOORS

HOME

CHILDREN

PETS

TRANSPORT

RESOURCES

GOING OUT
BEAUTY
FASHION
PARTIES
FOOD
HEALTH
ECO
OUTDOORS
HOME
CHILDREN
PETS
TRANSPORT
RESOURCES

Index

GOING OUT

BEAUTY

FASHION

PARTIES

FOOD

HEALTH

ECO

OUTDOORS

HOME

CHILDREN

PETS

TRANSPORT

RESOURCES

GOING OUT

BEAUTY

FASHION

PARTIES

FOOD

HEALTH

ECO

OUTDOORS

HOME

CHILDREN

PETS

TRANSPORT

RESOURCES

GOING OUT

BEAUTY

FASHION

PARTIES

FOOD

HEALTH

ECO

OUTDOORS

HOME

CHILDREN

PETS

TRANSPORT

RESOURCES

GOING OUT
BEAUTY
FASHION
PARTIES
FOOD
HEALTH
ECO
OUTDOORS
HOME
CHILDREN
PETS
TRANSPORT
RESOURCES

GOING OUT

BEAUTY

FASHION

PARTIES

FOOD

HEALTH

ECO

OUTDOORS

HOME

CHILDREN

PETS

TRANSPORT

RESOURCES